# THE ART OF THE

# Lapidary

## FRANCIS J. SPERISEN

LAPIDARY

SAN FRANCISCO, CALIFORNIA

THE BRUCE PUBLISHING COMPANY ⁖ MILWAUKEE

DEDICATED TO THE AMATEUR

MAY HIS TRIBE INCREASE

# *Preface*

THROUGHOUT the ages, from the remote past to the present time, mankind has been attracted to and charmed by gems and precious stones. With the development of civilization and the growth of culture, the appreciation for these rare items of nature progressed, and as a result the art of the lapidary developed in like manner. Centuries before the beginning of the Christian era, various types of quartz as well as harder stones were cut, engraved, and polished with consummate skill into exquisite works of art. Many of these bits of miniature sculpture, some smaller than a man's fingernail, have remained to this day in a state of excellent preservation; they have defied both time and the elements alike, to give mute evidence of the civilized status of people almost forgotten.

Often a portrait or a figure engraved on a gemstone is the sole record of a celebrated personage or a statue that once graced some temple or edifice in ancient times. It is a singular fact that although the art of the lapidary antedates that of recorded history, and has spread to all lands, little had been known of the technique used by the skilled artisans. The numerous printed works on gems and precious stones that have appeared in the past rarely devoted a chapter to the fascinating subject of the lapidary art and usually the information so offered is of a scanty nature.

In the past the main reason for this absence of information seems to have been an almost universal reticence on the part of the lapidaries who devoted their entire occupational lives in an effort to become proficient and expert in their work. The processes and improvements in processes and materials quite naturally became "secrets of the trade," and were often handed down from father to son. As a result these processes were rarely divulged and more rarely recorded in writing. The present book which records the knowledge and experience gained by the author during a period of over forty years as an amateur and professional lapidary has been written in the belief that the entire industry will profit from its publication.

Long contact with and practical experience in the cutting and polishing of gemstones provide the best means of gaining an intimate knowledge of gemmology. The experienced lapidary can usually identify gemstones rapidly and accurately without the use of special instruments. As skill in identifying gemstones is a necessary requirement of any lapidary if he aspires to become expert, a chapter on this subject has been included in this book.

In the preface to the first edition a hope was expressed that the treatise on *The Art of the Lapidary,* would fill a gap that has existed since the beginning of time, and that it might cause readers to pursue the pleasurable study of as well as cutting and polishing of gemstones. In the half score of years since its publication this hope had been realized. It is altogether fitting and proper to express sincere thanks and appreciation to the hundreds of individuals from all parts of the world who have written to express their pleasure as well as satisfaction as a result of reading the book and applying the knowledge contained therein.

The artisans of few professions can list as friends and patrons the world's illustrious men from ancient to modern times. Alexander, Mithradates, Caesar, Augustus, and Hadrian were ardent collectors of gem stones, and the latter among other accomplishments was also an amateur lapidary. Many of the famous museums of the world now house the collections of illustrious patrons of the arts, the Medici, Francis I, Rudolph II, and in our own land the collections of Isaac Lea, Morgan and Pratt are justly famous.

Many of the items illustrated in this book, the work of the author, and described for the first time have never before been made in America by a professional lapidary. As the principal requirements are patience and continued practice, and the tools required being of the simplest sort, it is sincerely hoped that all who read this book may follow in like manner.

F. J. S.

# Acknowledgments

THE author wishes to express his sincere thanks and appreciation to the many friends who have contributed suggestions, help, and encouragement during the writing of this manuscript.

Thanks in particular are extended to the late Dr. Austin F. Rogers of Stanford University for suggestions, criticism, and comments on the original manuscript; to Dr. Edward H. Kraus of the University of Michigan for permission to use illustrations showing hardness direction in the diamond; for the kind interest and co-operation of the late Fred V. Cole of the Jewelers' Circular-Keystone; to Lloyd M. Demrick for special care in photographing the author's equipment used in part to illustrate this work, as well as to George H. Needham, F.R.M.S., for equal interest in the preparation of the photomicrographs; to Bartling & Co., and Paul F. Hester, diamond cutters; and to Albert A. Sperisen, all of San Francisco, Calif.

Appreciation also is extended to the following contributors whose co-operation has aided materially in the completion of this book:

American Museum of Natural History, New York, Fig. 9–24
Bausch & Lomb Optical Co., Figs. 2–20, 21
British Museum, Fig. 9-1
Chang-Wen-Ti, Figs. 9-13 to 17 incl.
Max Fine & Sons, New York, Fig. 7–37
Paul Drury, Figs. 6–43, 7–47
Jewelers' Circular-Keystone, New York, Figs. 11–5, 6, 11
Kunsthistorischen Museum, Vienna, Austria, Figs. 1–2, 9–3, 22, 23
Metropolitan Museum of Art, New York, Figs. 6-3 to 5 incl., 6-60, 66, 8-7, 9-2
Museum of Fine Arts, Boston, Fig. 9-4
Norton Co., Worcester, Mass., Figs. 4-2, 3, 5, 6, 12-6
Wm. B. Pitts, San Francisco, Calif., Fig. 2-6
J. Louis Renton, Portland, Ore., Fig. 2-5
M. Rosendorff, Fig. 7-11
Stark Tool Co., Waltham, Mass., Fig. 8-4
M. D. Taylor Co. Soquel, Calif., Figs. 4-45, 8-10
Shreve and Co., San Francisco, Calif., Fig. 12–13
Dirk van Erp, San Francisco, Calif., Fig. 12-15
Harry Kazanjian and Kazanjian Foundation, Los Angeles, Calif., Fig. 9–6
M.D.R. Mfg. Co., Inc., Los Angeles, Calif., Fig. 4–46
Highland Park Mfg. Co., So. Pasadena, Calif., Figs. 4–33, 34, 42
Felker Di-Met, Torrance, Calif., Figs. 4–39, 40
Geo. Zwillinger, San Francisco, Calif., Figs. 10-1, 2
National Museum, Cairo, Egypt, Fig. 1-1
Paul Drury, Figs. 6–43, 7–47
M. de Patta, Napa, Calif., 12–15, 16, 17, 18
Henry Seuter, Color Photography, San Francisco, Calif.

For all of this kind and helpful assistance, the author is deeply grateful.

FRANCIS J. SPERISEN

# Contents

CONTENTS

# ART OF THE LAPIDARY

# CHAPTER 1

# Gems and Precious Stones

AMONG the many varieties of minerals found in the earth, a large number possess such qualities as beauty of color and marking, rarity and durability that have caused them to be highly prized as personal possessions, for adornment, or for utility.

Before the dawn of history, these colorful minerals were collected by man and used as amulets and finally as ornaments, an appeal that was felt by mankind often remotely separated on all continents. Even before the beginning of recorded history, colorful minerals were sought

**Fig. 1-1.** Bracelets of Queen Zer.

1. Central rosette of gold, small beads of turquoise and gold, large round beads of amethyst; 2. Hour glass beads of amethyst, gold and dark brown limestone; turquoise beads with conical gold caps; 3. Turquoise and hollow gold beads; dark round beads are lapis lazuli; 4. Alternate plaques of gold and turquoise, surmounted with royal hawk.

1

after, extracted from the stream beds or mountain fastness, and sometimes transported great distances to a waiting market.

Proof of this is shown from time to time by archaeological research and discoveries through treasure exposed to the light of day. In the year 1900 under the guidance of Wm. F. Petrie an important discovery was made at Abydos, Egypt. In clearing out the debris of the burial place of King Zer, a ruler in the second dynasty (4500 B.C.), a portion of a mummy of the Queen was found which upon examination disclosed four bracelets of exceptional workmanship (Fig. 1–1). One of these, No. 3, contained in combination with gold and turquoise, a number of beads fashioned from lapis lazuli. As lapis lazuli is not native to Egypt but is found in a remote portion of Afghanistan, it indicates that trade even in that ancient time existed between the two countries. More recently a considerable quantity of lapis lazuli was found in Ur of the Chaldees, in the burial pit of Mes-Kalum-Dug, a monarch who ruled in Mesopotamia about 3000 B.C.

Among the early historians whose works have survived, Theophrastus (315 B.C.) who largely through personal research compiled a history of stones describes a great number that are in use today. He also commented on the high prices that some of them brought and it is from the Greek that we derive many of the names of the respective stones; carbunculus, sapphiros, smaragdus, amethystos, and topazos are but a few.

From Roman antiquity we obtain the name gemma signifying an engraved stone, the surface of which was carved with an image. This design usually depicted an image of the owner, one of favorite gods or deities, or it might even depict some image the meaning of which is unknown at the present time.

Gemma ultimately became contracted to gem, and until recent times, this term, particularly when used with the prefix "antique," referred to all of those relics of ancient times that were recovered from the ruins or burial grounds of nations that have passed into ancient history (Fig. 1–2).

Although the custom of using cylinder seals was practiced by the Babylonians as early as 2000 B.C. (Fig. 9–1), and the use of seals in Greece by the seventh century B.C., it was not until the first century B.C. that the custom became popular to the Romans. Prior to that time the wearing of seal rings was restricted to the knights and to the senators.

Fig. 1-2. "Gemma Augustea."

The "Gemma Augustea" is one of the finest pictures to survive from ancient times; dating from the Augustean era, it is a superb cameo, an onyx of two layers the figures being carved in white on a brown ground, and in size it measures 190 by 230 mm. (7.48 by 9.05 in.) approximately 7.5 by 9 inches.

Augustus in the character of Jupiter is seated upon his throne holding in one hand the lituus and with the other leans on a long staff. A shield serves as his footstool indicating peace, the eagle indicating royalty stands beneath.

Above and before Augustus is Capricorn his horoscope. Behind the throne stands Neptune with his dripping locks and Cybele who is in the act of placing a civic crown upon the head of Augustus thus alludes to the restoration of peace and indicates him as being the savior of the state and sovereign over sea and land.

Livia as the goddess Roma is seated beside him. Drusus her son in full armor stands beside her. Tiberius with a laurel wreath as a crown is descending from a chariot which is guided by Victory in reference to his recent triumph.

Seated beside the throne Antonio the wife of Drusus depicts the character of Abundantia and beside her are her two children Germanicus and Claudius.

In the exergue, the lower half of the cameo, Roman soldiers are erecting a trophy while seated below are barbarian prisoners, two others are also in custody of two warriors. This scene represents the victories of Drusus over the Rhaeti and Vindelici (17 B.C.) as well as the successes of his brother Tiberius over the Pannonians.

Pliny (A.D. 23–79) states that the enormous quantity of treasure exhibited by Pompey in his triumph at Rome 62 B.C., after defeating Mithradates, king of Pontus, created a great demand for such items, not only among the wealthy but even among those of modest means. In the treasure house of the defeated king at Talaura in Pontus was found quantities of gold and other items of great value, gems in large numbers and 2000 cups made of onyx and a varigated agate of a type called murrha.* The carving of various forms of quartz became the vogue. Agate and rock crystal were usually carved into cups, dishes and amphora, some of which had a capacity of several pints, and the onyx and sardonyx were usually carved into the likeness of the ruler or to depict some noteworthy event (Fig. 1–2). Many centuries later such lapidary art became known and was referred to as cameos.

Gem set cups and tableware in gold and silver became the rage among the wealthy as noted in Jeuvenal's satire A.D. 100:

> To count the gems a saucy slave stands by
>     And marks your sharpened claws with curious eye.
> Excuse his freedom, and discreet, forbear
>     To handle such an emerald so rare.
> Thus fashions change; till now the finger bore
>     The gem that graced the scabbard long before
> Now rings are in disuse, and beryls shine,
>     And rubies lend their ruddy light to wine.

In other lands, mineral substances of various kinds were sought after and used in similar fashion. Soon after his landing in Mexico, Cortez received gifts sent by Montezuma and among these were four chalchihuitls each of which was worth more than a load of gold. Although the chalchihuitl is generally acknowledged as being jadeite, and most of the stones were cut in bead form (Fig. 6–67) other green minerals are also included under this term, e.g., green quartz, feldspar, green turquoise, serpentine, green chlorite, and quartzite. Numerous carvings of jadeite have since been found, and they exhibit a technical skill of considerable merit, especially as metal tools were practically unknown. The degree of polish on the beads illustrated is equal to that performed in most commercial shops today.

Although the chalchihuitl was highly prized by the Aztecs (as well

---

* Pliny records that in his day gold and silver had become commonplace and that the Roman patrician emphasized his wealth through the possession of murrhine goblets and rock crystal vases, items of such delicate nature that their very fragility increased their value.

as by the Mayas), the Spaniards regarded it as of little importance and when Alvarado gambled with Montezuma, the latter paid his losses in gold, the former in chalchihuitl and thus the cupidity of each was gratified.

The practice of burying stone ornaments with the deceased in many lands has been of great value to all students of gemmology for in exposing the contents of burial pits to the light of day, we have learned the nature of the stones also buried, stones that were esteemed and highly prized thousands of years ago.

For many centuries before the beginning of the Christian era a lively traffic existed in jade (nephrite) found in the river streams and mountains of Chinese Turkestan. By camel caravan these stones were transported to Peking where they were cut into various forms by the local lapidaries. Although Chinese nephrite is found in a number of colors, none of these exhibited the brilliant tones of the finer quality Burmese jade (jadeite) introduced to the trade by the middle of the eighteenth century, nevertheless the ancient jade was one of the most highly prized possessions. One type of nephrite of a certain white tint known as "mutton fat" jade was particularly esteemed.

From this brief historical survey, it will thus be observed that from century to century and from country to country, the whims of fashion or custom have determined man's use of a great variety of minerals. Many of these are not rare and in recent years because of a greater interest, they have been found in widely distributed areas. Within the past quarter century as a result of persistent searching by the avid amateur many new gem minerals have been discovered, particularly in our Western States. As late as 1928 the noted authority, the late Dr. Geo. F. Kunz lamented that a source of jade was unknown in America, although he predicted that it would be found. Within a few years after his death both nephrite and jadeite have been found in a number of areas, some of which have been of considerable commercial importance.

Because a limited number of minerals have been highly prized, sought after and bargained over from the earliest times, it became customary to refer to these minerals as "precious stones," particularly in the jewelry trade and to the greater number of gem minerals remaining the term "semiprecious" was given. Further qualifications were also given, the mineral substance must be rare, and colorful and of suitable hardness so that wear in use is at a minimum. In this group is listed the diamond, emerald, ruby, and sapphire.

This list however is an arbitrary one for it has varied from time to time and from place to place according to availability, custom, or usage. Because of the widespread dissemination of knowledge resulting from interest in the various sciences and the particular interest of the amateur, the old classification of precious and semiprecious stones is no longer valid. It is difficult to understand how in an exacting profession the term semiprecious could ever have been used. Either the stone is worth something — or nothing. At the present time it has become customary to refer to all gem minerals that are suitable for personal use or adornment as gemstones. Although the majority of gem minerals so used are cut and polished into some definite form, an increasing number are added to collections both private and public.

To state that the diamond, emerald, ruby, and sapphire are precious stones without specific qualifications is misleading, for all of these minerals are found in quantities but of such low quality that sizable stones can be obtained for a few dollars.

It thus becomes apparent that the most important characteristic of a gem mineral is perfection, for it is this quality, of equal importance to color, that governs the cost of a large number of gem minerals and thus causes them to be regarded as precious. To be perfect, a gemstone must be free of all cracks, flaws, inclusions, or blemishes when examined under a magnifying glass. Common usage stipulates that the magnifying power of the glass should be 10 times, although lenses of 15x are commonly used; particularly in the diamond trade. A magnifying glass of 10 power has a focal point one inch from the object; a 15x lens is about ⅗ of an inch from the object when in focus.

Color is possibly the most important characteristic of a gem mineral, for this quality quickly attracts the eye, whether the gemstone be a brightly colored pebble in the gravel bed of a river or on the seashore, or a perfectly formed crystal. Minerals that lack fine color because of imperfections and impurities have little interest or value for anyone but the mineralogist.

Durability, which is the quality possessed by gem minerals in varying degree, is important. To be durable, a gemstone must be equal in hardness or harder than quartz, because the particles of dust and grit that come in contact with it in normal use consist chiefly of quartz. Toughness is also a desirable quality. Because a number of minerals lack this quality, they cannot be classed and used satisfactorily as gemstones.

Rarity has been stressed as a quality of gemstones. As has been shown, the importance of this factor is debatable. Three of the most popular gemstones, carnelian, lapis lazuli, and turquoise have been widely used for more than 5000 years and they are not rare. Carnelian is quite common, while fine quality lapis lazuli and turquoise although scarce are not rare. The popularity of these gemstones can be explained by only one fact — they are fashionable.

In modern times fashion is a compelling force and its influence is exerted upon gemstones as well as the thousands of other commodities that are bought, sold, and used in everyday life. Occasionally this force causes demands for one item and later for simple or numerous reasons, as the case may be, the same item may be almost completely ignored. A simple example familiar to most is the rock crystal necklace, which was in fashion from 1920 to 1930. At the present time, it is rare indeed to see a single strand being worn.

For several centuries the diamond has been the most popular of all gemstones. Even though the diamond had been known for over 2000 years, its popularity was not achieved until its hidden beauty was revealed through the precise skill of the trained lapidary. Thereafter this popularity increased until the diamond has become the most important and valuable gemstone of all time.

Economically, the diamond is the most valuable of gemstones. About 80 per cent of the value of gemstones imported and sold in America is derived from the sale of diamonds. The diamond, during periods of prosperity or adversity, may be more readily sold and at a higher proportional price than other gemstones.

Industrially, through its widespread application, the diamond is the most valuable gemstone known. Because of its natural hardness, defective diamonds, or those stones not suited for gemstone use, are useful as abrasives. Clear, off-color, diamonds are extensively used for turning tools or for other industrial applications, principally in grinding operations.

Emeralds and rubies of exceptional quality are sometimes more costly than diamonds, but are not more valuable.

In the past the ruby was cherished as a precious gemstone, yet for more than 25 years it had been neglected because of the difficulty experienced by most dealers in distinguishing the natural gemstone and its synthetic copy. With a greater knowledge on the part of the dealer, this difficulty has been overcome and once again this beautiful red gemstone is popular.

Certain minerals, e.g. benitoite, hiddenite, and sphene, possessing many of the characteristics required of gemstones will never be fashionable because of their rarity. They are rarely seen in the jeweler's stock;

rather, they are sought by the discriminating collector of gemstones and become prized possessions when obtained.

To derive the greatest benefit from the study of gemstones, a knowledge of chemistry and mineralogy is essential, for after all, the science of gemstones or gemmology, as it is now called, is only specialized mineralogy. Unlike the gemmologist, who usually examines only cut gemstones, the lapidary is often called upon to ascertain the nature of rough gem minerals. For this purpose, a knowledge of mineralogy and its companion science, crystallography, is invaluable.

Through the study of mineralogy or gemmology, we learn that many gemstones that have different color or appearance may be closely related; thus, rock crystal, amethyst, citrine, cairngorm, and smoky quartz are all transparent varieties of the mineral quartz and differ only in color. Similarly, the mineral beryl includes many species, *e.g.*, emerald, aquamarine, goshenite, morganite, and golden beryl. Each of these has a different color, and yet all are easily recognized by the mineralogist as varieties of one mineral, beryl. This is because of similarity in their physical and optical characteristics.

# CHAPTER 2

# Physical Characteristics of Gems

THE physical and optical characteristics of gems provide the easiest means of correctly classifying the several varieties. In fact, the careful study and analysis of these characteristics are used in identifying the gem minerals which are similar in appearance.

Color is of first importance in a gem. Many varieties of minerals have sufficient hardness and durability to rank as gemstones and could be so classified but for the fact that they lack the necessary attractiveness of color and perfection.

In designating colors, a hue refers to a definite part of the spectrum. When a color is lighter than the standard or hue shown in the spectrum, it is spoken of as a tint; if a color is darker than the standard, it is called a shade of the color.

A gem mineral which has a given color as its chief characteristic owing to the presence of a definite constituent which is the coloring medium, is known as an idiochromatic mineral. Malachite, azurite, and hematite are typical idiochromatic minerals.

In the majority of gem minerals the color is caused by some impurity, usually in minute quantity. These minerals are colorless in the pure state. A large number of gem minerals are found in a variety of colors. Corundum, beryl, and quartz are typical of these gems. Some gem minerals are parti-colored (Figs. 2–1 and 3–12), *i.e.*, they occur with two or more colors in one crystal. Examples of these are tourmaline and

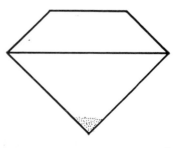

◀ **Fig. 2-1.** Growth phenomena in tourmaline. Basal section, "watermelon" tourmaline; green outer shell; two-tone pink inner section.

▶ **Fig. 2-2.** Cross section of "patchy" colored stone showing location of color at culet to obtain best results.

9

corundum. Finally, some gems derive their pigment from an included mineral in suspension, sometimes finely disseminated throughout the mass. Aventurine and Myrickite are examples. All of these are spoken of as allochromatic minerals.

In allochromatic minerals the pigment is often distributed in patches, stripes, or zones. These stones, if transparent, must be properly oriented so that the cut stone will appear to be uniformly colored. This is accomplished by grinding so that the darker part will be in the back of the stone (Fig. 2–2). Amethyst almost invariably occurs with patches of color, which sometimes are in distinct triangular form (Fig. 2–3).

Agate is a common gem with the colors arranged in stripes (Fig. 2–4).

Tourmaline is the most prominent gem mineral which has color in zones. Often the distinction of color is sharp and well defined with contrasting colors. Sometimes the color differs on opposite ends of the crystal, or it may be arranged in horizontal bands or radiate from the center in sharply defined zones. Occasionally the color varies gradually through the length of a crystal from deep pink on one end to no color at the other (Fig. 3–12).

Numerous gem minerals have been found in which the color is ar-

**Fig. 2-3.** Amethyst (Arizona), 6x. Amethyst in thin section showing zonal distribution of color. In this picture, which is a section of a quartz crystal, the amethyst (dark portions) are clearly seen in contrast to the clear or rock crystal remainder.

Fig. 2-4. California agate showing concentric banding. Pattern often called "Fortification agate."

Fig. 2-5. Scenic moss agates, manganese dioxide.

ranged in such a manner as to produce attractive markings, scenes, and pictures or figures. Moss agate is typical, and the quartz family abounds with many types (Fig. 2–5).

Inclusions, that is, foreign bodies in mineral which give color to a crystal, are of various types. The treelike figures in moss agate are inclusions of manganese oxide or of chlorite and form black or green markings (Fig. 2–5). Cinnabar or iron compounds form red markings. Chiastolite, when cut across the crystal, exhibits crosslike markings which are inclusions of a carbonaceous material (Fig. 2–6). Rutile and sometimes tourmaline in fine needle or hairlike crystals are also found as inclusions in quartz (Fig. 2–7).

Inclusions of rutile in fine hairlike crystals also are found in spinel and garnet as well as in ruby and sapphire. These inclusions provide a

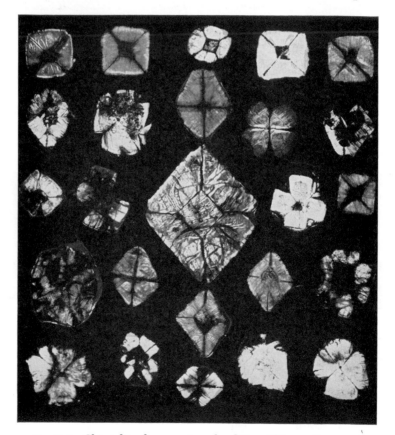

Fig. 2-6. Chiastolite from various localities. Thin sections cut across the chiastolite crystals exhibit unusual markings and crosslike patterns. Specimens natural size.

Fig. 2-7.
Heart shape in rock
crystal enclosing hairlike
crystals of rutile. Venus
Hair Stone, size
32 x 32 x 13 mm.

simple method for determining the genuineness of a ruby or garnet, for they are often present and are arranged in an orderly manner. They are never present in the synthetic transparent gem material. Synthetic star rubies and sapphires contain small particles of rutile, but these are never seen in the form illustrated in Figure 3–10.

Minerals may be classified according to their ability to transmit light. Those which permit light to be transmitted freely are transparent; those which transmit light feebly are translucent; those which completely resist the passage of light are opaque. The terms "semitransparent" and "semitranslucent" are applied to gems which are, roughly speaking, less than fully transparent or translucent.

In structure, gem minerals may be classified as crystalline, crypto-crystalline, and amorphous. Crystalline minerals are those which have a definite crystal form. The majority of gem minerals occur with distinct crystal forms which are often characteristic of the mineral and constitute an excellent means of identification.

The diamond is found in a crystal form called an octahedron, which is a solid bounded by eight equal equilateral triangles. By this means it is readily distinguished from all other colorless crystals.*

* Spinel also occurs in this form; colorless crystals, however, are practically unknown.

## QUARTZ

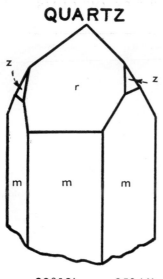

mr—38°13′    rr —85°46′
rz —46°16′   mz—66°52′
mm—60°

## TOPAZ

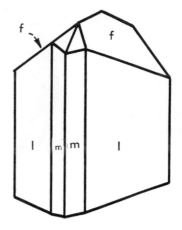

mm—55°43′    ll—86°49′
ml —18°44′   ff—87°18′

## ZIRCON

## VESUVIANITE

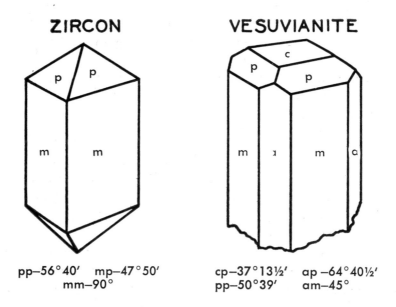

pp—56°40′    mp—47°50′
mm—90°

cp—37°13½′    ap —64°40½′
pp—50°39′    am—45°

**Fig. 2-8.** Outstanding crystal forms with interfacial angles.

Citrine, the yellow to brown transparent quartz sold as quartz-topaz, is readily distinguished from true topaz (called precious topaz) by its crystal form. Spodumene (kunzite and hiddenite), benitoite, and axinite all have distinctive forms by which the rough stones may be recognized. Many other minerals, less rare, are equally distinctive (Fig. 2–8).

In spite of varying sizes and unevenly developed faces or irregular growth, the angle between any two faces of a crystal is constant for all crystals of that species. Thus, if the specimen being examined is a fragment of a whole crystal, which often is the case, identification is simplified by checking the interfacial angle with a contact goniometer (Fig. 2–9) and comparing the angles with tables on crystallography.

Cryptocrystalline minerals are so finely crystalline that the crystal structure can be detected only through the use of a microscope. Agate, chalcedony, jasper, and flint are familiar types. Amorphous gems are rare. These are mineral substances without crystalline form. Opal is the best known type. Obsidian, a volcanic glass, and amber, a fossil resin, also belong to this class.

An important quality of gems is resistibility to abrasion. Commonly the minimum resistance to abrasion, or hardness, of a gem must be equal to or higher than quartz. A scale of hardness is a convenient and useful method of testing gems and of determining at least one aspect of value.

Many years ago the scientist Friedrich Mohs systematized the study of hardness as a quality of minerals by listing the common minerals, beginning with the softest and progressing to the hardest as follows:

| | |
|---|---|
| 1. Talc | 6. Feldspar |
| 2. Gypsum | 7. Quartz |
| 3. Calcite | 8. Topaz |
| 4. Fluorite | 9. Corundum |
| 5. Apatite | 10. Diamond |

Thus calcite will scratch gypsum if rubbed across it with moderate pressure; fluorite scratches calcite, and in like manner each of the harder minerals will scratch a softer one. Often minerals and gems are found which do not correspond to a fixed hardness value. They may be harder than one of the standards but softer than the next higher on the scale. Tourmaline and zircon are typical; both are capable of scratching quartz, hardness 7 on the scale, yet in turn tourmaline and zircon are scratched by topaz, hardness 8. The hardness value in this case is rated at 7½. Sometimes other values are listed, as for example 7¼. To detect such minor differences, however, requires considerable skill.

Most minerals are of a uniform hardness, varying only slightly according to the atomic structure. This uniformity of hardness is one of the chief qualities which assist in determining the identity of minerals. A few minerals, however, have marked differences in hardness when the same crystal is scratched in different directions. Thus, kyanite has a

Fig. 2-9. Two types of contact goniometers.

hardness of 7 across the crystal and a hardness of 5 parallel to its length. Again minerals from widely separated portions of the globe vary. The diamonds from South Africa are the softest, while those produced in Borneo and Australia are the hardest stones. The hardness rating of 10 given the diamond is an average.

In 1884, Pfaff, using a standard boring point, investigated the degree of hardness in minerals and found that Mohs' scale varied in a fairly uniform manner. Using the hardness of corundum at 1000, he developed the following table:

| | | |
|---|---|---|
| 9. | corundum | 1000 |
| 8. | topaz | 459 |
| 7. | quartz | 254 |
| 6. | orthoclase | 191 |
| 5. | apatite | 53.5 |
| 4. | fluorite | 37.3 |
| 3. | calcite | 15.3 |
| 2. | gypsum | 12.03 |

When hardness values of minerals are to be determined for research purposes, a sclerometer is useful. This instrument is so arranged that a lapped diamond point, under a definite weight, is drawn back and forth across a uniformly flat surface of the substance tested. The width of the scratch produced is measured with the aid of a microscope, and the hardness value is assigned according to the width of the scratch.

In Mohs' scale of hardness the values of hardness from points 1 to 9 are fairly uniform, but the jump from point 9 to 10 is so great, that the diamond which is rated at hardness 10 is not truly represented. In relation to other minerals in the scale the diamond should have a hardness value of 50.

It is unfortunate that Mohs placed the diamond at point 10 for this has caused endless misunderstanding among the uninformed who have been led to misjudge the relative hardness of gemstones compared with the diamond. The hardness of the ruby, or sapphire, which is placed at 9 on the scale, is most frequently exaggerated. Thus a five-carat synthetic ruby, hardness 9, may be reduced to powder in less than three minutes by grinding on an 8 by 1-inch silicon carbide wheel, while a diamond five carats in weight, when used as a dresser, will turn down the same wheels daily and may continue to give years of service.

As a result of the more recent development of various hard products of the electric furnace, a new scale of hardness has been proposed. This scale* places the diamond in truer relationship to other substances and has numerous advantages in commercial use.

While the scale is useful in identifying gems, care and judgment must be exercised in its use. To scratch the surface of a gem stone is unthinkable and unnecessary when the girdle may be used. It is, in fact, advisable whenever possible to use the girdle edge of a gem to scratch other minerals as a clue to its hardness. If the stone is mounted in a closed bezel, this is impossible and other tests must be relied on. The customary use of small sharp-edged chips of minerals of known hardness as testing units may be simplified by setting these chips or points in holders. The chips may be pointed by grinding or may be shaped to a special form.

A set of hardness testers designed by the writer (Fig. 2–10) has been found superior to the older type of conical point which usually breaks off at the first application. The set which consists of a rectangular prism, set in a convenient holder, provides four points, five

Fig. 2-10. Hardness point.

flats, and eight edges, so arranged that a point, a flat, or a broad edge may be used. This hardness tester may be used as a scraper on the girdle edge of a stone mounted in claws so that the girdle edge is exposed. If the stone tested is harder than the test point, the point or edge will glide over it without effect. If the stone is softer, the cutting of the scraper will be felt as it digs into the stone and removes a small amount of the stone in powder form. The powder removed from the scratch should be tested by wiping with the finger to determine which has been scratched — the stone or the scraper. In no case should it be necessary to make the scratch longer than 1/16 in.

The test outlined may be applied without harm to a small portion of the girdle which in most stones remains unpolished. Perhaps it may be well to add that care should be taken not to apply a hardness test to a surface of a gem in such a manner that its appearance and value are harmed. If the tester point is harder than the stone tested, the resulting scratch or furrow may cause permanent damage. A file may be used to test a rough stone, but it should never be applied to a fine gemstone. Although most gems are very hard, many are very brittle so that the

* The scale is the result of researches by Charles E. Woodell, research chemical engineer, the Carborundum Co., Niagara Falls, N. Y.

rasping action of a file may cause the edge to grizzle and chip.

Toughness or ability to resist shock is a characteristic possessed by few gems. Jade (nephrite and jadeite) and to a lesser degree agate, rhodonite, and californite are among the toughest stones known and will resist shock. Certain varieties of minerals, rated at the same hardness as others of the same group, are less difficult to work than the equally hard substances. Thus cryptocrystalline varieties of quartz (chalcedony and agate) are rated as hard as rock crystal and other crystalline varieties of quartz, but they are more difficult to saw and to grind because of their toughness.

Some gems having a brittle structure are easily chipped or broken, while others split or cleave along definite planes (Fig. 2–11). These cleavage planes are characteristic of certain mineral species and when the stones are in the rough, uncut state, cleavage cracks are often present and serve as distinguishing features. The direction of the planes of cleavage is not constant for all minerals but varies according to

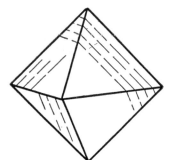

OCTAHEDRAL – DIAMOND

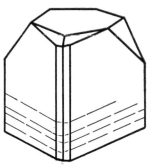

BASAL – TOPAZ

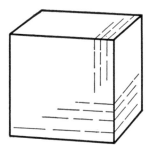

CUBIC – GALENA

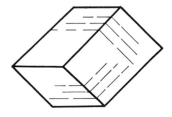

RHOMBOHEDRAL – CALCITE

Fig. 2-11.  Illustrating cleavage planes.

the laws of crystallography. In the diamond these planes are parallel to the face of the octahedron regardless of the shape of the crystal. Topaz has a basal cleavage (normal to the c axis), that is, its cleavage is at a right angle to the prism face, while in kunzite the cleavage is parallel to the c axis in two directions. In certain minerals and gems, cleavage is perfect, and in others it is imperfect or uneven.

In the case of the diamond, the cleavage planes are of definite value to the cutter, and cleaving is an important process in the diamond cutter's art. Cleaving is resorted to whenever it is necessary to remove imperfections or to reduce large stones to smaller pieces for economic reasons as well as to trim malformed crystals for cutting. In some cases, where a gem mineral possesses perfect cleavage planes and the structure of the stone is very weak on these planes, as in the spodumene, kunzite, and hiddenite, the cutting of the stone becomes difficult. The shock of the grinding or lapping action often develops cleavage cracks resulting in split stones.

If the stone is small, it is cemented on a holder to facilitate handling.

To cleave a stone, a small groove is made in it on the cleavage plane. An edged steel blade is placed truly in the groove parallel to the cleavage plane, and the blade is given a sharp blow with a metal rod (Fig. 2–12). The stone will part in the proper direction.

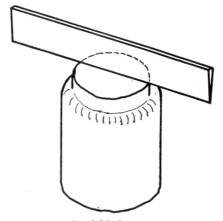

Fig. 2-12. Steel blade in position on cleavage plane for cleaving; stone cemented to block.

Although some gem minerals possess perfect cleavage, the tenacity of the minerals varies considerably. Mica cleaves under moderate pressure alone; calcite, fluorite, and kunzite are easily cleaved with a slight blow, while topaz and diamond require a sharp forceful blow. When Asscher cleaved the Cullinan diamond, the first blow broke the cleaving knife but did not split the stone.

Some minerals have imperfect cleavage planes; others have none. In gem minerals having perfect cleavage planes, the cleavage face produced by cleaving is bright and smooth. A large variety of gem minerals possess no planes of cleavage but, when struck a sharp blow, they will fracture or break with a characteristic surface. For example, the fracture of rock crystal is conchoidal or shell-like. Opal and obsidian show this type of fracture perfectly (Fig. 2–13). Turquoise and lapis lazuli show granular fracture, while minerals having a fibrous structure exhibit a splintery fracture when broken. Jade and tiger's-eye are typical.

Parting is sometimes present in gem minerals. This is usually due to polysynthetic twinning or it may be caused by pressure in definite directions. Corundum is the best known example.

Luster is an important quality in gems and varies according to the refractive index of the stone. When viewed by reflected light, the surface glitter or luster of gems differs widely. *Adamantine* luster is possessed by gems having a refractive index 1.90 or greater. The diamond and the zircon are the best known examples. *Sub-adamantine* luster is recognized in stones having a lower refractive index, ranging between 1.75 and 1.90. Included in this class are the corundum gems as well as several types of garnets.

*Vitreous* luster is characteristic of quartz and the majority of gems which are silicates.

The surface luster of many gems is accurately descriptive: thus, amber and copal are said to have a *resinous* luster; the turquoise is *waxy*; the mother-of-pearl is *pearly*; the fibrous minerals like satin spar are *silky*.

A few gem minerals, which are beautiful even in the rough state, react to light with a play of varied colors. Of these the opal is best known. White opal, black opal, fire opal, and noble opal are a few of the body colors or types which describe the phenomenal variety of hues which

**Fig. 2-13.** Conchoidal fracture, obsidian.

this gem mineral reflects as the stone is moved or turned under light.

Fire opal and water opal are clear types; the fire opal is red and is often cut faceted; the water opal is milky or *opalescent*. Black opal, as the name implies, is a dark gray to black type, the fine specimens of which give off myriad colored flashes of light. The terms *pin point, harlequin,* and *flash* refer to the character of the pattern in black opals.

*Opalescence* is a property possessed by few minerals; it is the pearly reflection seen in moonstone.

Fibrous minerals possess *chatoyance*. Of the gems which are chatoyant, cat's-eye, tiger's-eye, and the satin spar are typical. These stones are nearly always cut cabochon for the best effect. *Asterism*, similar to chatoyance, owing to regularly arranged inclusions in gems, is caused by the action of light on the internal structure of the stone. When cut cabochon and properly oriented, these gems exhibit a silky star with rays radiating from the center of the stone, the number of rays varying with the type of mineral. Asteriated rubies and sapphires, known as star rubies and star sapphires, have a six-rayed star. Some rose quartz also has *asterism*. Garnets sometimes exhibit this property, and in these gems the rays are four in number. On rare occasions the rays in asteriated stones may be multiple owing to twinning in the crystal.

*Schiller* is the bright sheenlike reflection caused by light acting upon inclusions arranged in parallel position within a stone. This is commonly seen in the sunstone.

*Iridescence* consists of spectrumlike colors reflected from the surface or from the interior of a mineral. Upon the surface the phenomenon has been observed as a result of alteration of the mineral. Iridescence, common in corundum gems, ruby and sapphire, seen in the interior of a mineral is caused by light reflecting upon regularly arranged inclusions.

Dispersion is that property of a gemstone which breaks up the white light into its component colors. Some stones possess this property to a high degree. Thus, when properly cut and polished, the diamond, zircon, demantoid, sphene, and benitoite exhibit flashing rainbowlike colors which may be seen by the unaided eye. Other stones, *e.g.,* amethyst, citrine, rock crystal, aquamarine, topaz, are very weak in dispersion.

In a large number of cases it may be observed that the imitation stones show a greater degree of dispersion than the stones which they imitate, for high dispersion is possessed by few gemstones. The admixture of a large amount of lead oxide to the other substances forming the glass (strass) used in the imitations is not only responsible for the fine dispersion possessed by the glass, but it also increases the density of the material. These two qualities, excellent dispersion and high specific gravity, are characteristic of most imitations and usually differ widely from the genuine stone they imitate.

Specific gravity is the ratio of the weight of a substance to the weight of an equal volume of water. The specific gravity of a gem is always greater than 1.00. To illustrate: one cubic centimeter of water weighs one gram, and one cubic centimeter of rock crystal weighs 2.65 grams. The specific gravity of rock crystal is therefore stated as 2.65. Specific gravity is an important means of identifying gems. The composition of ordinary minerals varies greatly and the specific gravity of small quantities varies as widely as a result of these differences. Gem minerals on the contrary are usually pure and nearly constant in composition, and their specific gravity is so uniform that identification by determination of specific gravity is quite accurate.

Several methods of ascertaining the specific gravity of gems are available. The simplest and quickest of these is with the use of heavy liquids of predetermined specific gravity. Methylene iodide, which is commonly used, has specific gravity of 3.31 and may be thinned with benzine to any desired specific gravity of lower density. When kept on hand for use as an indicator, it is particularly valuable and time saving for the rapid identification of gems of similar color or appearance. Thus, if four colorless stones — rock crystal, beryl (goshenite), phenacite, and topaz — are placed in methylene iodide solution of 2.67 sp. gr., the rock crystal will float because its specific gravity is only 2.65; the beryl (sp. gr., 2.67 to 2.7) will remain suspended in the liquid or will sink very slowly; phenacite (specific gravity 3.1) and topaz (specific gravity 3.6) will sink at once. If the specific gravity of the liquid is changed to 3.2, the phenacite will float and the topaz will sink to the bottom of the vessel. Gemstones, previously identified and of known specific gravity, may be kept in the liquid as reference pieces or indicators. Methylene iodide has one disadvantage: upon exposure to light, the iodine is liberated and the liquid becomes dark so that the motion of the gems is difficult to observe.

It is a familiar phenomenon that water has a buoyant effect upon a body when it is immersed. This fact makes it possible to determine the relative density, or weight, of a body by comparing its weight in water with the weight of the volume of the water displaced. For determining the specific gravity of small gems or fragments of precious stones, the pyncnometer may be used.

The specific gravity of large bodies may be determined by displace-

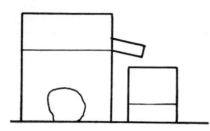

Fig. **2-14.** Determination of specific gravity by the displacement method.

ment with the use of simple apparatus. The stone is first weighed in air and is then inserted in a water-filled container fitted with an outlet arranged to maintain the water at a uniform level (Fig. 2–14). When the stone is immersed, an amount of water equal in volume to the volume of the stone drains off into a glass. The weight of the water drawn off is determined by deducting the weight of the dry glass from the weight of the glass with the water. The specific gravity is then determined by the simple equation:

$$\text{Specific gravity:} \quad \frac{\text{Weight of the stone in the air}}{\text{Weight of the contents of the glass}}$$

Specific gravity is accurately determined by means of the analytical balance (Fig. 2–15). The additional equipment required consists of a small table or platform constructed to clear the pan while placed between the bow. Upon this platform a beaker is placed which contains water. A fine wire is suspended from the hook on the beam the end of which reaches into the water. The wire usually has the form of a small

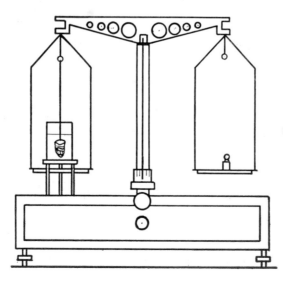

Fig. **2-15.** Analytical balance.

basket into which the stone is placed while being totally submerged in the water and weighed. Care should be exercised to prevent the wire or the bow from touching or rubbing against the beaker on the small table throughout the oscillation of the beam. The weight of the wire attached to the hook must be compensated for by the addition of proper weights on the opposite pan. To obtain the specific gravity of a gem, the stone is first weighed in the air, after which it is placed in the small basket on the end of the wire and is suspended in the water.

The wire as well as the stone must be free of air bubbles. By wetting the stone before placing it in the basket such air bubbles can be avoided. Having determined the weight of the stone while suspended in the water, a simple arithmetical calculation enables us to determine the specific gravity thus:

$$\text{Specific gravity:} \quad \frac{\text{Weight in air}}{\text{Weight in air} - \text{weight in water}}$$

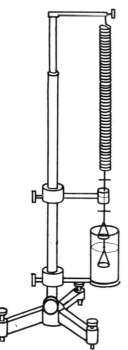

The specific gravity of a gem may be determined accurately and quickly with the use of the Jolly balance (Fig. 2-16). This balance consists of a vertical column fixed to a base fitted with leveling screws. To the column is attached a fixed scale and a movable rod having a right-angled extension at the top. To this extension is attached a coil spring with two pans fixed below, one of which is constantly submerged in water while making the tests. A simple Jolly-type balance like that illustrated has great accuracy and is at the same time simple and inexpensive to construct.

A simple and accurate specific-gravity balance is shown in Figure 2–17. This balance, the design of the late Prof. Austin F. Rogers of Stanford University, is simple in operation and may be constructed without difficulty. It will give accurate readings to the second place in decimals. This apparatus consists of a graduated beam supported near one end by a knife edge. Two pans are hung on the short end of the beam in such a manner that one pan is kept constantly submerged. The path of the long end of the beam is restricted by a guard which limits the motion of the beam.

**Fig. 2-16.** Jolly balance.

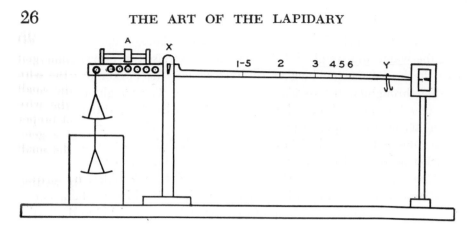

**Fig. 2-17.** Rogers specific-gravity balance.

The long arm of the beam is graduated so that the specific gravity is read directly. A counterpoise is placed in the notch at $y$ which is 15 in. from the fulcrum point $x$; above the beam at the short end is placed a compensating device consisting of a knurled nut on a screw $a$. The graduations up to 5 (more may be added, although they are not needed for weighing gems) are ratios of the distance between the two points $x$ and $y$. Thus, for specific gravity 2.00, the distance is ½ of 15 in., or 7.5 in. from $y$. Specific gravity 3.00 will be at a point 5 in. from $y$, and specific gravity 5.00 will be at a point 3 in. from $y$, and so on.

To operate, the beam is first balanced by means of the compensating device, the lower pan being submerged in the water. The stone is placed in the upper pan, and the counterpoise is placed at $y$. Sufficient riders, small bits of bent wire, are added to the counterpoise so that the beam becomes balanced and the beam point is in line with the indicator. The stone is then carefully wetted and placed in the lower pan, and care is taken to remove any air bubbles. In this position the counterpoise draws the beam end down owing to the buoyant force of the water upon the submerged stone. By sliding the counterpoise along the beam until a point is reached where the beam point is again even with the indicator, the specific gravity is read from the graduations and the result obtained is positive and accurate.

## OPTICAL PROPERTIES

The study of the optical properties of gems requires the use of special optical apparatus. While there are many types of optical instruments, each of which has special use, only those which are necessary to the practical classification of gems are described here.

**Fig. 2-18.** Single eye loupe. Louvers inside of frame prevent fogging of lens and permit normal sight with the eye when the loupe is used over long periods.

**Fig. 2-19.** Double eye loupe.

The most useful optical instrument required in the study of gems is the familiar magnifier or eye loupe (Figs. 2–18 and 2–19). This instrument may be had in a variety of powers, although the examination of the internal structure of stones a magnifying power from 10x to 15x is ample.

For the purpose of examining the surface of a gem, while it is being cut and polished, the use of a loupe of 3x is satisfactory. This instrument is particularly useful, for after a little practice it may be held in the eye socket thus leaving both hands free to properly hold and orient the stone while making an examination or to manipulate the grinding and polishing apparatus used to work a stone. The pocket magnifier (Fig. 2–20) may also be used.

Another form of magnifier, particularly useful for the examination of the internal structure of gems, is the triple aplanatic folding magnifier (Fig. 2–20). This instrument is composed of three lenses set in a folding frame which may be attached to a chain to safeguard against loss. The advantage of this instrument over the regular type loupe is in the optical corrections inherent in its construction, affording a clearer vision and freedom from distortion over a wider field. As all of these instruments are manually controlled, powers greater than 15x are not satisfactory for average use. Stronger glasses require greater steadiness in focusing than is possible with the unaided hand.

For special research work, monocular and wide-field binocular microscopes (Fig. 2–21) are useful. However, for the microscopical examina-

**Fig. 2-20.** Pocket magnifiers. First, Hastings triplet or triple aplanat, 20x; second, achromatic combination type, 3x, 7x, and 10x; third, Hastings triplet, 10x; fourth, Hastings triplet, 14x; fifth, doublet.

tion of gems, from a practical point of view, a magnifying power greater than 15x is unnecessary. The basic requirements for examining a gem are correct illumination and proper orientation of the stone rather than great magnifying power.

Certain transparent similarly colored stones are most readily distinguished by an instrument known as the dichroscope which permits the observer to determine whether they are single or double refracting stones (Fig. 2–22). In anisotropic or double-refracting minerals the absorption of light varies along the respective axes of the crystal. The stone

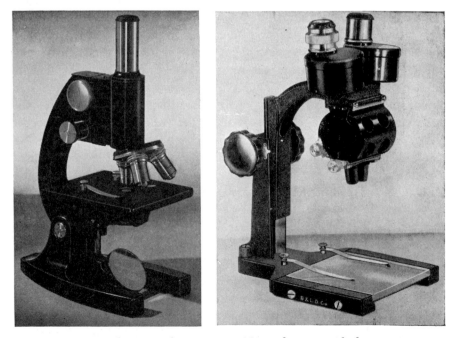

**Fig. 2-21.** Left: Research microscope. Monocular type with three-station revolving nosepiece. Right: Wide-field binocular microscope.

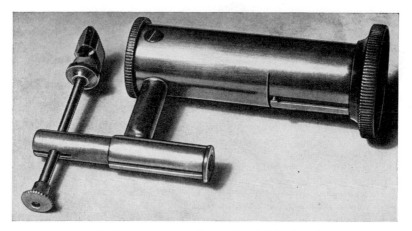

**Fig. 2-22.** Dichroscope. Stone fastened to holder for observation.

consequently appears to have different tones of color when viewed from different directions. Excellent examples of such stones are the deep-hued tourmaline and kunzite which show distinctly different tones when viewed along the main axis and at a right angle thereto.

In a cut stone this property of a clear, colored stone may not be strong enough to be seen by the unaided eye because of the refraction and interference of light in the cut facets. Here the use of a dichroscope (Fig. 2–22), consisting of a brass tube containing a cleavage of Iceland spar, is necessary. Stones to be examined are fixed to a small holder by means of wax, and the holder itself is moved or turned so that the stone may be viewed from all directions. As viewed through the lens, the opening appears double, and stones having pleochroism show two tones of the same color or different colors when properly oriented. This phenomenon is seen twice during each revolution of the stone, the respective colors alternating right and left. Because single-refracting stones show no change in the color tone regardless of the orientation, this instrument is valuable for distinguishing rubies from garnets and spinels, as well as for distinguishing between emerald and glass.

Colorless, double-refracting stones cannot be classified by the use of the dichroscope, and certain varieties of colored stones which have feeble dichroism or single-refracting synthetic spinels, which may possess dichroism owing to internal strain, must be determined by other methods. The most important instrument for this purpose is the refractometer (Figs. 2–23 and 2–24).

A number of portable refractometers are available, the usefulness of

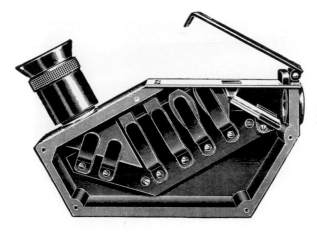

**Fig. 2-23.**
Rayner refractometer.

which is limited by the refractive index of the glass hemisphere. The principle of operation of these instruments is based on the total reflection of light entering the instrument onto a graduated scale from which the refractive index is read directly. This instrument is particularly valuable for the classification of mounted stones, the broad table being placed upon the hemispherical lens of the refractometer. Accurate results may be read to the second place of decimals.

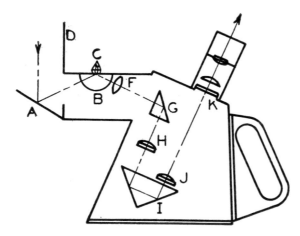

**Fig. 2-24.** Optical diagram of Tully refractometer: A, reflector; B, dense glass hemisphere; C, gem under test; D, velvet-lined screen; F, H, and J, lenses; G and I, prisms; K, scale.

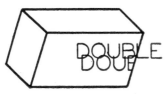

**Fig. 2-25.** Double refraction shown by transparent cleavage of calcite, called Iceland spar.

The property of double refraction, in varying degree inherent in most gemstones, is best shown by a transparent cleavage of calcite, called Iceland spar (Fig. 2–25). Objects viewed through the cleavage will appear double.

The refractive index also may be determined by immersion (Becke test).

# CHAPTER 3

# Classification of Gems

FOR centuries man has endeavored to imitate nature in the production of gemstones, and he has succeeded remarkably well in producing gems of commercial importance. In every reproduction, however, some peculiarity of internal structure remains which distinguishes these artificial gems from those produced by nature.

One of the simplest and most important optical instruments used in the classification of gems is the double eye loupe (Fig. 2–19), which has power of magnifying an object 14 to 15 times its actual size. While it is necessary to possess and to be able to use correctly and accurately the apparatus and instruments described in Chapter 2, if a wide variety of gems is to be classified or studied, all of this equipment seldom is required for a single classification.

Adequate lighting is essential. The most practical is a 100-watt Mazda lamp with reflector, the beam of light being normal to the line of sight when using the optical instruments.

When using the eye loupe, skillful handling is, of course, necessary. This skill can be acquired through constant practice and careful observation. A lapidary must have an accurate knowledge of the crystallographic structure as well as the types of faults characteristic of the gems he is studying, and with the ability to recognize these telltale signs a greater number of gems may be more readily recognized with a simple eye loupe than with any other optical instrument. The external as well as the internal markings or indicators may be examined with a loupe. Proper orientation of the gem being examined is also of great importance for only by proper orientation in an adequate light can the various fine lines, minute striae, bubbles, cavities, or inclusions be seen. Too little emphasis has been placed upon this important phase of the classification of gems. As a result, academic knowledge of gems gained by a student or layman in normal study and application is of little practical value without the use of needed scientific apparatus.

The majority of gemstones examined are cut and polished, and a large number of these are worn or abraded after they have been in use, which naturally results in altering the quality of the surface finish. Therefore, a full knowledge of all the characteristics of stones is necessary to make a lapidary proficient in gem classification. Some of the many characteristics possessed by gemstones that may be observed through the eye loupe are as follows:

SURFACE INDICATORS. Luster is a quality possessed by all gemstones in varying degrees. Provided a stone is perfectly cut and polished, the degree of luster will vary according to the nature of the material and its refractive index. An excellent example for study may be had in the various doublets composed of glass and garnet. The joining plane of these two materials is readily seen, and the quality of the luster on the polished surface of the two different substances composing the unit is in high contrast.

In the case of worn stones, the flat facets of the hard gem stones retain a considerable degree of polish and brilliance in spite of the abraded and rounded facet edges and points. By comparison, the worn surfaces of the softer imitations are quite dull. Badly worn soft gemstones cannot readily be distinguished from the imitation, but as the worn surface usually is the crown or top of the stone, the back facets invariably retain a large amount of their original luster. These soft stones are rarely seen, because the majority of gemstones in commerce are equal in hardness to or harder than quartz.

Should further analysis be necessary, a simple hardness test may prove necessary. The determination of the refractive index should follow if a refractometer is available, and a specific gravity test may be necessary.

Because of their greater hardness, properly finished gemstones usually possess a higher degree of polish and the facet edges are sharper than those of imitation stones. While this is generally true, a properly polished imitation stone may equal in appearance the stone which has been copied. In this case, a simple hardness test or the use of the dichroscope may be sufficient to distinguish between the two.

SURFACE FAULTS. Cleavage planes in a stone may leave small cracks, flakes on the surface of the facet, or small chips at the girdle edge (Fig. 3–1). These chips show bright flat surfaces and, if numerous, they may be arranged in a series of steps resulting from the blow or shock that removed portions of the stone from successive cleavage planes.

Parting planes resemble cleavage planes in a cut stone, although it is difficult to distinguish one from the other because they appear at the surface of the stone as flat chips or cracks, or fine parallel lines. These

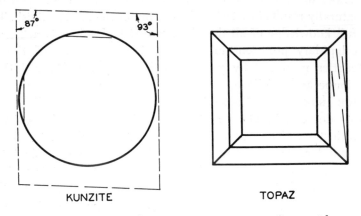

KUNZITE    TOPAZ

**Fig. 3-1.** Cleavage planes seen in gem stones. Stone with circular girdle shows cleavage planes and relationship to planes of cleavage in original crystal.

planes are conclusive proof that the stone is genuine and not imitation.

Etch figures are interesting surface faults which may be seen as small irregular hollow patches in an otherwise perfect surface. The polished facet may also exhibit a rippled surface, a structural defect seen in amethyst.

## PHOTOMICROGRAPHS OF INCLUSIONS IN GEMSTONES

In over a quarter of a century devoted to the study of gems, many thousands have been examined. With acquired familiarity, it often has been possible to classify a gem through the recognition of a small fault that is characteristic of the species (Fig. 3–1).

Although the majority of less valuable gems are usually free of imperfections, those that do contain faults are not always suitable for photographing. Therefore, many years may elapse before a representative collection has been acquired to illustrate all subjects mentioned.

The photomicrographs of gems in the author's collection, Figures 3–2 to 3–31, are typical. While a few of the pictures are from thin sections, the majority are from faceted stones. To counteract reflection and glare when viewing the stone by transmitted light through the microscope, the faceted stones were properly oriented, mounted in a cell with the aid of plasticene, and submerged in monobromonaphthalene.

**Fig. 3-2.** Synthetic ruby (old type), 40x. An early type showing the characteristic curved growth lines and great quantities of gas bubbles (dark spots). This stone was cut from a small boule which is responsible for the pronounced curves which have small radii. The dark curved lines are caused by sudden addition of the pigment which appears to have been poorly mixed with the alumina powder before fusion.

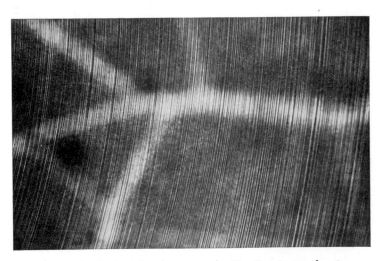

**Fig. 3-3.** Synthetic ruby (new type), 40x. Late type showing characteristic curved lines. The successive accumulations of material can readily be seen. This stone, cut from a large boule, shows the radii of the lines considerably larger than the preceding specimen. The dark spots are large gas bubbles out of focus in the field.

**Fig. 3-4.** Synthetic sapphire, 40x. Characteristic curved growth lines seen in synthetic sapphire having a dark blue tone (Oriental sapphire type). The brilliant straight line seen at the bottom of the picture is caused by light reflection at the juncture of two facets of the stone. By comparing the growth lines with this straight line, it can be readily seen that the growth lines are curved.

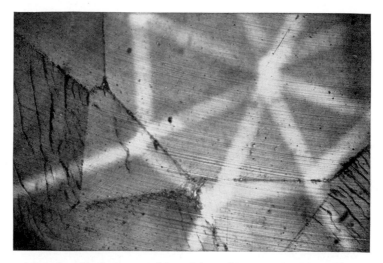

**Fig. 3-5.** Synthetic sapphire (alexandrite type), 20x. The characteristic curved growth lines, common in all synthetic corundum, may be readily seen across the field. Numerous gas bubbles also are present. The fissures or small crevices, in the surface of the facets at the left and bottom right, are often seen in the older synthetic corundum gems and are caused by improper polishing, referred to as burning.

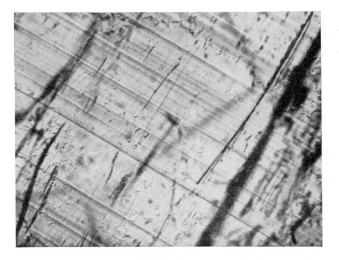

**Fig. 3-6.** Emerald (Colombia), 60x. Regularly oriented parallel growth lines may be seen crossing the field from top left to bottom right corners. These growth lines which vary in width and density may be seen by proper orientation of the gemstone. They are caused by successive accumulations of emerald differing slightly in color density. Numerous liquid filled cavities, fissures, and capillary tubes crossing at approximately right angles to the striae also may be seen.

In no case was it necessary to magnify beyond 60x in order to obtain sharp images and clear pictures.

Internal inclusions are many and varied, and although their presence has a detrimental effect on the value of the gem, as indicators, they are the most important means for identification. This is particularly true if the ruby, sapphire, or emerald is compared with the synthetic product.

The inclusions to be observed may be striae, growth pattern, lines or bands, capillary tubes, gas bubbles, cavities, liquid inclusions in cavities, gaseous inclusions in cavities, solid inclusions of primary minerals, negative crystals, flaws or cracks, feathers, or schiller (Figs. 3–2 to 3–31).

Striae may be seen as fine lines within the gem. These lines are similar to the lines or bands of color of various densities and hues which follow the growth pattern, for striae result from successive stages in the growth of the crystal. This defect may often be observed in the emerald. Because of the interference of light (owing to the accumulation of mineral during the growth of the crystal), the gem lacks limpidity and the streaked internal structure imparts a soft velvetlike appearance to the stone.

A similar effect may be seen in the synthetic corundum gems, particularly the ruby, in which striae result from accumulation. In this case, however, the striae are oriented in parallel curved streaks, the appearance by transmitted light being similar to curved brush marks on a painted surface (Fig. 3–3).

The striae observed in glass are characteristic of this material, because they are irregular, sometimes curving in all directions in the mass. The irregular nature of the striae is caused by agitation during the melting of the glass or through flow in the molding process. The presence of irregular striae seen in a gemlike substance are a certain indication of an imitation or glass (Fig. 3–7).

THE GROWTH PATTERN is a characteristic seen in varying degree in a wide variety of gemstones, natural as well as synthetic. This is a common feature of the corundum gems, ruby and sapphire, where it may be observed as straight bands of varying width (Fig. 3–8), straight bands intersecting at an angle of 60 or 120 degrees (Fig. 3–9), or as a complete hexagonal pattern.

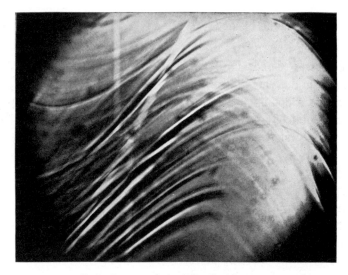

**Fig. 3-7.** Imitation amethyst (glass), 25x. Striae in glass imitations may be readily distinguished by the manner in which they curve in numerous directions. As most imitation stones are formed in molds by pressing a suitable blank of melted glass, the plastic mass flows, filling the mold, and in this process the striae are formed. The dark spots are gas bubbles out of focus.

**Fig. 3-8.** Sapphire (Ceylon), 60x. The parallel growth lines seen in this specimen are composed of successive depositions of clear, colorless sapphire alternating with clear, blue sapphire. High magnification fails to reveal rutile inclusions in the growth bands. Numerous slight cracks may be seen crossing the growth lines at an angle approximately 45 deg. thereto.

**Fig. 3-9.** Ruby (Burma), 40x. Regularly oriented minute rutile crystals in dense feltlike masses almost completely fill the field, causing opacity, and give a milky character to the stone. The bright portions of the picture free of inclusions are brilliant, clear ruby red. The rutile crystals follow the crystallographic law of the species and the growth lines which cross at 120 deg.

**Fig. 3-10.** Sapphire (Ceylon), 40x. Regularly oriented crystals of rutile in sapphire. These inclusions in slender, hairlike form crisscross at 60 or 120 deg., and follow the crystallographic law of the species. Rutile is invariably present in varying degrees in all of the corundum gems. Negative crystals, or liquid-filled cavities enclosing gas, also may be seen.

**Fig. 3-11.** Garnet (Ceylon), 40x. Regularly oriented hairlike crystals of rutile may be seen distributed throughout this specimen. These crystals crisscross at angles of 70 and 110 deg., corresponding to the angles on the face of the rhombic dodecahedron. Through inclusions of this type, garnet is readily distinguished from ruby or spinel.

The lines or bands of the growth pattern vary in character. They may be bands of a deeper hue or stripes a shade darker than the body of the stone. Again the bands or stripes may be opaque or translucent, resulting from myriad inclusions (Fig. 3–9).

High-power microscopic examination often reveals these bands as containing large quantities of fine hairlike crystals of rutile (Fig. 3–9). or the bands may contain a multitude of cavities with liquid inclusions, both of which are responsible for the opacity of the band.

At times numerous capillary tubes of microscopic size in parallel position may be seen exhibiting a silky texture by reflected light. This fault, known as "silk," is common in the corundum gems.

Large crystals of rutile may be oriented in directions parallel to one of the crystallographic axes of the crystal (Figs. 3–10 and 3–11), or they may crisscross exhibiting the characteristic hexagonal pattern. These oriented inclusions are readily discerned in the body of the stone by transmitted light.

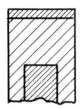

Fig. 3-12. Growth phenomena in tourmaline. Prism section: deep pink cap and core; remainder: pale pink.

The growth pattern and lines are seen in other transparent gems. Tourmaline is the most spectacular example, particularly the specimens having parti-colored cross sections (Figs. 2–1 and 3–12). Growth pattern also may be observed in the quartz gems, amethyst, citrine, and rock crystal. In amethyst the bands are of a darker shade, or smoky brown often may be seen. In rock crystal, phantoms are particularly prominent. Some remarkable examples recently found in Brazil appear almost like ribbon agate (Fig. 3–13).

As the growth lines and bands are parallel to a crystal face, measuring the angle of intersection of two lines will give the interfacial angle of two faces of the crystal. This may serve as an important clue to the identity of the mineral.

The growth pattern may be seen to advantage in a number of opaque stones as chalcedony of various types, particularly the agate. Nodules of this material sawed in half exhibit this growth pattern in a striking manner.

Parting planes are frequently seen in ruby and sapphire, particularly in the poor quality cabochon stones though less frequently in the clear faceted gems. They appear as bright parallel fissures within the stone, often similar to capillary tubes and as fine parallel grooves in the surface of the facets in the cut gemstone (Fig. 3–14).

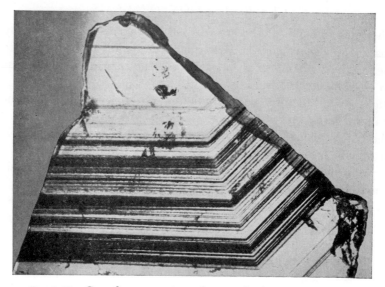

**Fig. 3-13.** Growth pattern in rock crystal, showing successive accumulations of rock crystal (light) and chlorite (dark) on the faces of the crystal. The angle (46° 16′) corresponds to the interfacial angle of the $r$ and $z$ faces of the rhombohedron.

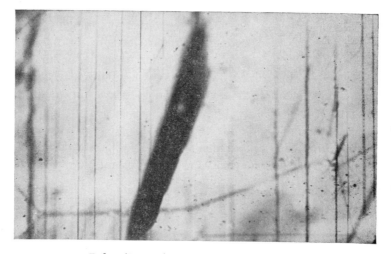

**Fig. 3-14.** Ruby (Burma), 40x. Parting planes are sometimes seen in faceted stones, particularly in the ruby. They appear as bright, parallel fissures within the stone and, as a result of cutting and polishing, fine grooves are left in the facets. In the specimen illustrated, the fine grooves extend across several adjacent facets and may be readily distinguished from polish marks on the facets. The large dark object in the center of the field is a bladelike fissure reflecting light.

**Fig. 3-15.** Green beryl (Brazil), 60x. Capillary tubes are a common occurrence in beryl and tourmaline. These are often oriented parallel to the prism face. Inclusions of this type are difficult to photograph, particularly when they are of small diameter, and in the picture above, they appear like striae. When the stone is properly oriented and viewed with transmitted light, these inclusions appear in brilliant hairlike clusters.

Capillary tubes, which are fine, hairlike, straight passages within a crystal, may be seen in a number of gems, particularly in aquamarine and other light-hued varieties of beryl as well as topaz and tourmaline (Fig. 3–15). These fine tubes are usually, though not always, oriented in a position parallel to a crystallographic axis. In the tourmaline they are sometimes present in dense masses parallel to the longitudinal or *c* axis. Cabochon stones cut from such material having the girdle edge parallel to the tubes will exhibit a cat's-eye effect. They are then called tourmaline cat's-eyes.

Gas bubbles are faults commonly seen in synthetic and imitation stones. They are usually round but they may also be oval, olive, or pear shaped. Occasionally three or more bubbles connected in line produce a wormlike form. Bubbles may be seen as isolated units in the finest type of glass imitation, synthetic spinel and corundum, or they may be seen in dense clouds, clusters, zones, and stripes or bands (Figs. 3–16 to 3–18).

In the synthetic corundum gems, particularly the blue sapphire, gas bubbles may be seen in curved pattern following the growth pattern or structure of the boule.

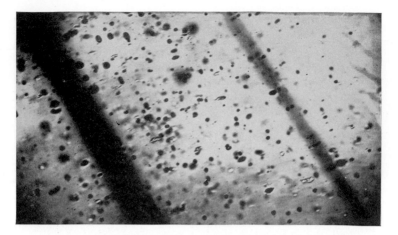

**Fig. 3-16.** Synthetic ruby, 25x. Gas bubbles are common in the synthetic corundum gems. In the specimen shown, a large number fill the field. These are in general round, glandular, or olive formed. Sometimes streams of gas bubbles may have an arclike disposition, being parallel to the curved growth lines.

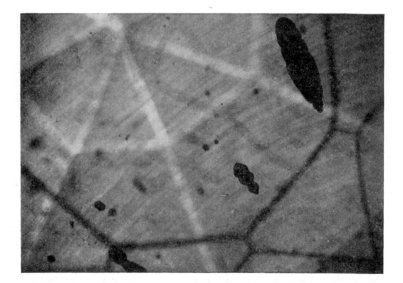

**Fig. 3-17.** Synthetic alexandrite (synthetic alexandrite like corundum), 20x, showing large wormlike gas-filled bubbles formed through the interconnection of several large bubbles during growth. The characteristic curved growth lines also may be seen.

**Fig. 3-18.** Imitation emerald, 45x. Large swarms of gas bubbles, caused by agitation, may be readily seen. These follow the striae and are induced in the glass to imitate natural feathers. They can be readily distinguished from the natural feathers by low-power magnification.

**Fig. 3-19.** Amethyst (Uruguay), 30x. This specimen contains one large and many small negative crystals. The form of these cavities resembles the large crystal of which they form inclusions. All of these cavities contain liquid accompanied with a balance fly gas bubble.

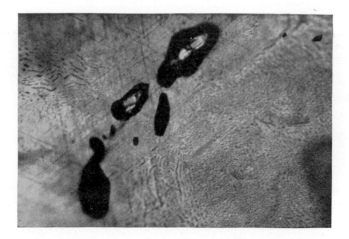

**Fig. 3-20.** Sapphire (Celyon), 60x. Large liquid-filled cavities of irregular shape, accompanied by gas, are in the center of the field. A large quantity of minute liquid-filled cavities fill the background. Numerous acicular crystals of rutile also may be seen.

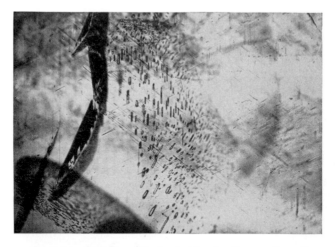

**Fig. 3-21.** Sapphire (Ceylon), 30x. Another portion of the stone pictured in Figure 3-20, showing the construction of the vanelike feathers common in sapphire. Vanes extending through the stone in a number of directions are formed of regularly oriented cavities enclosing liquid and gas. One series, normal to the line of sight, may be seen in the center of the picture. Others to the left and bottom left corner are in different planes and are out of focus. Numerous regularly oriented rutile crystals also may be seen.

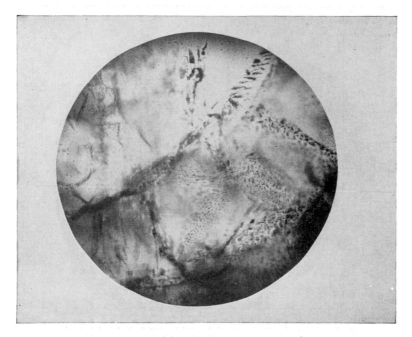

**Fig. 3-22.** 60x. Fine wisplike feathers composed of minute liquid-filled cavities are dispersed in all directions throughout the stone. This photomicrograph is from a thin section parallel to a prism face.

Cavities, which exist only in natural gemstones,* are usually irregular in outline. They always contain liquid inclusions, and sometimes gases are present (Figs. 3–19 to 3–27). At times the cavities may be large and filled with a considerable quantity of liquid (enhydros). At times the liquid may be so viscous that it will move only when the stone is heated. This is particularly true of topaz. In the majority of cases, however, the cavities in gems are small, and, in order to observe the nature of the included substance, examination by a glass of medium magnifying powder usually is necessary.

A cavity which contains gas in addition to liquid often reacts to the changed position of the stone, and, like a spirit level, the gas bubble will move to and fro as the position of the stone is altered. In rare instances inclusions of other minerals also may be present in a cavity.

Negative crystals are cavities resulting from interrupted growth of the crystal. These cavities invariably are of microscopic size and appear as voids having a form related to the parent crystal. They are oriented

---

* The sole exception being the Chatham gemstones (Figs. 3–22 and 23).

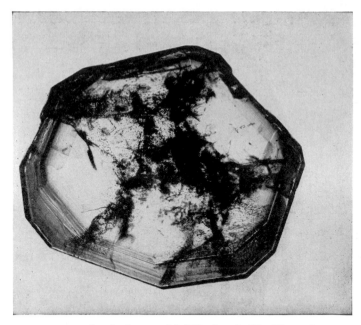

**Fig. 3-23.** Synthetic emerald (Chatham), 15x. Photomicrograph from a thin section cut parallel to the base of the crystal. The growth lines parallel to the faces of the crystal may be readily seen. Fine wisplike feathers characteristic of this substance radiate from the center of the crystal.

**Fig. 3-24.** Emerald (Colombia, 60x. Large fissures (dark areas), numerous cavities, and inclusions seen in a thin section parallel to the prism face of the crystal. All of the cavities forming *feathers* are liquid filled, and a number contain minute cubic crystals of halite, accompanied by balance fly bubble.

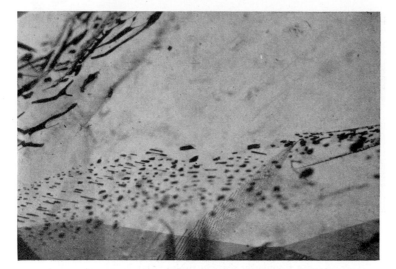

Fig. 3-25. Garnet (Ceylon), 25*x*. The irregular-shaped, liquid-filled cavities form feathers that extend throughout the stone. Several of the large cavities at the top left field are connected by capillary tubes.

in a direction corresponding to the crystal habit and are filled with liquid usually accompanied by gas (Figs. 3–19, 24 and 25).

Cavities are sometimes produced by successive stages of growth following solution. Growth projections (Fig. 3–28) formed on the faces of crystals may produce deep hollows or depressions. Many interesting types can be seen on the faces of diamond crystals.

When the etching caused by solution or the hollows formed by growth projections are filled by later growth, the mineral added to the parent crystal may be discerned as a small irregular outline or patch in the polished surface of a gemstone. Twinning in the crystal develops interesting patterns (Fig. 3–30).

SOLID INCLUSIONS. Besides the hairlike inclusions of rutile already mentioned, other primary minerals may also be included in a gem. Associated minerals which were present in the original magma often become attached to a face of the crystal during the growth of the latter. In the growth process these associated minerals become buried in the crystal, resulting in inclusions. Inclusions of primary minerals may be oriented parallel to the crystallographic axis of a gemstone (Figs. 3–9, 3–10, and 3–11), or they may be distributed in every direction throughout the crystal. At times, through metamorphism, the physical properties of the included mineral are altered to form a different substance.

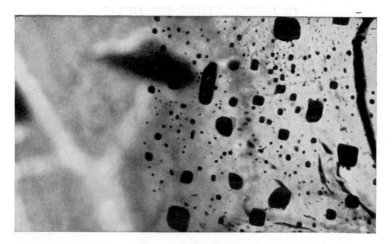

**Fig. 3-26.** Ruby (Burma), 40x. A large number of regularly oriented liquid-filled cavities (negative crystals) are concentrated in one portion of the gemstone. Cavities of this type are frequently seen in rubies from Burma.

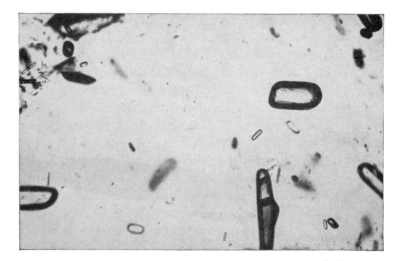

**Fig. 3-27.** Essonite (Ceylon), 30x. A large number of liquid-filled cavities (negative crystals) may be seen extending in all directions throughout the stone. Crystal faces may be seen on the inside wall of the large cavity in the right center. Negative crystals are very common in the essonite variety of garnet.

**Fig. 3-28.** Large garnet crystal showing characteristic growth projections. Weight 1940 grams. Illustration actual size.

**Fig. 3-29.** Synthetic ruby (Fremy), 7x. Photomicrograph of synthetic ruby crystals formed by Fremy, *circa* 1877. The crystals are tabular in habit and are generally formed in clusters of two or more. Numerous growth projections may be seen on the face of the largest crystal in the center of the field.

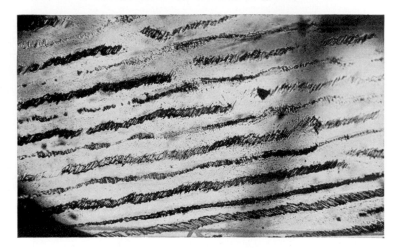

**Fig. 3-30.** Amethyst (Brazil), 30x.

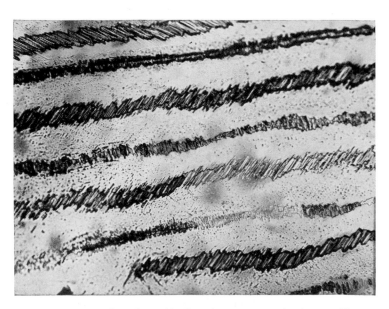

**Fig. 3-31.** Amethyst (Brazil), 70x. Photomicrograph of a vanelike feather of unusual structure completely fills the field. Feathers of this type, which are common in amethyst and citrine, are different from any previously shown. While these feathers appear to be caused by multiple twinning, higher magnification shows a strong resemblance to minute capillary tubes in parallel position.

The angle of intersection of the included crystals may serve as an indication of the species. Thus rutile, as regularly oriented inclusions in ruby, sapphire, and garnet, will cross at angles corresponding to the crystallographic laws of the species. If viewed normal to the bedding plane of the oriented inclusion, the rutile crystals in the corundum gems intersect at angles of 60 and 120 deg. (Figs. 3–9 and 3–10). In garnet the angles of intersection are 70 and 110 deg., the angles corresponding to the angles on the face of a rhombic dodecahedron (Fig. 3–11).

*Flaws or cracks* are common in gems, and when present they may be readily observed. These faults result from a number of causes, as sudden changes in temperature during the growth process, or from blows sustained in rolling about in stream beds, or from shock resulting from mining and handling operations.

In the majority of cases large flaws or cracks are removed in the cutting process, for these faults interfere with the passage of light through a stone and seriously impair its brilliance and beauty. Occasionally, through abuse, flaws or cracks are introduced into a gem after it has been cut and polished.

As a rule these cracks are bright bladelike fissures which may be seen by reflected light (Figs. 3–14 and 3–24). Sometimes the cracks exhibit brilliant interference colors. Flaws and cracks are common in the corundum gems, and they are often wholly or partly filled with iron oxide which imparts a brown stain to that portion of the stone. These latter faults serve as excellent indicators of natural gemstones, for they are never seen in synthetic stones.

*Flaws and cracks* may be seen in the synthetic gems as well. A peculiarity of this material is the small grizzly cracks seen in the surface of the polished facets (Fig. 3–5). These cracks are developed in the polishing of the stone, and they are probably a result of internal strain in the material. Cracks of this type are common in the synthetic corundum gems and are rarely seen in the natural stones, and then only as a result of improper polishing. It has been observed that these grizzled cracks have been seen only in the corundum gemstones.

*Feathers* are among the most interesting of the inclusions to be found in gems. These are cavities wholly filled or partly filled with a liquid accompanied by gas, arranged, as the name indicates, in a feather-like formation. Feathers are to be seen in a large variety of forms and shapes, ranging from small wisplike formations to cloudlike masses which may completely fill a stone and make it nearly opaque.

These formations may be fanlike, extending in a flat plane. This form is common in the amethyst (Fig. 3–30). Or they may be curved or irregular, as commonly found in the sapphire (Fig. 3–21). Small isolated inclusions of this nature may be seen and, as their orientation is not governed by crystallographic laws, series of feathers may intersect at various angles, filling the body of the stone. The fan type, which is the most common, usually consists of a series of long slender cavities arranged in a flat or curved plane, and when viewed by reflected light the fan exhibits a rippled formation.

*Feathers* in the synthetic emerald serve as an important means of distinguishing this gem from the natural stone. Feathers in both of these substances are characteristic and distinctive. The feathers in the synthetic gem are fine wisplike masses, extending in various directions like the branches of a tree, a type or form up to the present time peculiar to this gem. Feathers in the natural material are jagged cracks or cavities, with inclusions (Fig. 3–24), similar to those common in the other types of beryl. Dichroism in the synthetic emerald is also stronger. The yellow-green and blue-green are more pronounced.

Featherlike formations may also be seen in imitation stones, particularly in the imitation emerald. In this case, the featherlike fault is a fanlike series of gas or air bubbles which may readily be discerned by careful examination with a loupe or hand lens (Fig. 3–18).

In attempting to classify or identify the species of a gem in hand, careful examination of the surface of the stone should be made with the aid of an eye loupe by reflected light, searching for those indicators or telltale signs already described. The most prominent surface features to be observed are luster and the quality of the polish on the facets or surface of the stone. Often a gem may be recognized by the examination of the girdle edge alone. This is true of most imitations, doublets, triplets, and the diamond.

If further examination is necessary, the stone is carefully inspected by transmitted light. Holding the stone in the position illustrated in Figure 3–32 gives an effect similar to dark field illumination under the microscope, and prominently illuminates the interior of the stone, enabling one to see distinctly inclusions, etc. Further testing to determine the hardness of the gem may be necessary, and if this is not conclusive, the refractometer should then be used.

From practical experience, recourse to the specific gravity test is rarely necessary, and in the majority of cases, the eye loupe is the only instrument required.

It is well to begin the study of the various physical and optical proper-

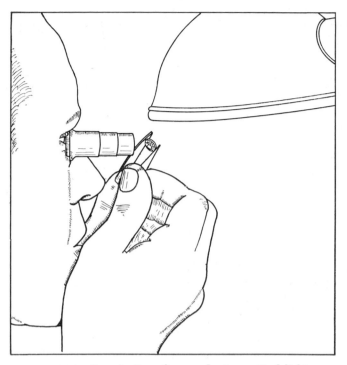

**Fig. 3-32.** Examination of a gem by transmitted light.

ties of gemstones with a stone that is unique. A typical example is the zircon.* Some of its characteristics are outstanding. Its high specific gravity is evident in its greater proportional weight compared with other stones of the same size; adamantine luster is easily noted, and the beautiful play of spectrum colors in sunlight is a feature possessed by few gems. In sunlight, the spectrum images cast upon a white card or paper lie in pairs in vivid color, one above the other, distinctly and widely separated. These features are indications of double refraction and high dispersive powers. The double refraction of this stone* is so great that when the edges of the back facets are carefully examined by means of a 10- to 15-power loupe, looking at them through the table or front of the stone by transmitted light, they appear to be doubled. The edges of the facets are duplicated and appear slightly offset (Fig. 3–33), the effect being somewhat similar to phantoms in rock crystal.*

As color play is the chief characteristic of the zircon, it follows that,

* Characteristics possessed by the heat-treated stones. Natural untreated zircons exhibit these features less prominently.

to obtain the best results, the stone must be properly cut and polished. The best results are obtained in a brilliant cut, with the front angle 43 deg. and the back angle 40 deg. with respect to the girdle edge. This gives a steeply sloped crown on the top, cut at an angle distinctly greater than is usual in other gems, and it is readily distinguished from the crown-facet angle on a properly polished diamond (front slope or angle from 33 to 35 deg.), the only other stone in common use that it resembles (Fig. 3–34). Most of these observations may be made with the eye alone or aided with a 10-power loupe.

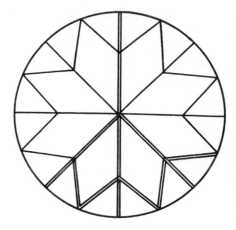

Fig. 3-33. Doubling of back facet edges in strongly doubly refracting stones, viewed through table with transmitted light. NOTE: Doubling effect is only partially drawn to avoid confusion as the eye can focus on only one set of facets at a time.

In a similar manner the diamond may be distinguished from all other colorless stones. It is capable of receiving and retaining the finest polish with high adamantine luster, with flat facets meeting in sharp edges and points free from any trace of roundness. As the stone polishes very slowly, the facets may be precisely spaced because the control is accurate. The facets are consequently more perfectly formed, and in the majority of cases the back facets are directly behind the front ones, which is seldom the case in other round stones.

The front slope or crown facets (fine modern cut) are at an angle of 33 to 35 deg. Dispersion and projected spectrum images of brilliant coloring are single because of the single refracting nature of the stone.

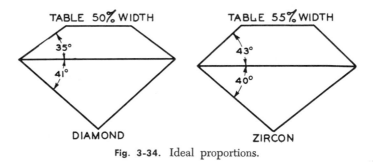

TABLE 50% WIDTH

35°

41°

DIAMOND

TABLE 55% WIDTH

43°

40°

ZIRCON

Fig. 3-34. Ideal proportions.

The girdle edge of a round, brilliant-cut diamond is rarely polished. In most cases the edge is rough, having a finish similar to finely ground glass. In some places it has a peculiar sheen, the result of minute particles having been cleaved off in rounding the stone on a lathe. If the girdle is polished, a series of small facets usually will surround the stone.*

In the majority of cases, several of the original crystal faces, ranging in number from one to four, according to the shape of the original stone, may be seen on the girdle edge. These are bright and brilliant, and close examination may disclose a slight irregularity of the surface, portions of the original crystal. As the material is very valuable, the cutter, in rounding up the stone, removes as little as possible; thus portions of the original crystal faces remain at the edge. An eye loupe or magnifying glass may disclose small matrix spots and inclusions, erroneously called carbon spots, also cracks or faults, all of which are characteristic.

Thus, with a knowledge of the subject and a proper light source supplementing an eye loupe, these as well as other gems may be distinguished without difficulty. The eye loupe or magnifier is the only instrument required to classify the synthetic corundums that possess definite hue, and to distinguish them from the natural stones. The curved lines in synthetic corundums (Figs. 3–2 to 3–5), owing to growth or uneven distribution of color, are well known and are characteristic of this material. The difficulty experienced by most students of gem science has been inability to locate or recognize these lines which are always curved and vary considerably in character. As a general rule, the lines in the blue sapphire are denser than the body color of the stone (Fig. 3–4). Sometimes these lines or zones are composed of streams of minute bubbles, and in rare cases (in light-tinted stones) the lines are so fine as to be distinguished only with difficulty. Often they have an appearance similar to the streaks left by a brush on a painted surface. With proper orientation, an adequate light source, and a 15-power loupe, the lines may be seen without difficulty. A well-shaded drop lamp of 100 watts capacity provides sufficient light. To understand what to look for and why in a synthetic corundum, it is necessary to study closely the material in the rough (Fig. 3–35). The rough masses, known as boules, are pear shaped. They are formed in an inverted position during the growth period and are built up on a little neck. This growth process causes the circular lines to appear at the outer surface of the boule, for the top is kept in a molten state while the fused alumina is assimilated drop by drop. During this process the top of

---

* One firm has introduced diamonds with circular polished girdle.

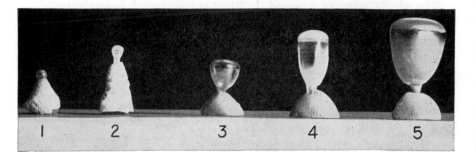

**Fig. 3-35.** Growth of boules (synthetic corundum). 1 and 2, small boules attached to clay pedestals; 3, 4, and 5, finished boules of various sizes. 1, 3, and 5, synthetic ruby; 2, synthetic colorless sapphire; 4, synthetic yellow sapphire. All boules show the characteristic domed top, outward form of growth lines or curved lines seen in all of the colored stones when cut. Boules 3, 4, and 5 are supported on plasticine bases.

the boule is crowned or domed and, as it flows from the addition of the molten material, the outer edge cools and the curved lines and zones are formed. Also, in the blue corundum the pigment tends to concentrate at the outer zone in the boule because of the turbulence caused by the pressure or blast of the gases and flame of the blowpipe. As a result, the center of the boule is often nearly colorless. After the process has been completed and the boule is cooled, it is under enormous internal strain. Sometimes cracks appear, and as a rule the boule will break in half longitudinally when the tip is broken off. The two halves are then ready and ideal for cutting. Thus, in cutting large stones, it is necessary to use the nearly flat broken face for the table and the curved surface of the boule for the back. Consequently the curved lines may be seen when viewed parallel to the longitudinal axis in a large cut stone. It is well, therefore, in studying synthetic stones, to begin with a synthetic blue sapphire, 12 mm. or more in length, for in a stone of this size the lines are easily discerned.

To hold the stone securely, a tweezer having a locking device is recommended as this enables rapid orientation and ease of handling with little risk of dropping the stone (Fig. 3–36). Large stones (15 carats and up) are more safely handled by the fingers. In making an examination, the stone is first cleaned so that it is free of surface marks or stains. It is then securely grasped between the jaws or tips of the tweezer and locked in position. The stone is then examined by transmitted light, and for best results it is held at the level of the edge of the lamp shade in line with the eye (Fig. 3–32). Here the eye loupe proves of great value for it may

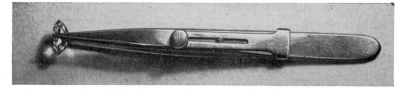

Fig. 3-36. Tweezer with locking device for holding stones.

be held by the eye socket, leaving both hands free to manipulate or hold the tweezer steadily. In using the hand lens, several of the fingers of the hand may steady the other hand holding the tweezer. The initial examination should be made by observation from the culet or back of the stone.

In case the lines are not seen at once, move the stone by tilting it slightly, and look into it from different directions while the light fully illuminates the interior. Clear uniform illumination free of glare is essential. Thus, in one or more positions, the curved lines characteristic of the synthetic corundum gems can be seen. The various types of lines already have been described, and they may be found in all densely to medium-colored synthetic corundums, ruby, sapphire, or alexandrite. In the lighter colored synthetic stones, these curved lines are more difficult to see, and in the colorless types they are impossible to detect. High-power magnification tends to lose the field entirely or cause the lines to appear straight or nearly so, for the arc examined is very short. Some stones have such faults as round gas bubbles, small or large, isolated or in dense concentration, in clouds or zones (Fig. 3–16), and the often present polish cracks in the facets of the stone (Fig. 3–5), which help distinguish them. The smaller stones may be cut from any portion of the boule and require greater dexterity in orientation. Sometimes it is necessary to view the stone from several positions successively before the proper position is attained where the curved lines or other faults may be seen. It is possible to prove that the curved lines viewed are curved and not straight, by comparing them with the facet edges whereby the curvature can be seen immediately (Figs. 3–4 and 3–5).

Natural corundum also has distinguishing characteristics. As the mineral crystallizes in the hexagonal system, the growth pattern is hexagonal and as a result the color lines are arranged in this manner having straight lines (Fig. 3–8). The prominence and the pattern formed by the lines vary considerably with the size of the cut stone. Sometimes a complete hexagonal pattern may be seen, or two or more sides of the hexagon may be observed. Also, the pattern may consist of straight lines filling the field of view, or they may crisscross in a manner parallel to the faces of the original crystal. Acicular rutile crystals in fine hairlike form are invariably included and arranged in this crisscross pattern (Figs. 3–9 and 3–10). These crystals were present before the corundum crystal was formed, or were formed at the same time, and during the growth of the latter they were arranged in the pattern mentioned following the crystallographic laws of this species.

Dense patches or zones of color often have been observed, particularly in the sapphire. This may be in sharp contrast with the remainder of the stone, or it may gradually alter in tint. As a general rule, these color zones show straight-line portions or even boundaries. Contrasting zones of color in the form of mineral inclusions or the concentration of iron-oxide stains in cracks or flaws are common and are readily seen.

Feathers, wisp or weblike inclusions (Fig. 3–21) formed by minute cavities enclosing liquid and bubbles, are common and are present in a majority of corundum gems. They vary in form and size and may be found in any portion of the crystal as their position is not governed by crystallographic laws. They vary also in size and may be only a small, straight, or curved, fanlike, or triangular wisp, or they may completely fill the body of the specimen, crossing in all directions. This defect is common in rock crystal, which provides excellent material for study.

Silk, a term which describes a common imperfection of corundum gems in a most fitting manner, is the shining silky luster exhibited when light is reflected from the stone. It is the effect caused by light acting on the acicular canals or tubes within the crystal. The corundum has microscopic inclusions (rutile) arranged in a pattern similar to the color lines already mentioned. The same crystallographic laws govern the arrangement and distribution of silk and the two are often found together. The crystal structure causing silk as well as asterism to appear have a close relationship.

Cavities are common in corundum, and invariably they are irregular in shape, having an oval, elongated, or worm form (Fig. 3–20). In rare cases, isolated, small, round, liquid-filled cavities have been observed by low-power magnification, not only in the corundum gems but in other minerals as well, including spinel, quartz, beryl, and garnet.

Another distinguishing feature, observed particularly in the ruby, is the presence of parting planes in the form of lines which, if present, may easily be observed in the surface polish when they extend to the surface of the cut stone (Fig. 3–14).

The types of marking, both internal as well as external, are typical of the gems noted and they are not common to both synthetic and natural gems.

Confusion has been experienced among students of gemmology as well as jewelers in regard to the synthetic alexandrite. This is because of a lack of knowledge, as few alexandrites are available on the market and there is little opportunity for study. The synthetic stone is not a synthetic alexandrite as the name implies, but it is a synthetic substance having the physical and chemical as well as optical properties of synthetic corundum. The sole resemblance to alexandrite is a change of color on exposure to artificial light. This change, however, is distinct and peculiar to the synthetic alexandrite. The body of this stone is a grayish green seen best by north light. In daylight the stone shows a magenta cast with green tones, while in artificial light the green is absent and the stone turns a reddish purple similar in tone to the Siberian amethyst. Two dichroic colors are tones of green — bluish green and brownish green.

Natural alexandrite, however, is usually a dark grass green when viewed in daylight (north light) uninfluenced by other light. The tone of color will vary, sometimes being a dark brownish green. The phenomenon of color change will also vary in different specimens, being influenced by the light absorption qualities of each individual gem. As a general rule, the color by match light is a brownish red, and in rare cases only is it a fine raspberry red. The two dichroic colors are green and reddish brown.

These characteristics differ widely from the synthetic alexandrite, for in the latter stone the body color is never free of the magenta cast; and in artificial light, the color is a vivid magenta or amethystine hue.

Even lacking the genuine alexandrite for comparison, no difficulty should be experienced in classifying the synthetic stone, for the telltale curved lines may be seen without difficulty (Fig. 3–5). Swarms of bubbles are nearly always present and polish cracks are also evident.

The synthetic spinels may be considered in a second class or group of synthetic stones. These comprise a large variety of colors, many of which closely resemble the natural stone. Fortunately, however, there is a great difference between these synthetic stones and the natural stones which they simulate. As a general rule, synthetic stones are harder and more brilliant because of their greater refractive index, and the specific gravity differs so greatly that they may be distinguished easily.

Although synthetic spinel is a hard substance, it is brittle, far more so than synthetic corundum. In this respect it resembles heat-treated zircons and is very susceptible to shock. Even mild attrition will cause chipping and spalling on the facets or facet intersections, the edges of which show the effect plainly.

Striation or growth lines in synthetic spinel are rare. As in the synthetic corundum, the lines are curved though rarely seen. Gas bubbles, whether isolated or in patches or clouds, are often present. Anomalous double refraction, caused by internal strain, may be present and may be observed with the use of the polariscope. This is an excellent means of distinguishing the synthetic from the natural spinel. The latter also has cavities, clouds, feathers, and flaws similar to the natural corundum gems.

One synthetic spinel likely to be difficult to distinguish from the natural stone is the light-blue stone resembling aquamarine. Lacking the refractometer, refractive index 1.72, which enables immediate determination, the stone may be classified by noting its greater degree of luster, higher dispersive qualities, and greater density (if unmounted). This is easily observed by heft (provided the specimen is of fair size), shaking the stone in the hand, the difference in specific gravity being distinctly greater (sp. gr. spinel 3.6; sp. gr. aquamarine 2.7).

So-called synthetic zircons (spinel) should cause no difficulty once the respective qualities are known, for the synthetic stone does not possess the brilliance, luster, fire, and degree of refraction characteristic of the natural zircon (heat-treated type). The doubling of the facets (Fig. 3–33) also is absent.

All of the colored varieties of synthetic spinel reflect red in varying degrees. This phenomenon may be observed distinctly in the deep blue stone when examined under incandescent light.

Colorless synthetic spinel can be distinguished from colorless topaz successfully only through proper scientific determination, refraction, and specific gravity.

Those stones which possess strong pleochroism, such as kunzite, hiddenite, iolite, and most tourmalines may be readily distinguished from imitation stones or from synthetic ones which may have a similar appearance. Some of these gems, exhibiting pleochroism, possess this property to such a degree that it may be readily observed by the unaided eye.

SYNTHETIC EMERALD. Feathers in synthetic emerald serve as an excellent means of distinguishing this substance from the natural stone. Small crystals, having the form and appearance of emeralds, were brought to the attention of the author in September, 1940, with the request that he ascertain their true nature.

From existing data these were recognized as being synthetic. A considerable number have since been cut by the author and they are now being produced in commercial quantities. Unlike the other synthetic gemlike substances already marketed (corundum and spinel that are formed in boules), the synthetic emerald occurs as euhedral crystals.

The fissures, inclusions, and growth lines (Figs. 3–22 and 3–23) are at first glance similar to those seen in the natural stone. A very careful examination, however, reveals considerable difference. Fissures are clean cracks in the stone commonly parallel to the c axis. Feathers consist of minute, liquid-filled cavities in fernlike form extending in various directions from the central portion of the crystal.

The dichroic property of the synthetic emerald is more pronounced than in the natural stone, being more intense. The blue-green and yellow-green may be readily observed in the dichroscope and, with a little practice, by the unaided eye. Under fluorescent light, the synthetic stone glows a deep dark red.

In one other respect the synthetic differs from the natural stone in a very pronounced manner for it possesses a very low coefficient of expansion. Heated to red heat, approximately 1450 deg. F. the stone may be plunged into water without injury. A gemstone possessing such a characteristic is appreciated immediately by the artisan, for repair or alteration to an article of jewelry can be made with the least possible danger from cracking as a result of heating.

In the early part of 1959, a number of rubies created by Carroll Chatham were cut by the author. These new gemstones possess the fine pigeon blood color of the best natural rubies, and although they are formed in a characteristic crystal form, it is interesting to note that feathered inclusions are also distinct and resemble those seen in the Chatham emerald (Fig. 3–22).

### TABLE 1. CHARACTERISTICS OF SYNTHETIC AND NATURAL EMERALD

| Origin | Sp. gr. | Refractive index |
|---|---|---|
| Germany synthetic ............... | 2.66 | 1.564–1.566[*] |
| America synthetic ............... | 2.667 | 1.573–1.578[**] |
| Colombia ...................... | 2.698 | 1.565–1.570 |
| South Africa ................... | 2.765 | 1.586–1.593 |
| Siberia ....................... | 2.703 | 1.573–1.579 |

[*] Anderson, B. W., and Payne, C. J., *Goldsmith's Journal and Gemmologist*, 37, 407–410 (1938). Foshag, W. F., *Jewelers' Circular-Keystone*, 104, 73, 75, 91 (1938).
[**] Rogers, A. F., and Sperisen, F. J., "American Synthetic Emerald," reprint, *American Mineralogist*, 27, 762–768 (1942). R.I. variable. W. J. Schaller reports R.I. of 1.569 (personal communication).

Synthetic star rubies and sapphires have been introduced to the trade. The production of these gems by an American firm is an outstanding technological achievement. Although asterism exhibited by these stones is well developed and pronounced, there should be no difficulty in distinguishing between the synthetic and the natural asterias.

The synthetic star rubies and sapphires possess curved growth lines and gas bubbles that are common to all synthetic corundum gems.

In the stones that were first introduced to the gem trade, the inclusions that produced the phenomenon of asterism penetrated the surface of the stone only slightly, approximately one millimeter. At the present time, as a result of improved technique, the regularly oriented rutile particles appear to extend throughout the entire stone. Together with the remainder of the synthetic corundum gemstones, the synthetic star stones possess a freedom from natural inclusions and such perfection that no difficulty should be experienced in distinguishing them.

Growth lines, regularly oriented inclusions or inclusions of primary minerals common in natural asterias are absent in the synthetic product.

The quartz gems, amethyst and citrine (golden or spanish topaz), are readily distinguished from imitations by the eye loupe. Because of the superior hardness of the amethyst and citrine, the polished facets will be flatter, if properly finished, and the edges of the adjoining facets should be sharper. Besides the flaws or feathers often present, zones or patches and streaks of deeper or contrasting color are commonly seen (Fig. 2–3). This is true in amethyst where the stone may show tints of varying hue, from crystal clear or very pale to dark purple, characteristics commonly seen in Siberian stones, as well as those from Arizona. Amethyst from Uruguay likewise possesses similar characteristics, the hue varying from a reddish purple to deep violet.

Another fault often seen, particularly in the medium to dark-colored stones, are smoky, brown stripes, usually present as straight lines through the stone. Sometimes lines (oriented crystal inclusions) may intersect at an angle corresponding to the interfacial angle of two faces of the crystal (Fig. 3–11). Similar lines and zones are to be seen in citrine, the yellow to brown variety of transparent quartz, in which case the lines are invariably of a darker hue. None of the faults mentioned are ever present in imitation stones. Citrine (called common topaz) may be readily distinguished from the true topaz of the same color by the poorer luster and polish as well as the lower specific gravity and inferior hardness.

After one has become thoroughly familiar with the characteristics of imitation stones, no difficulty should be experienced in distinguishing them from the genuine, although it is astonishing how often mistakes are made. Most of these errors occur because too much reliance is placed upon a sixth sense and too little time is devoted to the science of gems. In a large majority of cases, an ordinary eye loupe is the only optical instrument needed for accurate determination. Nearly all imitations possess round, brilliant bubbles, and in a large number striae may be seen (Fig. 3–7), these being commonly present where the stone has been finished from a molded or die-cast blank.

The cheapest form of imitation stone is the common molded type which is used directly without polishing as it comes from the mold. In this state, the girdle edge may be somewhat irregular or jagged, and the stone, if it is of the faceted type, will possess uneven, slightly hollow facets unlike any flat polished surface. In a better grade of imitation stone, the crown of the stone is polished and the back surface is left in the molded condition, the contrast being easily observed.

In the finest type of imitation stones where the entire stone is polished, closer observation is necessary. Commercial stones may show uneven mold marks on the girdle edge and in many cases, because of the high dispersive quality of the glass used (strass in most cases), the imitation may show finer color play than the genuine. Because of the large amount of lead oxide present in this glass, the imitation is invariably denser and possesses a higher specific gravity which may be easily observed, particularly in large stones, by the heft.

Because of the varying composition of glass, the specific gravity as well as the refractive index cannot be relied upon individually for a definite determination unless this value is different from that of the stone which the imitation simulates. The dichroscope is particularly useful, and the sunlight spectrum image test is always an unfailing means to determine the single refraction of glass. If the dichroscope or sunlight is not available and minute examination with a 15x loupe fails to reveal internal defects, bubbles, or striae, then the stone should be tested for hardness as already outlined, using a scraper made of feldspar.

One imitation often found in antique jewelry is imitation black onyx. This material, which is jet-black glass, if perfectly polished and set, can only be detected by the hardness test. If the stone has been worn, small percussion marks or scratches will show a chipped surface of a brilliant nature, the material having conchoidal fracture. Other opaque imitation stones, e.g., turquoise, lapis, jade, chalcedony, when chipped, exhibit fractures of like nature. In comparison, fractures on natural stones are dull.

A number of imitation stones have no counterpart among natural stones and have caused some confusion because of various trade names by which they are known. Goldstone is the name applied to glass to which copper filings have been added (Fig. 3–37). When cut and polished, a brilliant sparkling effect is obtained, somewhat resembling aventurine feldspar or sunstone. Microscopic thin sections show that the copper filings have crystallized, thus becoming more brilliant light reflectors with beneficial results to the material (Fig. 3–37).

Until recently "fire agate" was a term used to describe an imitation stone composed of glass of a distinct type, two layers of which were fused together. The back or bottom layer is irregular and reflects red and blue light. The clear or amber colored top layer gives the cabochon stone its proper thickness. The term is also used to describe a newly found brown agate showing green, red, and orange iridescence. When fine specimens are cut into cabochon forms, the effect is very striking and unique.

An interesting imitation stone offered to the trade a number of years ago was cut from champagne bottles that had gone through the San Francisco fire of 1906. Originally a transparent green, the glass had been changed to a translucent pale bluish color which, when cut into faceted stones, exhibited beautiful red fire.

Doublets and triplets are often used for gemstones and, once their characteristics are recognized, no difficulty should be experienced in their identification. These simulated stones are composed of two or more

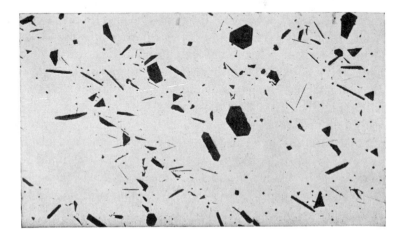

Fig. 3-37. Goldstone, 60x. Photomicrograph of a petrographic thin section showing the crystallization of copper particles. Courtesy: Prof. Austin F. Rogers, Stanford University.

units fused or cemented together. The units may be partly or wholly genuine. The majority of doublets in use are substitutes for the transparent gemstones they are designed to represent.

Imitation doublets are made by fusing colored transparent glass onto a thin piece of garnet which is used for the front of the stone. This surface receives the brunt of the wear or abrasive action while in use when mounted. In the majority of cases the garnet is thin and extends only half way to the girdle (Fig. 3-38). Only the finest doublets have the stone equally divided into two parts, the joining portion being at the girdle. In the first type where the garnet portion is thin, the doublet may be easily recognized by the dissimilarity of the polished surfaces on the facets of the crown. The garnet, because of its greater hardness, will possess a finer degree of polish, and its luster, because of the higher index of refraction, will be noticeably greater than the glass to which it is joined. The joining edge of the two units is invariably uneven because the garnet top is made from a chip of this material, and the glass

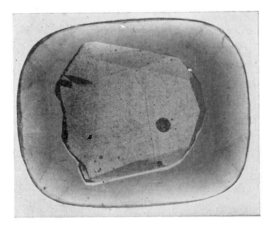

**Fig. 3-38.** Imitation topaz doublet, 6x. Low-power magnification of the stone in monobromonaphthalene. The garnet section on the top of the stone may be readily seen, the irregular jagged border edge of which extends only a short distance beyond the table facet. This is characteristic of a large number of the imitation doublets of medium to large size. The large black spot is a gas bubble between the garnet top and the glass back. Because of similarity of color and almost identical refractive indexes, the glass portion of the doublet was nearly invisible showing the garnet section in high relief.

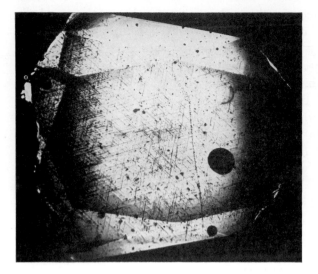

**Fig. 3-39.**
Imitation topaz doublet, 12x. Higher magnification of the imitation topaz doublet in Figure 3-38 discloses numerous gas bubbles in the glass as well as regularly oriented rutile crystal inclusions in the garnet top.

is fused thereto (Fig. 3–39). Rutile crystals are often present in the garnet portion (Fig. 3–40).

Colored doublets of blue, green, yellow, or brown invariably give off red flashes when viewed in sunlight or by reflected light, and the red tone may be distinctly seen when the stone is viewed from the back. Ruby doublets show the garnet top in a darker shade. When the garnet top extends to the girdle in the finer type of doublets, detection is equally simple even though the girdle edge is hidden by the bezel of the mounting. A higher degree of luster and finer polish than that possessed by the stones they represent (with the exception of the garnet, ruby, and sapphire) are the most noticeable difference. The garnet doublet will probably be the most difficult to detect if the garnet top covers the entire stone. However, by comparing the luster of the front and back surfaces, a distinction will be observed. A simple method by which transparent doublets as well as triplets may be recognized is the peculiar phantom or shadow effect (halation) (Fig. 3–41), produced when the stone is carefully observed by reflected light. This is an optical effect that may be relied upon as a positive means of identification, for it is not evident in any natural stone, and it is an exclusive characteristic of the transparent doublets and triplets. As light enters the stone, most of it is reflected from the back facets having previously passed through the garnet top as well as the glass bottom. A portion of the light (angular incident rays), however, is reflected from the joining surfaces and this

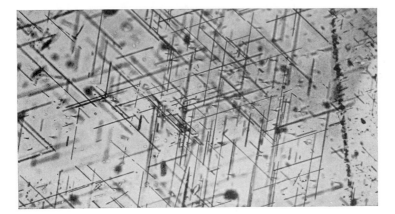

Fig. 3-40. Imitation topaz doublet, 60x. Increasing the magnification prominently reveals the regularly oriented rutile crystals included in the garnet. The stream of gas bubbles in a line at the right of the picture may be seen to the left of the large gas bubble in Figure 3-39.

may be seen as a peculiar reflection in the top facets (Fig. 3–41). This effect is particularly noticeable in the emerald triplets, or so-called soldered emeralds, which are made by joining two hard masses, such as pale aquamarine with gelatinous bonding material or cement, in a manner similar to that used in shatterproof glass. The bonding or cementing material, which is dark green, imparts this color to the pale top and bottom by reflected light. The phantom effect caused by the reflected light may be seen in the long facets surrounding the table of the stone. Triplets representing other gemstones have recently been produced, using rock crystal for the top and bottom units, joining these with a gelatinous bond of the proper hue.

Opal doublets are made to simulate the precious black opal. These

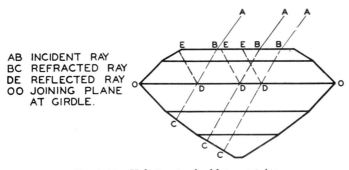

AB  INCIDENT RAY
BC  REFRACTED RAY
DE  REFLECTED RAY
OO  JOINING PLANE
     AT GIRDLE.

Fig. 3-41. Halation in doublet or triplet.

are made by joining a thin section of precious opal to a gray or black opaque back with black cement. When this combination has been cut and polished, its resemblance to a natural black opal is striking. The stones are particularly difficult to distinguish when they are well made and set in closed bezel mountings.

Star sapphires have been recently imitated by using asteriated rose quartz which is cut cabochon. Care is taken to obtain proper orientation of the star after which the stone is cemented to a small blue mirror which imparts a blue color to the stone when viewed from the front. If these stones are set in closed bezels, they resemble star sapphires. They are readily distinguished from the latter, however, by the pale rose color when viewed across the stone, by the lack of growth lines or pattern as well as feathers which are seen in true sapphire. Reflected light caused by the mirror back is very prominent at the apex of the stone when viewed in a strong lamplight.

After one has become proficient through repeated examination and study, all of the stones mentioned may be easily classified by the use of the simple optical instrument, the lens.

# CHAPTER 4

# Tools and Equipment

ABRASIVES. An abrasive for lapidary use is a hard, granular mineral or substance varying in composition and in grain size. After the abrasive has been applied to a suitable metal lap with a vehicle, such as water, it will abrade or lap a substance, leaving a dull surface, the smoothness of which varies according to the grain size used. Metal laps are specified, for under certain conditions of skill and technique, a fine abrasive may actually serve as a polishing material.

A polishing material is understood to be a finely divided mineral or other substance which, after having been applied to a metal or other type of lap, will result in producing a polished surface.

The abrasives required to cut and polish gems are few in number as well as in type. At the present time the most efficient, economical, and useful abrasive for lapidary use is silicon carbide. This is a product of the electric furnace and is composed of silicon and carbon. (The chemical formula is SiC.) The product is sold under various trade names such

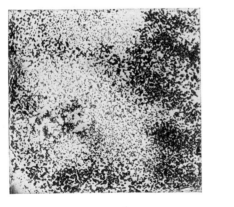

A        B

**Fig. 4-1.** Diamond grain 80 grit (No. 80): dispersed over a photographic plate and photographed with transmitted light, (A) natural size; (B) magnified, 25x. High magnification reveals characteristics of an excellent abrasive, angular particles, sharp corners, and edges.

71

as Carborundum, Crystolon, Natrolon, etc. In hardness, silicon carbide is superior to the ruby or sapphire, and it is, therefore, a suitable abrasive for cutting all gemstones excepting the diamond which can be cut only with diamond powder.

Abrasives of all types for lapidary use are accurately graded according to the size of the grain. The size designated corresponds to the mesh size of the screen through which the grain is sifted and means the number of openings per linear inch; thus a grain size No. 80 will pass through a screen having 80 meshes or small squares to the linear inch (Fig. 4–1). Standard-size grains are listed in Tables 2 and 3.

## TABLE 2.  GRIT SIZES*

*Standard Abrasive Grain Sizes*

| Size of mesh | 60 | 80 | 100 | 220 | 240 | 280 | 320 | 400 | 500 | 600 |
|---|---|---|---|---|---|---|---|---|---|---|
| Size of grain | .40 | .27 | .17 | .066 | .063 | .060 | .045 | .033 | .022 | .012 mm. |

Levigated alumina (regular grade) 3 microns (.003 mm.)

## TABLE 3.  DIAMOND GRIT SIZES

| No.** | | No.*** | |
|---|---|---|---|
| 0 | .18 mm. or coarser | 0 | 80–115 mesh |
| 1 | .12–.17 mm. | 1 | 115–200 mesh |
| 2 | .08–.12 mm. | 2 | 200–300 mesh |
| 3 | .05–.08 mm. | 3 | 300–400 mesh |
| 4 | .03–.05 mm. | 4 | 20–60 microns |
| 5 | .01–.025 mm. | 5 | 13–37 microns |
| 6 | .001–.005 mm. | 6 | 0–6 microns |
| | | 7 | 0–2 microns |

* Courtesy Norton Co. Research Laboratory, Abrasive Division.
** After Paul Grodzinski "Diamond and Gemstone Industrial Production."
*** Diamond grit sizes, courtesy Arthur A. Crafts Co., Inc., Boston, Mass.

In explanation of the varying grit sizes in any size number, Number 2, for example, will contain grains of such a size that all will pass through a 200-mesh sieve and will stop on a sieve of 300 mesh, etc. Number 3 will permit grains of size 300 mesh and finer to pass.

Alumina in the form of synthetic corundum, sold under such trade names as Alundum and Aloxite, has a limited use in the lapidary art. It has replaced to a great extent the natural corundum and emery, impure abrasives which were in common use several decades ago, before Acheson's discovery of silicon carbide. Alumina, particularly useful for the lapidary, is the finely divided powder known as "levigated alumina" used for polishing, and certain types of vitrified alumina wheels used for fine grinding, to which reference will be made later.

Boron carbide, Norbide, another electric furnace product is useful for lapping stones of great hardness. Norbide is the hardest abrasive known, except the diamond. Graded similarly to silicon carbide, its uses are also similar.

The diamond is the ideal abrasive, for it not only surpasses all other substances in hardness,* but it also possesses a unique quality which is its ability to charge a metal disk or lap. This quality of the diamond is owed, first, to its great compressive strength as well as hardness, for, although the diamond will break into fragments upon receiving a sharp blow, it offers great resistance to crushing when a load is applied gradually. It may actually be impressed into soft metal without damage. Second, the diamond on being crushed breaks into small sharp-pointed pieces (Fig. 4–1) which are easily impressed or rolled into metal where they remain until dislodged by the wearing away of the disk or lap.

Diamond is graded into various grain sizes from coarse particles, usually called crushing boart, to the finest powder. As a rule, individual firms that prepare and market diamond powder, use their own code as to the fineness of the diamond grain, the coarsest practical grain for lapping being No. 200. Diamond powder is prepared by crushing boart, or impure diamond crystals or fragments unsuited for other purposes, in a hardened steel mortar. This powder may be used directly in certain applications, but the best results are attained with the use of properly graded powder. These grades are obtained by mixing the powder with a quantity of olive oil, shaking well, and allowing the suspended diamond particles to settle. As the settling period varies according to the size of the grain, diamond powder of various degrees of fineness is readily obtained by simply observing closely the periods between decanting. American Machine Tool Standards have established the following grades:

After crushing mix with olive oil, stir thoroughly, permit to stand five minutes, and pour off contents. The residue in the container is No. 0. Stir the oil again and proceed as outlined above.

Stand 10 minutes and pour off contents, residue remaining is No. 1.
Stand 30 minutes and pour off contents, residue remaining is No. 2.
Stand 1 hour and pour off contents, residue remaining is No. 3.
Stand 2 hours and pour off contents, residue remaining is No. 4.
Stand 10 hours and pour off contents, residue remaining is No. 5.
Stand until oil is clear, pour off contents, residue remaining is No. 6.

PUMICE is a mild abrasive intermediate between a cutting and a polishing material. This abrasive is extensively used in the polishing of

---

* Borazon, a new product of the General Electric Co., produced by subjecting boron nitride to great heat and pressure, is said to be harder than the diamond. This is a laboratory curiosity however, and is not available commercially.

glass and is particularly useful in polishing opal. As pumice is a natural substance which is found in large quantities, it may be obtained at a low cost. It is graded and classed in a distinct system, as 0, 00, 000, etc. Double 0 or 2–0 is the best size for lapidary use.

POLISHING MATERIALS. The most widely used polishing powder is stannic oxide (tin oxide) sometimes called putty powder. This powder must be free of all grit and may be used to polish the majority of gems.

Levigated alumina is a finely powdered polishing medium which must be used on certain types of stone. It is harder than tin oxide and although it may be used as a substitute, the polish obtained will be duller or less brilliant.

Damascus ruby powder is a finely divided alumina, and in its application is identical to the levigated alumina.

Tripoli is a name given to a type of polishing medium consisting of certain decomposed rocks. It is generally used in lump form in the natural state. The best type of rock for polishing gemstones shows small brown spots when the lump is scratched with the fingernail. Gritty material should not be used. This polishing medium must not be confused with the tripoli used for polishing metal. The latter is a specially prepared material compressed into brick form with grease and is unsuited for stone polishing. Tripoli is extensively used to polish rubies and sapphires. As a rule, polishing powders are free of grit or foreign matter. In some cases, where an exceptionally fine finish is required, it may be necessary to reclassify or grade the powder. This is done by precipitation in water. The powder is thoroughly mixed and the resulting mixture allowed to settle. The suspended particles being finest are drawn off and are permitted to settle until the water is clear.

Linde A-5175 powder is slightly softer than levigated alumina, and it may be used with advantage on all stones polished with the alumina powder, particularly on spinel and garnet.

WHEELS. Abrasive wheels are made in a variety of forms or shapes and with different bonds, but grinding wheels best suited for lapidary work are of the vitrified silicon carbide type (Fig. 4–2). The silicon carbide in the required grain size is mixed with the proper proportion of clay,* which is the bonding material. It is then molded and finally fired. The clay becomes vitrified and holds the numerous sharp gritty particles thus forming an efficient grinding tool. The ratio of the clay to the grit in the mixture is the means for regulating the hardness of the wheel. Medium-grade wheels are best suited for grinding hard stones.

---

* Other substances may also be added, e.g., feldspar.

Fig. 4-2. Various types of grinding wheels.

At the present time, the markings on the grinding wheels, as made by the respective manufacturers, agree in principle. The user is thus able to interpret the code and decide whether the grinding wheel is suitable for the use intended. A typical wheel specification may be 37C 60-J8VK 10 by 1 by 1 in. This would indicate a wheel of medium hardness made by the vitrified process composed essentially of carborundum or crystalon (both of which are silicon carbide), the grain size of the grit passing through a No. 60 mesh screen. The figures given in inches refer to the diameter of the wheel, width of the face, and the diameter of the hole.

Finer grain wheels are used for special purposes as in the roughing of fragile stones where wheels of No. 80 or 100 grit may be preferred.

For finish grinding, No. 180 is the finest standard grit available in grinding wheels although finer grits, for example Nos. 220 and 240 should be used. Until recently, wheels composed of these fine grains were obtained on special order only. Because of the rapid growth of interest in lapidary work, many firms now have these wheels in stock for immediate delivery. Wherever possible standard size grinding wheels should be used. Abrasive wheels 8 in. and 10 in. in diameter and 1 in. to 1½ in. in thickness are the most popular sizes. For best results the finer grit wheels are somewhat harder than the coarser ones, a typical code being 37C 220-M7V.

Abrasive wheels made with other types of bonding materials, bakelite, resinoid bonds, and rubber are generally used for finish grinding. The grinding action of such wheels is slower than that of the standard vitrified wheels and consequently they produce a finer surface, often with considerable gloss. The rubber bonded wheels have a distinct polishing action.

Such bonded abrasive wheels are often sold under special trade names. "Brightboy" and "Cratex" are bonded with rubber and the "Lapidabrade" wheel is of the resinoid type.

Abrasive wheels with diamond as the grit may be had with all types of bonding medii, vitrified, resinoid, and metallic. Regular type resinoid bonded diamond grit wheels are excellent for grinding fragile stones.

Vitrified wheels with alumina as an abrasive have a limited use in the lapidary shop. Fine-cutting finishing wheels, however, are particularly useful in finishing stones like opal, glass, turquoise, malachite, and variscite. Their use is optional, as excellent results have been obtained with the fine-grained silicon carbide wheels. Some lapidary shops use sandstone wheels for finishing agate and onyx or the softer stones.

**Fig. 4-3.** Abrasive saws or cutoff wheels.

Thin disks, composed of silicon carbide grains bonded with natural or synthetic resins or gums, have long been used for cutting off or sawing operations (Fig. 4–3). Rocks and minerals of all kinds can be sawed with these thin cutoff wheels. When properly applied and used, various types of quartz may be sawed at the rate of one square inch in five minutes. Care and discretion should be exercised, however, as these wheels are fragile, and they should be properly shielded and mounted in a rigid machine.

WHEEL SPEEDS. Although it has been the custom among the manufacturers of abrasive wheels to recommend a surface speed of 5000 surface feet per minute (5000 s.f.p.m.), experience has shown that in the grinding of gemstones a surface speed of 4000 f.p.m. will give excellent results. As the majority of the stones ground are small, only a few minutes at most is required to grind the stone to the desired size. The lower speed recommended will also permit a more copious supply of coolant and thus prevent cracking of the gemstones during the grinding operation.

To obtain maximum results and the greatest value out of a grinding wheel, some method should be adopted which will provide for changing the number of revolutions per minute (r.p.m.) so that the normal speed in surface feet per minute may be maintained. A 10-in wheel rotating at the speed of 4000 s.f.p.m. should rotate at 1528 r.p.m. Should the revolutions per minute remain fixed, and the wheel be worn down to 5 in. in diameter, its efficiency as well as its grinding ability would be reduced over 50 per cent. This is because the grinding surface is reduced by half and also to the greater amount of work each grain in the surface of the wheel must do as it strikes the object more often in the same distance traveled.

When the diameter of the wheel is reduced from 10 inches to eight inches through grinding, the speed of rotation should be increased to 1910 r.p.m. in order to maintain the surface speed at 4000 s.f.p.m. (Note table 4.) A wheel 6 in. in diameter should rotate at 2546 r.p.m. to equal the same 4000 s.f.p.m.

In some cases the recommended speed may be altered to suit special requirements. Small vitrified wheels and mounted points are commonly used to carve gem stones. The wheels vary in diameter and thickness, and the sizes most frequently used are 1 to 2 in. in diameter and ¼ to ½ in. thick. These wheels are bushed with lead with a ¼-in. hole for use on a tapered threaded spindle (Fig. 4–4) upon which they can be mounted or removed at will. This is an important feature, for it is often necessary

## TABLE 4. SPEEDS

REVOLUTIONS PER MINUTE FOR VARIOUS DIAMETERS OF GRINDING WHEELS TO
GIVE PERIPHERAL SPEED IN FEET PER MINUTE AS INDICATED

| Diameter of Wheel in Inches | Peripheral speed in feet per minute | | | | | |
|---|---|---|---|---|---|---|
| | 4000 | 4500 | 5000 | 5500 | 6000 | 6500 |
| | Revolutions per minute | | | | | |
| 1 | 15,279 | 17,189 | 19,098 | 21,008 | 22,918 | 24,828 |
| 2 | 7,639 | 8,594 | 9,549 | 10,504 | 11,459 | 12,414 |
| 3 | 5,093 | 5,729 | 6,366 | 7,003 | 7,639 | 8,276 |
| 4 | 3,820 | 4,297 | 4,775 | 5,252 | 5,729 | 6,207 |
| 5 | 3,056 | 3,438 | 3,820 | 4,202 | 4,584 | 4,966 |
| 6 | 2,546 | 2,865 | 3,183 | 3,501 | 3,820 | 4,138 |
| 7 | 2,183 | 2,455 | 2,728 | 3,001 | 3,274 | 3,547 |
| 8 | 1,910 | 2,148 | 2,387 | 2,626 | 2,865 | 3,103 |
| 10 | 1,528 | 1,719 | 1,910 | 2,101 | 2,292 | 2,483 |
| 12 | 1,273 | 1,432 | 1,591 | 1,751 | 1,910 | 2,069 |
| 14 | 1,091 | 1,228 | 1,364 | 1,500 | 1,637 | 1,773 |
| 16 | 955 | 1,074 | 1,194 | 1,313 | 1,432 | 1,552 |

to use successively several wheels of different sizes. For special purposes soft rubber bonded wheels are useful. The grinding action is mild, and it actually rubs off the material, leaving a glossy surface free of chatter marks or the coarse grinding scratches which result from grinding with vitrified wheels.

All types of these small grinding wheels are used with water as a coolant which is customary in lapidary work. Their grinding ability may be assisted by the application of loose, wet, abrasive grain of the same grit size as that bonded in the wheel.

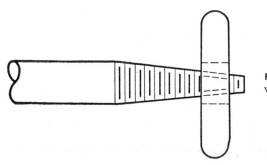

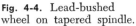

Fig. 4-4. Lead-bushed wheel on tapered spindle.

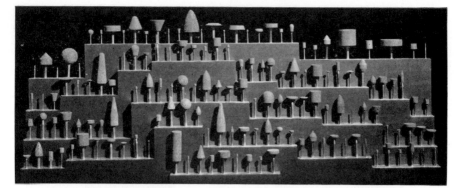

Fig. 4-5. Mounted points.

Mounted tool points (Fig. 4–5) are small grinding wheels of various sizes and shapes, usually ⅛ to 1 in. in diameter, secured to spindles. These tools must be held in a collet chuck for accuracy in grinding, and they are used in a manner similar to the small unmounted wheels.

Mild steel or iron tools, shaped like the tools in Figure 4–5, may be used in place of the grinding wheels. These, when fed with wet abrasive grain, act in a manner similar to grinding wheels. For work requiring small wheels, grinding units of this type have longer life as they wear less rapidly and maintain their contour over a longer period. They require greater skill in handling, however, as the abrasive must be applied constantly. The tools are operated at speeds from 1750 to 3500 r.p.m. Grain size for work should be 220 grit.

Diamond tools having forms similar to the above are usually made of metal, and are charged with diamond powder which is rolled into the metal and thus forms a very efficient cutting tool. They may be any size. Some may have cutting points or heads smaller than a pinhead, while diamond charged laps and saws may be 10 to 12 in. in diameter, or larger (Fig. 4–6).

With the exception of the laps and saws, diamond tools are usually small and are used for fine work in hard stone. They are usually made of mild steel rod, designed to be held in the collet chuck of a small lathe, and they are rotated at high speed. Although they are used particularly for carving and engraving, they find wide use in the lapidary shop for drilling, reaming, countersinking, slotting, counterboring, recessing, or grooving.

During operation it is customary to keep the tool moistened with a

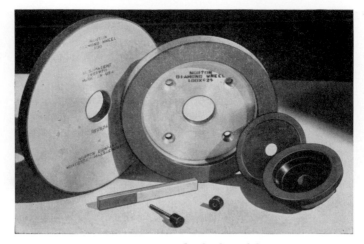

Fig. 4-6.   Diamond wheels and laps.

light oil. In some cases, however, where the oil may harm the stone or where it acts as a lubricant, water is preferable. The usual speeds are from 2000 to 7000 r.p.m., according to the size of the tool and the nature and amount of the work required.

In recent years mounted points shaped like those shown in Figure 4–5 in which diamond grain is held by a metallic bond have become very popular and their use is extensive, particularly in dentistry. The construction of these tools varies with different manufacturers and there are two types, one in which the diamond grain extends throughout the metal matrix of which the wheel or point is formed; and the other in which the diamond grain is held by the metallic bond and fastened to the metal core which gives to the tool its shape.

The latter type is less costly than the former and if carefully used, it will prove to be economical. In time the diamond charged shell or matrix will wear away or it may strip off the body or core of the tool, in which case the usefulness of the tools as a cutting medium is greatly impaired or ended. Force or heavy pressure should never be used with these tools. A light pressure, ample coolant and a high speed, from 5000 to 7000 r.p.m. will give maximum life.

GRINDING-WHEEL HEADS (Fig. 4–7). All grinding wheels should be suitably mounted on heads large enough and rigid enough to bear the load. Various types of grinding heads are available with definite wheel-size ratings which should not be exceeded. Wheel sizes most frequently used and their corresponding spindle sizes are given in Table 5.

## MINIMUM WHEEL-SPINDLE DIAMETERS*

No wheel of larger diameter or greater thickness than specified in Table 5 shall be used on any machine of given spindle diameter.

TABLE 5. MINIMUM DIAMETERS OF SPINDLES FOR WHEELS OF VARIOUS DIAMETERS AND THICKNESSES OPERATING AT SPEEDS UP TO 7000 PERIPHERAL FEET PER MINUTE

| Diameter of wheel in inches | Thickness of wheel — inches | | | | | | | | | | | |
|---|---|---|---|---|---|---|---|---|---|---|---|---|
| | $\frac{1}{4}$ | $\frac{3}{8}$ | $\frac{1}{2}$ | $\frac{5}{8}$ | $\frac{3}{4}$ | 1 | $1\frac{1}{4}$ | $1\frac{1}{2}$ | $1\frac{3}{4}$ | 2 | $2\frac{1}{4}$ | $2\frac{1}{2}$ |
| | Diameter of spindle — inches | | | | | | | | | | | |
| 6 | $\frac{1}{2}$ | $\frac{1}{2}$ | $\frac{1}{2}$ | $\frac{1}{2}$ | $\frac{1}{2}$ | $\frac{1}{2}$ | $\frac{5}{8}$ | $\frac{5}{8}$ | $\frac{3}{4}$ | $\frac{3}{4}$ | $\frac{3}{4}$ | $\frac{3}{4}$ |
| 7 | $\frac{1}{2}$ | $\frac{1}{2}$ | $\frac{1}{2}$ | $\frac{1}{2}$ | $\frac{5}{8}$ | $\frac{5}{8}$ | $\frac{5}{8}$ | $\frac{3}{4}$ | $\frac{3}{4}$ | $\frac{3}{4}$ | $\frac{3}{4}$ | $\frac{3}{4}$ |
| 8 | $\frac{5}{8}$ | $\frac{5}{8}$ | $\frac{5}{8}$ | $\frac{5}{8}$ | $\frac{5}{8}$ | $\frac{5}{8}$ | $\frac{3}{4}$ | $\frac{3}{4}$ | $\frac{3}{4}$ | 1 | 1 | 1 |
| 9 | $\frac{5}{8}$ | $\frac{5}{8}$ | $\frac{5}{8}$ | $\frac{5}{8}$ | $\frac{3}{4}$ | $\frac{3}{4}$ | $\frac{3}{4}$ | $\frac{3}{4}$ | 1 | 1 | 1 | 1 |
| 10 | $\frac{3}{4}$ | $\frac{3}{4}$ | $\frac{3}{4}$ | $\frac{3}{4}$ | $\frac{3}{4}$ | $\frac{3}{4}$ | $\frac{3}{4}$ | $\frac{3}{4}$ | 1 | 1 | 1 | $1\frac{1}{4}$ |
| 12 | $\frac{3}{4}$ | $\frac{3}{4}$ | $\frac{3}{4}$ | $\frac{3}{4}$ | $\frac{3}{4}$ | 1 | 1 | 1 | 1 | 1 | 1 | $1\frac{1}{4}$ |
| 14 | $\frac{7}{8}$ | $\frac{7}{8}$ | $\frac{7}{8}$ | $\frac{7}{8}$ | 1 | 1 | $1\frac{1}{4}$ | $1\frac{1}{4}$ | $1\frac{1}{4}$ | $1\frac{1}{4}$ | $1\frac{1}{4}$ | $1\frac{1}{4}$ |
| 16 | | | | | $1\frac{1}{4}$ | $1\frac{1}{4}$ | $1\frac{1}{4}$ | $1\frac{1}{4}$ | $1\frac{1}{4}$ | $1\frac{1}{4}$ | $1\frac{1}{2}$ | $1\frac{1}{2}$ |

Bearings for all grinding equipment should be sealed against the entrance of grit which is ever present. Modern grinding heads have integrally sealed ball bearings with built-in seals to retain the lubricant and to exclude all foreign matter. These are highly recommended and may be relied upon to give thousands of hours of trouble-free service.

Babbitt bearings have long been used in grinding heads. Wherever it is possible to keep out grit or abrasive particles from the lubricant, this type of bearing, if properly fitted, will give good service.

Figures 4–7 and 4–8 show the heads suitable for lapidary work. The head in Figure 4–8, designed and built by the author, has many features not found in other types. The bearings are precision ball-bearing, grease-seal type. The drive consists of a V-belt and step-cone pulley, affording a selection of four speeds and enabling the operator to select the proper speed according to the wheel diameter. The long spindle and rigid bearings provide excellent grinding clearance, enabling the operator to work under ideal conditions.

* "Grinding Wheel Manufacturers' Safety Code," The Norton Co.

**Fig. 4-7.**   Grinder head for wheels 10 by 1 by ¾ in.

The diameter of the flanges on the grinding heads of lapidary grinders should be at least one third of the wheel diameter. A packing washer is placed between the flange and the wheel. A thin rubber sheet or vellumoid packing is ideal for this purpose. These never wear out or become torn and may be used over and over again. The practice of using blotting paper should be discouraged wherever wet grinding prevails as the wet blotting paper quickly rusts iron or steel flanges, and whenever it is necessary to remove a wheel, the paper sticks to the flange surface and ruins it. Unless the flange face and the wheel are scraped clean, the wheel, when replaced, will not rotate truly but will wobble. Grinder heads should be securely bolted to a rigid base in order to prevent vibration All wheels in use should be trued and kept in balance.

**Fig. 4-8.**   Grinder head showing tapered polishing spindle and chuck spindle attached. Used for concaves, carving, engraving, etc.

Fig. 4-9. Small standard-type grinding spindle.

Other grinding spindles of simple design (Fig. 4–9) may be used, particularly where one wishes to do a limited amount of lapidary work, or where funds are limited. While the spindle illustrated was designed and intended to be used for sawing, the unit may readily be used for grinding, lapping, or polishing; and it is very efficient for carving when equipped with a suitable chuck.

A small portable lapidary machine utilizing this element is shown in Figures 4–10 and 4–11. The spindle is bolted to a heavy (6 in. by 6 in.) angle plate, which in turn is securely fastened to a baseboard upon which ⅓ h.p. motor is fastened. As the spindle diameter is ⅝ in., grinding wheels up to 6 in. by 1 in. may be used safely. Large spindle units of the same type are also available, and these can utilize grinding wheels 8 in. to 10 in. in diameter. A No. 2 Jacobs chuck may be attached

Fig. 4-10.
Mounted
grinding
spindle.

Fig. 4-11.  Portable grinder with splash guard.

to the threaded end, whereby additional tools, especially for carving, may be used.

Previously, lapidary lathes were unknown; consequently standard tools were adapted for such use. To eliminate the damage caused by grit in the bearings and spindle, a lathe (Figs. 4–12 and 4–13) was designed and built by the author. The spindle is mounted on grease-sealed ball bearings that in turn are mounted on a removable quill. In case of wear, the entire quill unit may be quickly removed and replaced; or quills with different spindle mountings may be used.

The bed of the lathe, which is used in the conventional manner for the support of turning tools or attachments of various kinds, is also removable. This feature provides a clear work space as required in the carving of large objects or for finishing the inside of bowls and vases. Although the lathe is often covered with grit resulting from splash, the streamlined design permits thorough cleaning in a few minutes. The effectively shielded bearings afford maximum protection even after years of constant use.

BELTS.  V-belts in the better grades are unexcelled for lapidary work. They are endless and uniform in cross section without hooks or fasteners, and they provide a smooth flow of power from the driving pulley, free

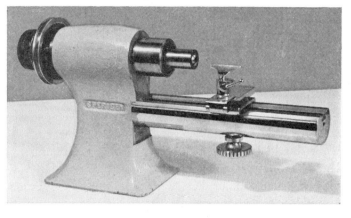

Fig. 4-12.
Lathe with
collet chuck
spindle and
standard base.

of jar or vibration. The belts can be obtained in all lengths with pulleys of various diameters to suit every need. The standard 17/32-in. belt, which is ideal for lapidary work, will transmit one horsepower. Exceptionally long life may be expected from V-belts, some having been in service for 10 years before failure.

LAPS. Laps are usually made of metal or alloys of various types, and it is customary to operate them in a horizontal plane mounted on a vertical spindle. With the exception of the diamond-charged lap, which remains charged over a long period of time, metal laps serve only as the vehicle for the abrasive which must be applied from time to time or

Fig. 4-13. Lathe with quill-type spindle and single-purpose chuck (⅜-in. capacity).

continuously in accordance with the work being done. Small stones may be lapped without the addition of abrasive through the small charge embedded in the lap, the surface of which requires wetting only. The lapping of large flat surfaces, however, requires a constant application of abrasive by means of a flat brush. If required, the application of the abrasive may be automatic as shown in Figure 6–38.

Iron laps are excellent for lapping or surfacing large flat areas. They are also used for diamond polishing. The speed of a lap for most flat work should be about 500 r.p.m. with a lap diameter of 10 in. In prolonged lapping of flat surfaces, the speed may be reduced to approximately 300 r.p.m. or less, according to the application. Although the lapping action at the reduced speed is not as rapid, there is less tendency for the abrasive to be thrown off the surface of the lap by centrifugal force. This in turn prevents the abrasive from splashing about, which is always a source of aggravation because of the danger of contaminating polishing wheels and equipment. Diamond polishing is usually done on laps 10 to 12 in. in diameter, rotating at speeds of 2000 to 2500 r.p.m.

Pewter laps are generally used for hand lapping, cutting, and sizing all gem stones with the exception of the diamond. They are ideal for facet work. Lead base babbit metal or linotype may also be used for such laps, and they are less costly than those made from pewter. Their operating speed is constant at about 400–500 r.p.m.

Tin laps are used solely for polishing, and while most cutting laps may be operated at a uniform speed of 400 to 500 r.p.m., tin laps may be operated at variable speeds according to the size and nature of the work. Large flat pieces may be polished at normal speed, the maximum being 500 r.p.m. Special operations and technique may require much lower speeds, sometimes only a few revolutions per minute being necessary.

Copper laps are charged with diamond powder for faceting hard stones and are operated at 500 r.p.m. In preparing a copper lap for cutting, the trued surface is scored with a fine abrasive stick, No. 180 grit will be excellent for this purpose. After the surface is completely scored and thoroughly cleaned, a carefully graded diamond grain, e.g., No. 400 is mixed with a small quantity of heavy oil to form a paste which is spread uniformly over the surface of the lap by means of a leather wiper. If desired, a prior coating of a light oil to the lap surface will permit a more uniform distribution of the diamond grit. After these operations have been completed, the grit is then rolled into the surface of the lap by means of a hard steel roller. The greater the length of time spent in this operation, the better charged will be the lap.

Although good results can be obtained by hand rolling, best results are obtained when the rolling is done in a lathe. One carat weight of diamond grain will be required to effectively charge the face of a 10-in. lap. After the rolling has been completed, the operation may require 10 or 15 minutes, the surface of the lap as well as the roller should be cleaned with kerosene. The excess diamond grain may be recovered by washing into a dish or metal basin and, after precipitation, saved for future use.

Diamond charged laps where the diamond grain is bonded with metal are available in many sizes and shapes. Although these laps are indispensable in industrial plants, their high cost prevent their use in the average lapidary shop.

Copper laps as well as bronze, zinc, and tin laps are used for polishing corundum gems.

In shape, these laps are flat disks (Fig. 4–14). Their standard size is 10 in. in diameter and 1 in. thick. Smaller or larger sizes are sometimes used; but laps smaller than 8 in. in diameter are not recommended. In any case the lap should be accurately machined and bored to fit the spindle and perfectly balanced so that upon rotating there is no vibration.

Laps that are cast in a hot iron mold invariably are in balance after machining. However, if cast in sand in the orthodox foundry manner, certain portions of the metal or alloy become chilled and are denser than other sections, and, unless properly vented, blow holes occur from the gases present.

**Fig. 4-14.** Section of standard lap.

Occasionally cavities of large size are produced in the interior of the lap which may not be disclosed upon machining, hence the necessity for accurate balancing. The balancing operation is simple. A tightly fitting mandrel or arbor is pressed into the center hole so that it projects an equal distance from each side of the lap. A pair of parallel knife edges or straight, thin steel plates are securely set on a frame at a height sufficient to clear the lap above the table upon which the fixture is mounted. The parallel guides are set level and a few inches apart so that the

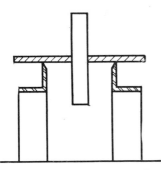

**Fig. 4-15.** Cross section of balancing ways.

mounted lap may rotate freely when placed upon the balancing ways
(Fig. 4–15). The face of the lap should be parallel to the guides midway
between them. The heaviest portion of the lap will draw it around resulting from the force of gravity and it will oscillate to and fro, finally coming
to rest. If desired, enough putty may be added to the opposite (uppermost) side, so that the lap will remain poised in any position. The
weight of the putty which is ascertained determines the weight of
the metal to be removed from the heavy side. This practice may
be dispensed with, however, by a simple trial-and-check method. It is
customary to file or scrape metal off the back of the lap from the heavier
portion until the lap remains in perfect balance in any position.

Felt wheels are finishing tools and are used with fine abrasive grain to
smooth or remove scratches from certain types of stones. They also may
be used with tin oxide to do polishing. Felt wheels are made of compressed wool and vary in size and hardness. Small wheels, 3 in. or less in
diameter and from ¼ to ½ in. thick, are used for polishing small concaves.
The larger sizes, 6 in. or more in diameter and 1 to 2 in. thick, are used
for finishing flat or convex surfaces. The abrasive grain or polishing
powder which is mixed with water is applied with a brush, and the consistency of the mixture is like thick cream. By altering the type and
size of the abrasive or polishing material a variety of finishes can be
produced. Felt wheels should not be operated at a speed greater than
2500 s.f.p.m. They must be kept wet constantly by the application of
wet abrasive, otherwise the heat caused by friction may quickly ruin
the stone being polished.

Sanders, a name applied to disks covered with abrasive cloth, are used
for smoothing surfaces after finish-grinding or lapping. This is actually
the first stage in polishing, for by the use of worn abrasive cloth a fine
finish with considerable gloss may be imparted to a stone.

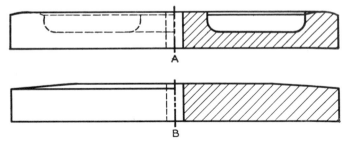

Fig. 4-16. Two types of sanders: A, cross section of
drum-type sanding or polishing wheel for cabochon
work; B, section of crowned wheel for flat specimens.

Fig. 4-18. 3-in. belt sander using standard parts. Author's creation.

Fig. 4-17. 6-in. vertical-horizontal belt sander (Sears).

While gemstones may be sanded by hand by briskly rubbing the stone on the abrasive cloth, a practice which should always be followed in the working of delicate stones, most of the sanding is done by machine. This saves considerable time as well as labor, particularly where a large number of stones are to be polished. Two sanders in common use are shown in Figure 4–16.

Two types are shown. One, slightly crowned, is used for flat surfaces only. The abrasive cloth is cemented to the surface of the wheel. On the other drumlike sander, the abrasive cloth is tightly stretched across and usually fastened with a hoop, which facilitates removal and replacement of the cloth when worn. This wheel may be used for a variety of purposes, for the flat outer rim is used for smoothing flats while the drum portion over which the cloth is stretched is used to polish convex surfaces. Occasionally the hollow portion of the wheel is filled with a spongy rubber which offers some resistance to the pressure imposed upon the abrasive cloth during the smoothing operation. The crowned sanding wheels may also be covered with a thin layer of rubber which imparts a cushion effect to the sanding cloth in operation. Sanders which are operated dry may overheat the stone being polished through prolonged operation, and care should be exercised at all times in their use. A speed of 500 r.p.m. for a wheel 10 in. in diameter is ample.

Other sanders are also used. These include the sleeve type, usually of small diameter rarely exceeding three inches, and the belt type. The latter, used extensively in woodworking as well as metalworking industries has found great popularity in the lapidary field as well. Abrasive belts of various sizes and widths may be had in various grits and in some cases a wet sanding attachment may also be used. By utilizing fixtures of various kinds, a wide variety of surfaces from round to flat, or combinations thereof may be finished (Figs. 4–17 and 4–18).

Specially prepared sanding wheels are sometimes used. These wheels are felt of proper size and turned to the desired shape; abrasive grain is glued to the face or contour of such wheels. Although wheels of this type are regularly used in the metalworking industry, they are rarely used in the lapidary shop.

Buffs, made of stitched muslin, are used for finish polishing stones of many types. Those commonly used are 6 in. or more in diameter, and a speed of 2500 s.f.p.m. is best.

Leather-covered polishing wheels offer the best medium for polishing surfaces of all kinds with the exception of facet work. The construction of these wheels is similar to that of the drum wheel used for smoothing. The wood for the wheel is turned with a hollow face, having a flat surface at the periphery. Two layers of calfskin or cowhide, with the hair side out, are tightly stretched across and over the edge of the wheel and firmly tacked in place. The best leather to use is cowhide and if this can be obtained approximately ⅛ in. thick, only one layer is required. The tiny pores in the hair side of the skin form excellent cups in which the polishing powder lodges. For a 10 to 12-in. wheel, a speed of 500 r.p.m. is sufficient.

Speeds are listed either as r.p.m., or revolutions per minute, and s.f.p.m., surface feet per minute. Where the speed of the wheel remains constant throughout its life, as in the case of laps, the speed in r.p.m. is a fixed value, but for wheels which are consumed or ground away with the gradual changing of the diameter, the speeds are recorded under s.f.p.m.

WOODEN WHEELS. Wheels made of various hard woods are used extensively by the lapidary. Wheels made of southern gum, or poplar, are ideal for fine smoothing prior to polishing on the felt wheel. Cabochon as well as flat stones are treated with equal ease on these wheels. To the faces of these wheels FFF silicon carbide is applied wet with a brush.

Maple is used in the form of a lap for polishing flat surfaces and soft faceted stones of various types.

Polishing wheels made of rosewood or boxwood are used with diamond-powder tripoli or tin oxide to polish cabochon sapphires or carvings of various types.

MOTORS. For continuous use and heavy service the repulsion-induction type of motor, commonly referred to as a heavy-duty motor, is a necessity. A ½ to ¾-h.p. motor will be required to drive a head with 10-in. diameter wheels at the recommended speed. Smaller heads for light work or for the home workshop may be driven by a ⅓-h.p. motor. A cutout or overloading switch should be included in the circuit to protect the motor and the line against damage.

Motors with grease-sealed bearings only should be used. These motors are superior to the sleeve-bearing type for lapidary work for the particles of loose abrasive which float in the air are an ever present menace to the life of a sleeve bearing, inevitably resulting in costly replacement. In every case it is better to have a reserve of power available than to drive equipment with a motor too small for the load. Serious overloading of an electric motor, which causes stalling, results in overheating and causes breakdown of the insulation, thus ruining the motor.

A capacitor-type motor may be used in place of a heavy-duty motor where the load or starting conditions are less severe.

The regular split-phase or light-duty motor will be found satisfactory for driving light equipment, such as small grinders, buffers, polishing wheels, or laps. A ⅓-h.p. motor will provide ample power for driving a 10-in. lap under all normal service conditions.

When electricity is not available, lapidary apparatus may be driven by hand or by foot, or with the aid of a gasoline engine. In the hand or footpower apparatus, drive is direct, and with the gasoline engine the drive is arranged through a countershaft with a suitable clutch. A motor-generator set may be installed and used in connection with a storage battery in a manner similar to the electric system in automobiles, with the drive to the laps or wheels through a 6- or 12-volt motor.

If lineshafting is used, small ball-bearing pillow blocks or bearings are recommended. They are inexpensive and need oiling only once a year.

RESTS. Facet-stick rests used by the lapidary in faceting stones by the hand method are of two types. The jamb peg is a trumpet-shaped wooden support attached to a steel column. A series of holes on the face of the rest permits the cutting of facets, the angularity of which is gov-

**Fig. 4-19.** Hand faceting rest. Conventional lapidary equipment.

erned by the inclination of the lap stick at angles between the horizontal and the vertical.

The adjustable back rest (Fig. 4–19) is superior because of its adjustable feature. The rest is fastened to a pin which is friction tight in the holder, permitting a slight rotating motion. This affects the vertical position of rows of holes with respect to the lap, thereby affording an infinite amount of adjustment. Thus by altering the inclination of the back rest, the same facet angle may be obtained conveniently by placing the pointed end of the facet stick in any of two series or rows of holes.

LAP STICKS AND CEMENT.   To facilitate handling after roughing, stones are fastened onto lap sticks by means of cement of various types. Lap sticks (Fig. 4–20) are made of hard wood, and in size and appearance they are similar to penholders, which actually may be used for this purpose. Ordinary round dowels or meat pegs may be used, but for ease of handling, these substitutes are far inferior to the properly turned lapidary stick. For handling small stones as small as the head of a pin to 5/16 in. or 8 mm. diameter, sticks are turned from ¼-in. dowel (turned birch sticks). Larger stones naturally require larger diameter sticks for comfortable handling. For most stones of ordinary ring-stone size a stick ⅜ in. in diameter is used. The largest stones require a stick ½ in. in diameter. The most satisfactory length for all of these sticks is 5½ in.

Lap sticks for faceting (Fig. 4–21) are similar to those used in cabochon work, but they are made of harder wood and one end is pointed to fit into the jamb peg or back rest (Fig. 4–19) used to obtain proper facet angles. Mexican rosewood (cocobolo) is an ideal hard wood for this purpose. This wood may be easily turned; it is hard and rigid, has a fine even grain, and cement adheres well to it. Ebony, tulip, and Brazilian rosewood also are excellent for lap sticks.

In commercial shops where a number of stones are cut at one time these sticks, by reason of the different color of the wood, provide an excellent means of segregating various stones when they require polishing treatment, or when identical stones of different lots must be kept separate to prevent confusion or error.

To cement a small stone is a simple operation, and little time is required for the process. Large stones, however, take longer to set up because the large mass of cement necessary to support the stone must be thoroughly heated. After the stone has been mounted in place, some time must elapse before the cement has sufficiently set and hardened so that the stick may be left without danger of the stone tilting because of its weight. To save time when a number of large stones are to be cut,

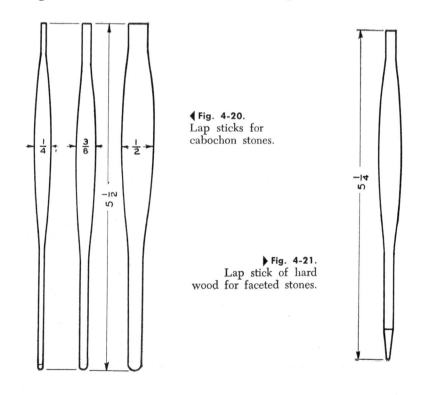

◀ Fig. 4-20.
Lap sticks for
cabochon stones.

▶ Fig. 4-21.
Lap stick of hard
wood for faceted stones.

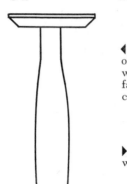

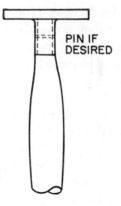

PIN IF
DESIRED

◀ **Fig. 4-22.** Lap stick of turned aluminum, with flattened surface at top, for cabochon stones.

▶ **Fig. 4-23.** Lap stick with aluminum head.

the lap stick shown in Figure 4–22 was designed by the author. This is made of turned aluminum with a flattened surface at the top, slightly smaller than the stone that is to be cemented. To use, the stick is held in a flame which heats the metal rapidly; cement is applied to the top plate, and the stone, which has been warmed, at the same time is placed on the plate. Here it is firmly pressed and centered by the hand and eye. As the top plate of the stick is turned truly and at a right angle to the axis of the stick, it is obvious that the stone also will be set truly. The entire unit may be set aside to cool without loss of time or danger of tilting before cooling.

An improved version utilizes an aluminum plate and socket unit into which the hardwood is pressed (Fig. 4–23). The wood stick serves as an insulator. The aluminum stick because of the rapid heat transmission, becomes quite hot during the cementing operation. Furthermore, the wooden stick is far more comfortable to manipulate during the subsequent operations.

Cement used for all cabochon or flat stones is ordinary red sealing wax. A ¼-lb. bar will suffice for many lap sticks. Sealing wax has considerable tenacity and it is readily applied to the lap sticks when needed by first heating the end of the wax stick in a Bunsen or alcohol flame. The melted wax or cement then is rubbed onto the end of the lap stick and rolled to a cylindrical shape. If the cement is properly applied, it will hold the stone securely throughout all operations, whether the stone is as small as a pinhead or a slab 6 by 6 in. in size.

For faceting, special stone cement is required. This is harder and firmer than sealing wax, although in some cases the latter may be used. Faceting cement is made from equal parts, by weight, of sealing wax

Fig. 4-24. Equipment for cementing: Bunsen burner, cementing plate, knockoff block, alcohol pot, knife, tweezer; in background, stones cemented on lap sticks.

and diamond cement. This cement, used by diamond polishers in rounding up diamonds, also is used to cement corundum gems for faceting.

To facilitate the handling of the cement, a cementing plate (Fig. 4-24) is necessary. This may be an ordinary, cold-rolled steel bar about 1½ in. wide and 6 in. long, or it may be mounted on legs as shown. A lap-stick holder is necessary, which is simply a stand with a number of holes in which the sticks are placed for the cement to cool after sticking or cementing. A tweezer is used to hold the stone for the cementing operation, because the stone must be heated sufficiently so that the cement will stick to it. A knockingoff stick for removing the cemented stone and a small paring knife for scraping off adhering cement are necessary. A small cold-cream jar is excellent for an alcohol pot into which the finished stones are placed to remove all traces of adhering cement. Denatured alcohol is the best solvent for this purpose.

For accurate sizing and calibration of stones, gauges or calipers (Fig. 4-25) are essential. It has been customary to cut stones to definite standard sizes and shapes, with dimensions in millimeters. The metric system is convenient and easy to use. The majority of millimeter gauges are

**Fig. 4-25.** Gauges used by lapidaries (author's collection).
(1) Folding gauge, showing stone size in millimeters,
stone-size number, and weight in carats. (2) Millimeter
gauge with vernier to read in tenths. (3) Gauge for
oval (elliptical) stones. (4) Spring gauge, graduations
in tenths of millimeters. (5) Stone-size gauge, graduations similar to No. 1. (6 and 7) Contact gauges used
in diamond polishing. (6) Gauge for measuring angle
of table and top main facet. (7) Gauge for measuring
angle of table and back main facet, 40 and 41 deg.
respectively.

equipped with a vernier so that measurements may be read to 1/10 mm.
which is equivalent to .0039 in.

Stone plates are gauges or templates with accurately sized holes of
various shapes and sizes. These usually are made of nonferrous metals,
such as aluminum, copper, or brass, as well as nickel silver, about 1/32 in.
thick. Gauges of various types are shown in Figure 4–25, and their uses
are described under cutting of gemstones.

LAPIDARY MACHINES (benches or lathes). Wherever there is an incen-
tive to manufacture or construct something, thought and ingenuity will

**Fig. 4-26.** "At Work," from *The Gem Cutter's Craft* by Leopold Clarement. Painting by John Harrison, 1902. London, England.

provide the method. The author's first lapidary bench, built when a boy fifteen years of age, was constructed from an old sewing machine frame complete with foot treadle, which had been bought for 50 cents. Later on, he bought a machined spindle for $3.50 and built himself a hand-driven machine of conventional design. The inspiration to build this machine came from the illustration in *The Gem Cutters Craft* which showed the author of the book, Leopold Claremont, at work (Fig. 4–26). The provision of a flywheel of the required size and weight was a problem because of the lack of funds. This difficulty was finally solved by the use of an old bicycle wheel which was weighted with scrap iron held in place by wire and further secured by filling with plaster of Paris. Driven by means of a round belt, this apparatus worked in a most satisfactory manner and provided many happy hours of work.

Hand-driven lapidary machines are in common use in many shops. For certain purposes, such as cutting and polishing small faceted stones, called "caliber," very efficient work can be done with this machine because there is better wheel-speed control.

**Fig. 4-27.** Portable lapidaries apparatus. *Familiar Lessons on Mineralogy and Geology and a Practical Description of the Use of Lapidaries Apparatus* by John Mawe, London, 1822.° An early type of simple hand-driven lapidaries apparatus.

(° Although 139 years old, it is astonishing how concise and accurate this brief treatise on the fashioning of gemstones is.)

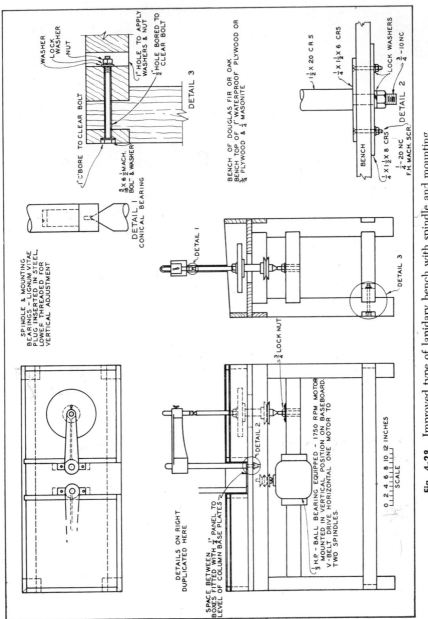

Fig. 4-28. Improved type of lapidary bench with spindle and mounting.

Fig. 4-29. Sawing through rock cemented to angle plate held in vise. Small, portable lapidary machine for sawing, lapping, grinding, polishing, and faceting gem materials (author's creation).

Fig. 4-30. Small, table-type lapping machine, with splash pan, used in finish-grinding quartz crystal oscillators for radio.

**Fig. 4-31.** Small table-type lapping machine in operation. Edging rock-crystal blanks for use in radio

**Fig. 4-32.** Ancient-type lapidary lathe.

For many years, a lapidary known to the author, J. J. Kinrade, who worked exclusively in cabochon stones, did all of his work including the sawing of large stones with a hand-driven machine.

Lapidary machines of the simplest form (Fig. 4–32) in which a spindle is actuated by a belt through foot power have been used in China for many centuries. By means of this simple lathe, Chinese lapidaries have produced some of the finest lapidary art the world has seen (Figs. 9–13 to 9–17).

Where a small amount of work is to be done, a simple grinding spindle (Figs. 4–9 to 4–11) will suffice, and when this unit is completely equipped a skilled lapidary can produce an impressive variety of work. Although the machine shown in Figure 4–29 was designed for amateur use, it has proved to be very efficient and practical for commercial use, particularly in rock analysis in geological work, in mining as well as oil exploration.*

For an inexpensive outfit, all parts required for a practical machine, such as flywheel, spindle, bearings, etc., may be obtained from any auto-wrecking firm. However, if one is seriously interested in the lapidary art, complete satisfaction can only be obtained with properly designed and built equipment.

MACHINE DESIGN. To saw, grind, finish, and polish ordinary specimen or cabochon work, use the regular grinding head (Fig. 4–7), properly equipped. The type and size of head are governed by the size and quantity of work to be done.

Fig. 4-33.
Combination lapidary grinding and polishing unit.

---

* Over 100 machines are in operation in U. S. A., Saudia Arabia, P. P. Islands, Ecuador, and Venezuela.

Fig. 4-34.
General-purpose
lapidary machine.

However, for all-round use, the horizontal lap is superior because a greater variety of work may be done with it. Machines of various types are shown in Figures 4–27 to 4–31. In recent years combination machines have proved to be popular (Figs. 4–33 and 34).

Commercial lap benches are of simple design with vertical spindles which fit through a hole in the table top. A conventional spindle of approved design is shown in Figure 4–35. This unit is made of hot-rolled machine steel, preferably heat treated, and has a collar of substantial size shrunk onto it upon which the lap rests. The ends of the spindle are pointed at an angle of 60 deg. and are left soft. This facilitates the periodical truing of worn points which is a simple lathe operation. Hardened points may also be used but these when worn require regrinding. These spindles operate in wood bearings (*lignum vitae*) and will give daily service for years. The spindle points require truing only about once a year. Metal bearings should be avoided for they rapidly cut the points of the spindle wherever abrasive is present and where a horizontal lap is used with loose abrasive grain.

In machining spindles of this type, the shaft is rough turned to approximate measurements and the collar is shrunk on, after which the spindle is pointed and finished between female centers. Only in this manner is concentricity and accuracy assured. Spindles of this type are

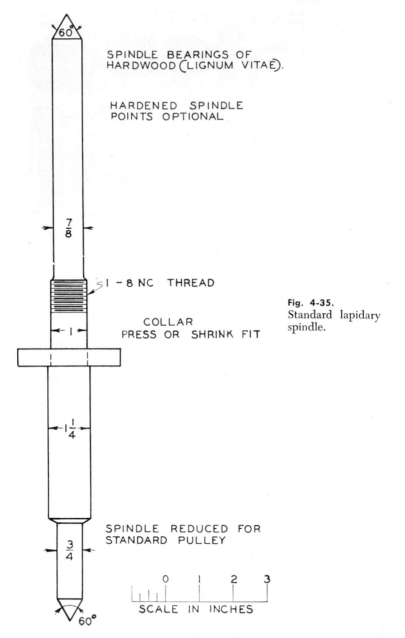

SPINDLE BEARINGS OF
HARDWOOD (LIGNUM VITAE).

HARDENED SPINDLE
POINTS OPTIONAL

$\frac{7}{8}$

≤1 - 8 NC THREAD

COLLAR
PRESS OR SHRINK FIT

Fig. 4-35.
Standard lapidary
spindle.

1

$1\frac{1}{4}$

SPINDLE REDUCED FOR
STANDARD PULLEY

$\frac{3}{4}$

60°

SCALE IN INCHES

standard equipment and are used in lapidary shops all over the world.

Grinding spindles of modern design are shown in Figures 4–36 and 4–37. These are self-contained units mounted on precision, felt-seal-type bearings which in practice have been found to give satisfactory service

**Fig. 4-36.** Machine spindles, Senior and Junior models, for lapidary work.

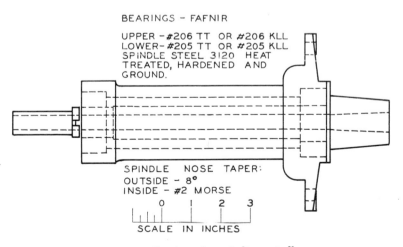

BEARINGS - FAFNIR

UPPER - #206 TT OR #206 KLL
LOWER - #205 TT OR #205 KLL
SPINDLE STEEL 3120 HEAT
TREATED, HARDENED AND
GROUND.

SPINDLE NOSE TAPER:
OUTSIDE - 8°
INSIDE - #2 MORSE

0    1    2    3

SCALE IN INCHES

**Fig. 4-37.** Sperisen Sr. grinding spindle.

over long periods of time. The spindle ("Sr." model) is made of nickel alloy steel, heat treated, hardened, and ground. The tapered spindle nose permits the accurate mounting of laps and grinding wheels as well as their rapid removal and replacement where a number of necessary operations may be performed on a single unit. An interesting feature is the hollow-bored spindle with a No. 2 Morse taper in the spindle nose. This permits the accurate mounting of arbors, reamers, chucks, laps, or saws, as well as special tools thereby increasing the scope of the work and the usefulness of the machine. As the spindle is soundly and ruggedly built, grinding wheels, saws, or laps of all types may be mounted thereon. With a five-step pulley a wide range of speeds is obtained. A maximum speed of 5000 r.p.m. is possible.

Simplified grinding spindles (Sperisen Jr., Fig. 4–36) are giving thousands of hours of satisfactory service.

SAWS AND SAWING OR SLITTING MACHINES.  Saws used in lapidary apparatus are designated as mud saws, abrasive saws, or cutoff wheels and diamond saws.

Circular saws are used, and the diameters may be any dimension from 1 in. upward; however, for the sawing or slitting of rocks or gem minerals into suitable pieces, the diameters most commonly used are 8, 10, and 12 in. Larger diameters also are available.

The saw blades are mounted on suitable spindles well shielded and protected from the entrance of grit and enclosed in a housing. The latter may be a simple shield if a small amount of sawing is required, or an elaborate system including circulating pumps and splash guards may be required in addition for large-scale production work. The popular fully automatic sawing machine, shown in Figure 4–38, is provided with

Fig. 4-38. Petrified wood being sawed on conventional-type diamond saw.

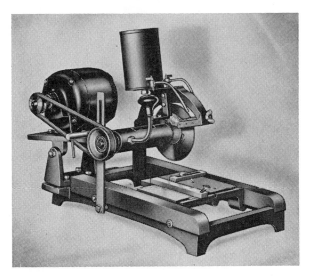

Fig. 4-39.
Felker Di-met model
11-B lapidary machine.

splash system for the coolant, and the feed to bring pressure on the specimen being sawed is by a weight acting through gravity.

A 12-in. diameter saw, used with a machine of this type, will saw through a boulder 4½ by 6 in. with the standard clamping device. With a well-built machine, a surprising degree of accuracy is achieved in the sawing of slabs. Many have been checked with a micrometer caliper that showed parallelism within .005 in. in slabs 4 by 4 in.

Larger sawing machines utilizing diamond saws up to 24 in. in diameter and equipped with adjustable mechanical or hydraulic feed are also available (Figs. 4–39 to 4–41). Small sawing machines commonly called trim saws utilizing blades from four to eight inches in diameter are important tools in the lapidary shop (Fig. 4–42). Trim saws using the larger blades are in fact universal sawing machines, as a blade of this diameter, eight inches, can saw a boulder in half measuring over three inches in the cut.

MECHANICAL FACETING HEADS. To aid the lapidary in the accurate cutting of facets rather than to depend upon skill alone, mechanical devices may be used.

The apparatus shown in Figures 4–43 and 4–44 has many unique features. It is completely mobile being separable from the trunnion support, thus permitting ease of examination. Fine and rapid adjustment in all planes, to change the position of the stone being faceted, also is provided.

The hollow body with chucking device permits the rapid, accurate

Fig. 4-40. Felker Di-met model 80 diamond sawing machine.

Fig. 4-41.
Duplex sawing machine for large rock masses (author's creation; patent applied for).

Fig. 4-42.   Trim saw.

handling of a quantity of stones, eliminating the necessity of recementing the stones to special holders. Figures 4–45 and 4–46 illustrate other versions of faceting units.

Many types of faceting tools are obtainable at the present time, some of which have as many as 96 divisions. The principle of operation, however, is the same in all cases. It is important, for successful operation,

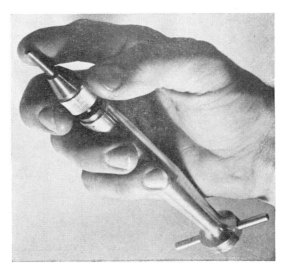

Fig. 4-43.
Hand piece Sperisen
faceting tool.

Fig. 4-44.
Universal faceting tool.

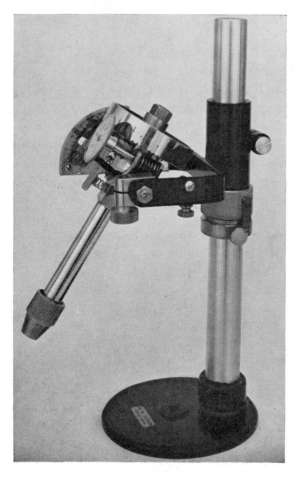

Fig. 4-45.
Taylor faceting tool.

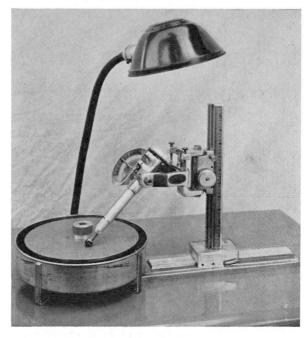

Fig. 4-46.
Master facet unit.

that the lap and the spindle upon which it is mounted are accurate.

For classroom work or for a small commercial shop, it is more practical to install individual units. Figure 4–47 shows a compact grouping of three units, a diamond saw with a 12-in. blade, a grinder head with 10-in. wheels, and a vertical spindle with a 10-in. lap. For this grouping, the elements shown in Figures 4–7, 4–36, and 4–38 were used.

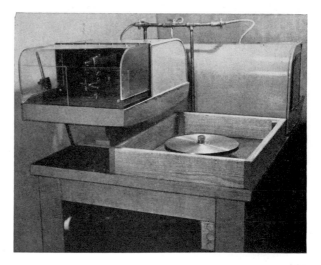

Fig. 4-47.
Complete lapidary unit.
Bench top 30 x 48 in.
(author's creation).

CHAPTER 5

# Sawing, Specimen Grinding, and Polishing

A STONE may be sawed or slit in a number of ways, with saws or sawing media of various types. A mud saw, an abrasive saw, commonly called cutoff wheel, or a diamond saw can be used. Each of these saws has its advantages and limitations. The mud saw and the diamond saw are commonly used in all lapidary shops. Although certain types of resinoid bonded abrasive saws are useful to the lapidary, they are more widely used in the industrial field for cutting marble and granite slabs into strips or sections.

Formerly, the simplest and least costly means of parting or slitting a hard stone was by means of a "mud saw," which is still the best method to use in the sawing of gold quartz having dense metallic concentration. Meteorites may also be slit in this manner. Sheet-metal disks

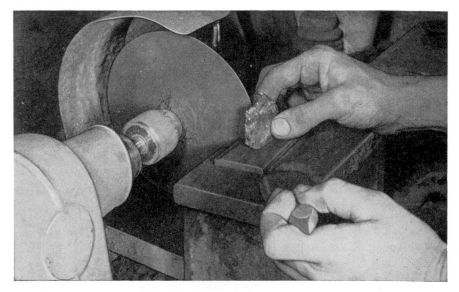

Fig. 5-1. Position of stone for sawing on a mud saw.

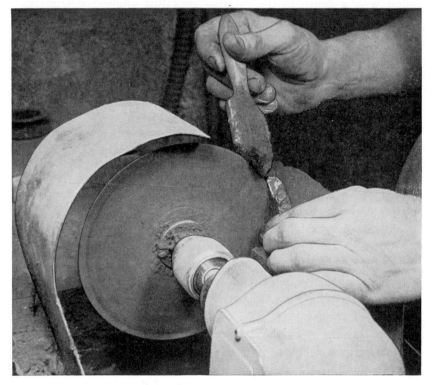

**Fig. 5-2.** Applying abrasive with a brush to a mud saw.

are commonly used, and those made of soft iron will give the best results. The majority of saws are circular and vary in thickness according to their diameter. A 20- or 22-gauge metal will be satisfactory for a disk 6 to 8 in. in diameter, but to provide sufficient stiffness, a thicker sheet is required for saws of larger diameter. Thin blades operated at high speed will wear unevenly and the edge may collapse within a short time.

Wet abrasive is applied with a brush to the periphery of a mud saw, and for fast sawing the blade is rotated at a speed of 2500 s.f.p.m. This saw derives its name from the muddy condition of the abrasive and apparatus after a few hours of work. As the saw operates, the abrasive grain wears down, and the material removed by the saw combines with the abrasive to form the mudlike mixture. Water should be used at all times and, as heat develops during operation, more water must be added to maintain the muddy mixture at proper consistency.

A simple type of mud saw is shown in Figures 5–1 and 5–2. If silicon carbide grit No. 220 or 180 is used, and the wet abrasive is constantly applied with a brush to the rotating disk just above the stone being sawed, a cut can be made through quartz at the rate of 1 sq. in. in five minutes or less.

Sometimes it is advisable to use thinner gauge metal of soft steel, such as 20 or 22 gauge (.032 and .025 in.), with an abrasive of finer grit, either FFF or 320. In sawing thin slabs of gold quartz for inlay work, as shown in Figure 10–7, superior and more economical results were obtained with FFF grit and a saw blade 6 in. in diameter and .020 in. thick.

When a saw unit of this type is operated, the stone or object to be sawed should rest on the table in front of the saw and be firmly held and pressed against the saw. Stones larger than 2 by 2 in. should be held in a clamp; smaller pieces may be conveniently held by the hand. If the hand method is followed, the stone should be grasped firmly so that it will not slip. A brushful of the wet abrasive applied against the rotating saw above the stone will cause the saw to begin cutting immediately. The pressure on the stone should be firm and steady, and the thumb of the hand should be to one side of the plane of the saw, for if the stone should part the thumb would be cut.

Because of its simplicity, usefulness, and adaptability, this type of saw is universally used by lapidaries to cut all types of inexpensive specimens.

To saw large specimens, mud saws may be made to operate automatically. To do this, the speed of the saw is reduced to approximately 500 s.f.p.m. to prevent excessive spattering of the abrasive. The sawing rate is slow, and because the operation is automatic, a large number of slabs or specimens may be sawed with little personal attention.

Mud saws include such types as band saws, consisting of endless bands of steel to which wet abrasive grain is applied. The band operates on the conventional saw frame.

Gang saws with numerous steel bands in parallel position within an oscillating frame are unsurpassable for quantity production. With this saw it was possible to slit agate boulders cemented together into a block 2 cu. ft. in size within 24 hours. The saw blades were placed ½ in. apart, and the total area of the sawed surface was 48 sq. ft.

Mud saws also are made of wire. The ends of the wire may be welded together and these wires used in a manner similar to the band saw, or the ends may be fastened to a bent sapling or bow and used in a reciprocating manner. Chinese lapidaries use such saws to cut large masses of stone. Although a great amount of labor is expended in this process, wonderful results have been achieved. The 18,000-lb. jade boulder used to make the altar of the sacred Jade Pagoda (Fig. 9–17) was sawed in this manner. It is necessary always to feed a thin stream of muddy abrasive to the metal element. Although the mud saw is convenient and economical, it is difficult to control the grit and prevent the mud from spattering.

Some abrasive saws or cutoff wheels are suitable for lapidary work. Bonded with resins or gums and abrasive, the silicon carbide cutoff wheel will perform efficiently and economically on the softer stones and rocks and on various types of quartz.

Experience has shown that the resinoid bonded cutoff wheel 3760 L.7.T.2., Norton Co., 8 or 10 in. in diameter and 1/16 in. thick, operating at 5000 s.f.p.m. will saw through quartz at the rate of 1 sq. in. in five minutes. More time is required to cut large masses of quartz if the cut is to be made in one through pass. Thus a piece of chalcedony 2 by 2 in. sawed in this manner required 40 minutes. To cut larger specimens, more time and increased power are required. This difficulty can be overcome by rotating or oscillating the work, thus decreasing the arc of contact as the cut deepens. On test, jasper 3 by 4 in. was sawed at the rate of 1 sq. in. in five minutes. For this work, however, a rotating work holder and a special machine were required.

On softer rocks, clean cuts can be made with a minimum of effort. Granite may be sawed at the rate of 30 seconds per square inch. Water is used as a coolant, and a solution of various compounds, such as codol or soda, prevent rusting of the steel spindle and other ferrous parts of the machine.

Cutoff wheels are fragile and must be handled carefully. Cuts should be started in the plane of the saw without deviation. Resinoid bonded diamond abrasive cutoff wheels, available in small sizes and in thin blades, are excellent for cutting precious gemstones although their high cost and danger of breakage prevent their universal use. Abrasive cutoff wheels should be used only on equipment designed for their use.

Diamond saws in common use are made of metal — copper, phosphor bronze, or steel — and have diamond grain or coarse powder rolled or embedded in the periphery. Operating conditions and performances vary widely with saws of different manufacturers. Speeds may range from 1500 to 5000 s.f.p.m. With a well-made saw, the cutting rate in quartz will be 1 sq. in. in two minutes or less.

The life and performance of these saws vary according to the type of saw, speed of operation, nature of the material sawed, and skill in operation. The softer minerals and rocks will allow a longer life and more speed in a saw, while chalcedony and various agates afford the greatest resistance to sawing and cut down the useful life of a saw.

Small sections may be sawed without the use of clamps (Fig. 5–3) by holding the stone in the hand as is done when mud sawing. However, clamps and vises of various types are commonly used. While these may be parallel wood clamps operated by screws, a screw vise as commonly used in the machine shop will be of the greatest value in holding small specimens. Thin wooden packing is used between the jaws to assist in holding the stone and to prevent twisting or crushing it. Stones also may be secured to a cement block by means of sealing wax, cement, or plaster of Paris. A low melting point, modified Wood's alloy, which melts and runs freely at a temperature below the melting point of sealing wax, used in conjunction with a cup-shaped holder that may be readily fixed to the sawing frame, is very useful in holding stones securely. It affords a positive grip, making it impossible for the stone to shift or to become dislodged while sawing. The holding unit (Fig. 5–4) is small in proportion to the rock being held, takes little space, and is easily adapted to any holding or clamping fixture.

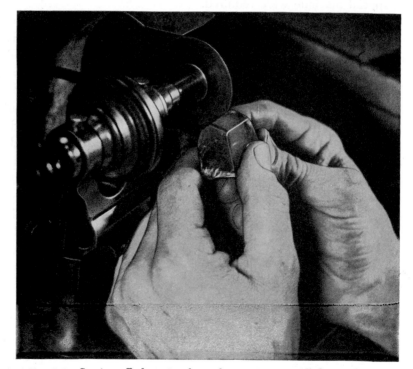

**Fig. 5-3.** Sawing off clear tip of amethyst, using a small diamond saw.

**Fig. 5-4.**
Stone holder for sawing.

Into this unit the stone is placed, and the alloy which has been pre-viously melted in hot water is poured over the stone. The alloy fills the cup-shaped holder displacing what water remains therein. The unit then is cooled or quenched under a flow of cold water to develop a fine grain structure and to solidify the alloy. Unlike most metals or alloys that shrink on cooling, this alloy expands, thus holding the stone securely in the cup. To remove the stone after sawing has been completed, the unit is placed in a pot of hot water which melts the alloy and frees the stone. Although this alloy is more expensive than other cements, it may be used repeatedly and, therefore, is far more economical.

During the sawing operations a coolant is used. It has been customary to use a mixture of four parts of kerosene to one of light motor oil. Auto-engine flushing oil, or if the diamond saw is properly made, water or a non-rusting cutting solution, may be used.

Although a four to one oil solution is standard practice in sawing large masses of rock into suitable slabs, this solution is not practical for use in small trim saws in the commercial shop. Water or other solu-tions or compounds are used for this purpose. Soluble oil has been used in the past, but recently a number of chemical compounds have become available for use in the machine tool industry. These compounds are readily soluble in water, are pleasant to use and have no disagreeable aftereffects. One of these, "HOCUT" No. 237, has been found to give excellent results. The aqueous solution is not only a coolant and lubri-cant but also of equal economic value; the sawing time per unit area is lessened.

Diamond saws may be purchased or the operator may prefer to make them. Small saws (Fig. 5–3) are made of bronze or sheet iron about .005 to .010 in. thick. They are readily charged by the application of a mixture of a carat of No. 3 or 300 diamond powder and about 10 drops of olive oil. A flat piece of agate is held against the properly trued disk, and the diamond in oil is applied to the edge of the saw. After a few moments the disk will begin cutting. Prior to charging small nicks should be made with a sharp knife in the periphery of the blade to achieve best results. After the saw has been completely charged by the application of sufficient diamond, oil is added as a coolant and lubricant, and only intermittent applications of the diamond-oil mixture will be needed.

Larger saws, 8 to 12 in. in diameter, are usually made of 18 (.040 in.) or 20-gauge (.032 in.) iron sheet, the larger diameter requiring thicker sheet metal. Nicks are cut in the periphery with a knife or chisel, and No. 80 or 100 grit diamond grain mixed to a thick paste with heavy oil is affixed in the nicks and is peened or rolled in place. The disposition, pitch, and depth of the nicks will vary, depending on the manufacturer; but the average pitch is ⅟₁₆ in. (distance from nick to nick) and the average depth is ⅟₁₆–³⁄₃₂ in. deep. Two to four carats of diamond grain, depending on the number of notches, will be required to charge a well-made saw 10 in. in diameter.

The life and performance of the saw will vary according to the method of operation and the type of material cut, as well as the efficiency of the machine in which the saw is operated. Carefully compiled data amassed over a period of four years' testing shows that a 10 or 12-in. diamond saw will produce from 400 to 2500 sq. in. of sawed quartz during its life, according to the amount of diamond in the saw. The saws that were poorly made or lacking in the charge of diamond grain gave correspondingly poor results.

In the use of a diamond saw, the same general principles apply as those which govern the use and operation of the mud saw. Although it is possible to saw small stones without the use of a clamping device, the best results are obtained by the rigid clamping of the stone during the sawing operation (Fig. 5–5). Should the stone shift or become loosened in the clamp while it is being sawed, the saw blade will be bent or nicked and possibly ruined. Saws made from rolled sheet metal, if damaged, may be straightened by a skilled smith.

Diamond saws manufactured by bonding diamond grain in a sintered alloy or plastic are fragile and will break if improperly used.

**Fig. 5-5.** Twelve-inch diamond saw skillfully operated by a 13-year-old boy.

Because of this weakness, improvements have been effected in recent years whereby the diamond grain bonded in a sintered alloy is firmly held to the periphery of a solid metal disk or it may also be a filling in slots milled about the edge.

Research carried out by the author from June, 1938, to August, 1939, proved the excellence of self-made, slot-filled, metal-bonded diamond saws. At a low speed (650 r.p.m.) a 12-in diamond saw cut through quartz at the rate of 1 sq. in. in 58 seconds. Similar performance was also recorded on large slabs. A stone 6 by 7 in. was sawed through in one hour.

A commercial blade of this type, 12 in. in diameter, yielded over 3450 sq. in. of sawed slabs before it was completely worn out. Most of the material cut was chalcedony and nephrite (Wyoming jade).

Large-diameter diamond saws are invariably used with small clamping collars in order to utilize the maximum sawing area. As a result, a considerable amount of flexibility is present. Therefore, it is important, when sawing a large stone, that the saw be started at a point on the stone that is in the plane of the saw. Correct starting is easily accomplished when the stone to be sawed has a flat surface perpendicular to the plane of the saw. If the surface of the stone is irregular or forms an angle tangent to the plane of the saw, it will be necessary to guide the saw where it strikes the stone so that the cut may be started correctly. This may be done by holding a small block on the stone so that the periphery of the saw will bear against the stone and the saw blade will not be diverted from its true path.

An alternate method is to feed the stone carefully to the saw. The feed is stopped when contact has been made, thus permitting the rotating saw blade to cut a groove in the surface of the stone. The sawing then progresses in the usual manner.

Under normal operating conditions a pull of 5 lbs., usually applied by a weight suspended from a cord attached to the moving carriage, will be sufficient to cause the carriage to travel along the ways provided in the machine. By carefully starting the saw and controlling it as it emerges through the cut the saw will be useful over a long period. If it is necessary to saw slabs of about 1 mm. thickness, most satisfactory results will be obtained if a flat surface of the stone is cemented to a suitable holder which is mounted parallel to the saw. Then, by proper adjustment, the stone is severed so that the path of the saw is the required distance from the cemented face.

Small stones that must be sawed into a number of pieces may be cemented to a slab of marble or slate held rigidly in a vise. The saw can cut through the stone and the slate backing without hindrance.

Large, thin slabs that require sawing into strips or other forms should be cemented to plates as mentioned to prevent breaking. Regardless of the type of saw used, an important factor in successful operation is the rigid and secure holding of the stone (Fig. 5–6).

Fig. 5-6. Holding fixtures for sawing rocks into slabs. First, iron angle plate; second, rock cemented; third, section sawed; fourth, rock cemented to special plate to be bolted to fixture on saw.

▲ **Fig. 5-8.** Blank for smoky crystal compote ready to be rounded and finished.

◀ **Fig. 5-7.** Smoky crystal "roughed out" by sawing; blank is cemented to plate.

When sawing rocks or gem minerals, fixtures of various types are not only useful but timesaving as well. Figures 5–7 and 5–8 show apparatus used for "roughing out" a block of smoky crystal for making a compote.

A flat face was prepared on the blank, after which the blank was carefully cemented to a circular steel holder of appropriate size. By means of a centralized stud bolt, the cement plate was held in position for sawing. A steel plate bent to the desired angle and held securely in a vise permitted holding the cement plate in the correct position. By means of successive saw cuts, the surplus material was removed and a considerable amount of grinding time was saved.

In a similar manner, by means of proper indexing, a number of cuts, six, eight, ten, or more, would enable the operator to accurately saw to size and shape a multiple faceted unit.

Although the apparatus illustrated (Fig. 5–7) utilizes a diamond saw operating in a horizontal plane, the same principle of operation can also be used with diamond saws operating in a vertical plane. If a number of stones of the same size and shape are to be cut from a slab, careful marking out will often yield a greater number of stones (Fig. 5–9).

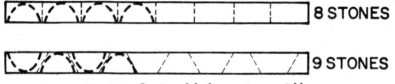

**Fig. 5-9.** Sawing slab for maximum yield.

## SPECIMEN POLISHING

Specimen polishing is the simplest form of lapidary work. The polishing of large surfaces may be difficult and may require the use of large machinery, but the technique is essentially the same as that used in polishing small specimens. "Spotting" is the polishing of a small surface to show the predominant color, pattern, or markings.

In polishing specimens, it soon becomes apparent that mineral species not only vary in hardness but also in texture. Moreover, it may be observed that these varying qualities of hardness and texture are frequently present in the same stone. All stones that are to be polished as specimens or as cabochons have been divided into two classes. To obtain best results a slight change in the polishing technique has been followed in each class.

While it is possible to polish all stones by the technique recommended for the stones listed in Group 1, the polishing of the stones listed in Group 2 is speeded by the introduction of an additional step.

Group 1 includes all soft stones such as malachite, turquoise, azurite, variscite, and lapis lazuli; all hard stones having granular or uneven structure caused by materials of varying hardness; stones having a fibrous texture, or those containing inclusions of various types such as the rhodonite, jasper, dumortierite, jade, and tiger's-eye.

Group 2 consists of all stones which have a dense uniform structure like glass, opal, agate or chalcedony, rock crystal, amethyst, or tourmaline.

Following are the steps used to polish stones:

### Group 1

Rough grind on silicon carbide, 60 or 80 grit.
Finish grind on silicon carbide, 180 or 220 grit.
Smooth on silicon carbide, abrasive cloth, 180, 220, or 320 grit.
Polish on leather wheel with tin oxide.

### Group 2

Rough grind as for Group 1.
Finish grind as for Group 1.
Smooth as for Group 1.
First, polish with a felt wheel using silicon carbide grain FFF.
Finish polishing with a leather wheel using tin oxide.

When small specimens are to be ground and polished, or when a limited amount of work is to be done, simple and inexpensive equipment may be used. All grinding must be done wet and an adequate supply of coolant, usually water, should be directed upon the wheel. For the first attempt at polishing, it is best to select a piece of agate or chalcedony. Montana agate is ideal for this purpose for it possesses a fine, even grain, and it can be given and retains an excellent polish. Many attractive patterns also are available in this stone thus assuring fine cabinet specimens.

A stone not over 2 sq. in. in area will serve well. This size can be easily handled, and the grinding and polishing operations to follow will not be too prolonged and tiresome.

The agate is included in the second group. The following technique for polishing stones in this group should be adhered to regardless of the size, shape, or form the article ultimately will assume. If the stone selected is a waterworn pebble, the rough and nicked surface must be removed by grinding. If the stone is a small, sawed piece, the flat surface resulting from sawing will require only finish-grinding to prepare it for polishing.

If the pebble has been selected for grinding, it should be grasped firmly by the first three fingers of both hands and pressed against the 60-grit coarse grinding wheel. It it is easier to hold the stone with

**Fig. 5-10.** Roughing out stone on coarse grinding wheel, 60 or 80 grit.

one hand only, the hand holding the stone is aided and supported by the other. To gain accurate control of the grinding operation, the forearms should rest on a firm support. In this manner through the support, the arms, wrists, hands, and fingers are able to exert considerable pressure against the grinding wheel and at the same time exercise complete control of the grinding operation (Fig. 5–10). The grinding wheel should rotate at a speed approximately 4000 s.f.p.m., and it must be kept wet during the entire operation. During the grinding operation care should be exercised to prevent running off the face of the wheel which could result in severe injury to the fingers or hand. However, the unskilled student or the amateur lapidary who does grinding for the first time should have no fear or be timid about it. Confidence together with skill come with practice.

During rough-grinding all surface cracks and nicks should be removed. The stone is rotated by turning on the face of the wheel, and at the same time it is given a slight up and down or radial movement to produce a moderate convex surface, for this surface is easier to polish than a flat surface. The stone may be examined from time to time in order to observe the progress made.

When the stone has been properly ground, the entire surface will be uniform, showing the grit marks left by the coarse grinding wheel. The stone now should be examined through a magnifier or loupe of 3x power. The time required to rough grind an agate or chalcedony pebble 1½ in. square will be from one to five minutes, depending upon the condition of the stone and the type of apparatus used.

In finish-grinding, the technique is the same as roughing, but as less material is to be removed, the operation is quicker. When the stone has been properly ground, the entire surface will be of a uniform nature showing the grit marks left by the 180- or 220-grit finish-grinding wheel. These grit marks will be finer than those left by the coarse grinding wheel, and any grinding marks left by the coarse grinding wheel which may not have been removed will be easily seen with an eye loupe. During the finish-grinding operation care should be exercised to produce as uniform a surface as possible, free from bumps or hollows, for the polishing processes that follow wear the stone very slowly. If the grinding steps are not properly performed, much unnecessary time will be spent in removing the grinding marks in the operations following. In finish-grinding, the amount of material to be removed is relatively small and as a result the time consumed is about half that of rough-grinding.

The finish-grinding wheels should rotate at the same rate of surface speed as the rough-grinding wheels, approximately 4000 f.p.m.

The next step is smoothing, commonly called "sanding," which is the first step in polishing. This is a simple operation and it may be performed manually by briskly rubbing the surface of the stone on abrasive cloth held in the hand, or a rotating abrasive disk may be used (Fig. 6–18). Both methods have advantages as well as limitations. In smoothing by hand the sole requirement is briskly rubbing the stone on a piece of abrasive cloth held flat on a board or on a table. By giving the stone a slight universal motion (turning in all directions), the entire surface will be smoothed, and the grit marks or slight irregularities which have been left from the finish-grinding will be eliminated. The operation is performed without danger of heating due to friction. Small stones may be sanded in a minute or two, but large surfaces may require from five minutes upward according to the size of the specimen. Although large slabs or specimens may be smoothed in this manner, the process is laborious and time consuming. For smoothing large surfaces, power-driven sanding belts, wheels or drums are recommended (Figs. 4–17 and 4–18; 6–18). When operating a power-driven sanding wheel, moderate pressure should be used when applying the stone. Too much pressure would develop excessive heat which could flake, crack, or otherwise ruin a stone. For regular use, the sander should operate at a speed not to exceed 1500 s.f.p.m. A 10- or 12-in. disk wheel operating at 500 r.p.m. will give satisfactory results.

When two sanding disks are on hand, a great deal of time can be saved. The initial work of removing grinding scratches is performed with a fresh or slightly used cloth, and the final sanding may be done on a cloth which has become worn. An optional method of sanding where two units are available is to use a 180 or 220 grit abrasive cloth on one machine and a 320 or 400 grit abrasive cloth on the other. If the foregoing steps are carefully followed, the stone will be smooth and glossy, and if examined with a lens or with an eye loupe, the stone will present a smooth uniform surface with very fine scratches made by the smoothing cloth.

The next step in polishing is to thoroughly scrub and clean the specimen, as well as the operator's hands, using a stiff brush, soap and water. All traces of grit also must be carefully removed from the specimen because any remaining grit would contaminate all polishing materials and produce scratches on the surface of the polished stone.

After thorough cleaning, the next step in polishing is to present the smooth face of the specimen to the surface of a hard felt wheel,

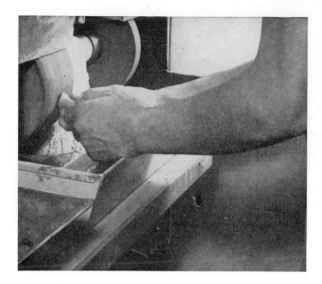

Fig. 5-11.
Polishing a cabochon
stone on a felt wheel.

to which FFF silicon carbide has been applied with a brush (Figs.
5–11 and 5–12). The fine abrasive material is mixed with water to
form a thin paste. The operating speed of the felt wheel should be about
2000 s.f.p.m. When beginning work with a new felt wheel, the stone
should be applied to the wheel with only slight pressure. By the continuous application of wet abrasive to the wheel surface immediately in front
of the specimen, the abrasive is compressed into the wheel which thus becomes charged, the stone and its surface at the point of contact remain

Fig. 5-12.
Polishing the face of
a large agate specimen
on a felt wheel.

cool, and the surface of the stone gradually receives a dull glossy polish. When the operation has been completed, the entire surface will be free of scratches left by the previous operations. When polishing with a felt wheel, excess pressure or prolonged contact with the wheel without the application of wet abrasive must be avoided. Heat is quickly generated if the wheel is permitted to become dry, and the stone may be cracked, burned, or otherwise ruined in an instant. It is not difficult to hold a small stone on the wheel face or side with one hand while a brushful of wet abrasive is applied with the other hand every few seconds. The time required to polish a specimen of 2 sq. in. may be five minutes or less depending on the thoroughness of the preceding operations and the equipment used.

In polishing surfaces that are nearly flat, streaks or minute polish gouges, resulting from the action of the felt wheel and the abrasive used, may appear in the surface of the stone if considerable pressure is applied. By holding the stone so that the felt wheel polishes at a right angle to the previous action, and by gentle pressure, all of the streaks may be removed.

While it is customary to use felt wheels on a grinding head running in a vertical plane, there are distinct advantages in operating the wheel in a horizontal plane like a lap (Fig. 6–19). In this manner both the work and the polishing material may be applied with ease to the surface of the lap, resulting in a sustained polishing action and a lessening of the time required to polish the stone. This will minimize fatigue. As the operator does not stand in the same plane with the abrasive thrown off by the rapidly rotating wheel, the danger of wet abrasive spattering the operator's face is eliminated.

If an examination with the $3x$ loupe fails to reveal grit scratches or removable blemishes on the stone left by preceding operations, it is again thoroughly cleaned with soap and water after which it is ready for the final polishing.

For superior results on the majority of stones having a convex or flat surface, a cowhide-covered drum or crowned wheel should be used (Fig. 6–19). Tin oxide is the most satisfactory polishing powder, although on hard stones levigated alumina, applied wet with a brush, will give good results. When new wheels are used or when a new leather covering has replaced a worn covering, the polishing material should be applied as a thick paste and worked into the leather by means of the stone to be polished. After the pores of the leather have been thoroughly impregnated with the polishing powder, a thin creamlike mixture may be used, or if preferred, the powder may be applied by dipping a wet brush into it and then placing it on the surface of the wheel.

A constant application of the polishing material is not always necessary. The surface of the wheel can be touched occasionally with the wet brush in order to maintain the proper amount of dampness which enables the charged leather to do its work. The best results have been obtained when the condition of the leather is such that it pulls or tugs at the work as it is applied to the surface of the wheel. When polishing a large surface, this pulling force is very great and it is necessary to obtain a firm grip upon the stone during the operation. While working large stones, too great a pressure must not be placed upon the wheel for the braking effect is so strong that it is an easy matter to stall a ⅛ h.p. motor which may result in blown fuses or a ruined motor.

If the stone has been properly prepared in the previous operations, the time required to finish polish the surface of 2 sq. in. will not take more than two minutes.

Prolonged polishing may result in wetting the leather on the wheel to such a degree that it will not polish but cause the stone to slide over the surface without effect. Should the leather become too wet, the wheel should be allowed to run for several minutes until it is dry, when the operation of polishing may be resumed. A speed of 1500 s.f.p.m. will give satisfactory results.

An alternative method of polishing is to use a stitched muslin buff to which the wet polishing material has been applied in the usual manner. These wheels can be used satisfactorily on dense, close-grained stones, but they are not recommended for the polishing of stones composed of particles of varying hardness. They are useful in the polishing of irregular surfaces, hollows, or concaves. Buffs with concentric stitching should be used. These stitches are cut through with a knife when the buff has been worn down and the surface begins to harden. Best results can be obtained with a speed of 2500 s.f.p.m., keeping the buff wet or damp. A dry wheel and forceful application of the work may cause the stone to spall or crack.

Specimens listed in Group 1, such as turquoise, malachite, tiger's-eye, or jasper are treated in a similar manner, the first three steps being rough grinding, finish grinding, and sanding. Because of their granular structure or varying hardness, polishing on the felt wheel is eliminated. The stone is carefully smoothed with the regular sanding cloth to remove all fine grinding marks, and then it is finished on a cloth which has been worn smooth. This method of finishing imparts a smooth glossy surface to the stone. When all coarse scratches have been removed, the specimen is thoroughly scrubbed with soap and water to remove all traces of grit after which it is ready for polishing on the leather wheel. This operation requires a little more time than the previously described method but the results are far more satisfactory, for if stones in Group 1 were treated on the felt wheel, all soft particles would be worked out, leaving the surface uneven and irregular.

Through careful attention to detail, the process and technique just described will give excellent results. Careless or halfhearted attempts should not be tolerated, and a high polish with deep scratches, the so-called "California finish," should be avoided.

Through care and diligence ability can be acquired to perfectly polish specimens of all kinds. Thus, a broad field is open to the lapidary and this newly developed skill may be applied to produce countless objects, the nature of which is limited solely by the imagination and skill of the operator.

TUMBLING. In the past decade, "tumbled" gemstones have become very popular. Although gemstones cut and polished in this manner have been used for many centuries, only in recent times has their popularity grown to such an extent that hand finishing became impractical commercially and machinery was used to produce the polished stones in the quantities required.

Tumbling machines are to be seen in great variety. The principle of operation is simple: the stones being kept in constant agitation with grits respectively finer till a polished surface is attained.

A simple tumbling machine designed and built by the author is shown in Figures 5–13 and 5–14. This design possesses many advantages over the single or double barrel units available. Although four units are shown, as many as twenty tumbling barrels may be used on a column six feet high, and having the same floor space. Various types of inexpensive tumbling units can be used. Two pound coffee cans may be used, but owing to the internal pressure developed, it is difficult to prevent leaks unless some venting device is used, or the cover is soldered in place.

One gallon paint cans proved to be excellent for this purpose. The lids were not only pressure tight, but also the wire handle permitted the use of a wooden wedge as a safety factor. The cans are fastened to the six inch iron pulley wheels by means of three bolts (No. 10–24 by 1 in.) spaced equidistantly for ease in mounting; wheels are driven by V-belts. The initial drive is by means of a small motor having a

Fig. 5-13.
Driving unit of
tumbling machine.

gear reduction unit with connecting chain drive. As each "tumbler" conveniently holds five pounds of stones to be finished, as much as 100 pounds of gemstones may be treated on one battery of units. All pulleys are mounted on ball bearing pillow blocks having double end

Fig. 5-14.
Tumbling machine
(author's creation).

shafts. Should one wish to check the progress of a definite unit, releasing the hollow head setscrew on the pulley hub permits the removal of the unit desired without disturbing the remainder. As the covers of the gallon cans can be readily removed, cleaning is simple. Improved action is obtained by cementing a thin ribbed plastic liner to the inside of the can.

For best results, the stones to be finished should be of approximately the same size, hardness, and contour. Stones having a rounded surface will require less time to finish, while those having flat faces, such as small flat pieces left from trim sawing, will require the maximum amount of time to finish. The usual practice is to start grinding with No. 100 grit silicon carbide although if care is given to the selection of the stones and selected pieces are used, No. 220 grit may be used instead. The grit mixed with the stones to form a "charge" should fill the container from ½ to ⅔ and sufficient water added to permit easy movement. Adding a tablespoon of detergent will eliminate frothing. By adding small steel screws to the "charge" (20–25 per cent of the volume), as much as ten hours first-stage grinding time was saved. Old iron wood screws are ideal for this purpose and these carriers act as small iron laps. A total of fifty hours time was required to prepare the surfaces of the stones for the second stage of grinding. The speed of rotation was 30 r.p.m. and this with the cans used was equivalent to 45 s.f.p.m.

After thorough cleaning, should examination disclose that a number of the pebbles have not been uniformly ground, they should be rejected and reground till a satisfactory surface is developed. A second charge is then prepared using FFF and the unit is treated for another fifty hours.

In like manner a third (No. 600) and fourth (No. 1200) stage followed with finer grit. At the third stage using No. 600 grit, carriers were fashioned from strip tin approximately ³⁄₃₂ in. thick. These strips were further scored by peening with a coarse file and the strips were then cut into small, approximately ½ in., triangular sections. These carriers, acting as small laps, developed a fine uniform surface.

In the final stage, the stones thoroughly cleansed of all remaining grit were placed in the polishing unit together with tin oxide. The carriers used were small hardwood blocks and chips of heavy sole leather. For an intermediate polishing stage use levigated alumina as the polishing agent. In any case, the time required for polishing is considerably longer; at least 150 hours is required to develop a satisfactory polish.

## POLISHING LARGE, FLAT SPECIMEN STONES

Flat stones of all kinds are polished by the lapidary. These stones may vary in size and in type from the small flat or table-cut gems used in caliber work to large slabs of jasper or petrified wood used in the manufacture of table tops, clocks, or desk sets.

To prepare and polish flat surfaces of large size, several methods are available. The method usually followed is to grind the surface of the stone on an iron lap with a suitable abrasive. Surfaces prepared and rough-ground on a silicon carbide grinding wheel may be quickly flattened by using SiC (silicon carbide) grain No. 220 on an iron lap, provided the original surface is reasonably flat. In a similar manner sawed slabs may be trued and made flat. The flatness of the surface is next checked with a surface gauge, and after this has been done, the slab is thoroughly cleaned and all grit is removed by a thorough scrubbing. The surface of the stone is then brought to a finer finish by similar lapping, but with the use of a finer grit. FFF silicon carbide will give excellent results, and grit No. 600 also may be used.

After the surface of the stone has been worked and the coarse grit marks have been removed, the stone is thoroughly cleaned and it is then ready for polishing. In polishing hard stones, varieties of quartz or the hard silicates, the best results can be obtained by polishing on a flat tin lap, using tin oxide as a polishing medium. The lap should be thoroughly roughened or scored with a knife so that the powder, which may be applied to the surface in the form of a thick paste, will adhere. The flat stone then is brought in contact with the lap (Fig. 5–15).

The largest size slab which may be conveniently handled on a flat tin lap is about 5 by 5 in. Larger pieces may be handled, but special holding fixtures will be required in order to prevent damage to the stone, the lap, or to the operator.

The powder on the lap should be kept wet by adding water from time to time, and the stone should be moved on the lap surface so that all portions of the stone receive a uniform lapping action. After a few moments' operation, the surface of the stone may be examined and the progress observed. If the slab has been properly lapped, and the laps, grinding, and polishing, are flat, the polish marks on the slab will be evenly distributed. Irregularities on the surface of the slab, caused by improper handling or by untrue laps, will show by polished spots and contrasting dull hollows. Should the hollows be slight, which can be proved by checking with a straightedge, the surface may be corrected

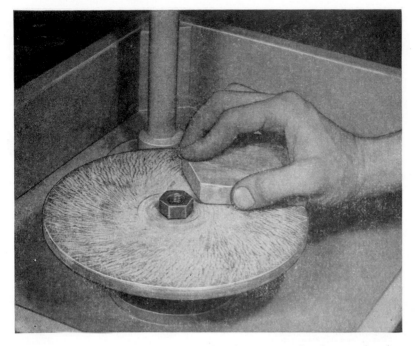

**Fig. 5-15.** Polishing flat slab on a tin lap (Sperisen Jr. lapidary machine).

by continued polishing. If deep hollows or rounded portions exist, the work must be corrected on a properly trued and faced lap.

After the surface of the stone has been polished in a uniform manner, the polishing marks or scratches remaining are removed by continued action. This is done by permitting the powder on the wheel to slowly dry out, then adding a small quantity of water from time to time so that the powder remains slightly damp. The entire surface of the stone is treated with the polishing wheel in this condition, and in a short time, the surface of the stone becomes brilliantly polished, free of irregularities. The time required to polish a flat surface in this manner varies with the size and the nature of the stone. The surface of a properly prepared specimen of chalcedony or jasper 1 in. in area may be perfectly polished within five minutes. Slabs of agate, jasper, etc., 3 by 4 in. in size, usually require 15 minutes to ½ hour to completely polish the surface after it has been correctly lapped. The desk set shown in Figure 5–16 was finished in this manner.

An alternative method that requires less skill, and one that is followed in polishing soft stones, such as malachite, turquoise, or variscite,

**Fig. 5-16.** Desk set in jasper. Pen base 4¾" x 6" x 1". (From author's workshop.)

eliminates the use of the tin lap. The stone is flattened on the iron lap in the manner previously described, after which it is smoothed on a special, crowned sander (Fig. 4–16), to which silicon carbide abrasive cloth grit No. 320 has been applied. If possible, two sanders should be used, one having a fresh cloth (a coarser grit may be used; e.g., No. 220) which is used for the initial sanding, and a second one having a worn cloth, the function of which is to impart a glossy finish to the surface being worked. Sanding belts are excellent for large work. Most machines are equipped with a platen or table upon which the work may rest and little effort is required to produce a well-sanded surface.

Final polishing is done with a leather-covered polishing wheel, of like form, using tin oxide. A large stitched muslin buff also may be used. Harder stones may be treated in a similar manner using, in addition, a felt wheel, following the same technique described in specimen polishing.

The felt wheel should be slightly crowned if the polishing is done on the flat portion of the wheel. Polishing also may be done on the cylindrical portion and, in the case of large stones, the stone or slab must be kept in constant motion so that hollow surfaces are not worked into the surface of the slab (Fig. 5–12).

Large specimens, too heavy to handle, may be polished on a rubbing bed. This is regular practice in polishing marble and granite slabs. In machines of this kind, the work is stationary and fastened on a level plane. A vertical spindle operating on a pantographic principle is usually used. Grinding laps and polishing wheels are attached to the spindle end; consequently, a considerable area may be finished at one time. A practical application of polished slabs may be seen in Figure 5–17.

**Fig. 5-17.** Practical application of polished slabs. This hearthstone made of over 90 types of gem and ornamental stones from our western states has an area of 8.1 sq. ft. The border tiles consist of lapis lazuli. The hearthstone was designed and built by Harry St. John Dixon and the stones were from the author's workshop.

# CHAPTER 6

# Cabochon Cutting and Polishing

THE simplest form of a cut stone suitable for conventional jewelry is called a *cabochon*. Cabochon stones may have any geometrical outline — round, square, rectangular, oblong, triangular, etc. (Fig. 6–1). The top or visible surface of the stone, however, is domed, and it can be any proportion of height and length to width. The back of the stone usually is flat, or nearly so. The edge or outline of the stone is known as the *girdle*.

A stone may be classified as a regular cabochon, a high cabochon, or a low cabochon according to its thickness. In the regular cabochon, the thickness is approximately one half the width of the stone; in a high cabochon, the thickness is about two thirds the width of the stone, and in a low cabochon, the thickness is less than one half its width.

Double cabochon stones are those that have a cabochon or domed surface on each side of the plane formed by the girdle edge. When both of these sides are uniform the stones are used for pendants or charms. The outline usually is elliptical, oval, or pear shaped. Hollow cabochon stones are those on which the backs are concave to permit light to be transmitted more freely. This form of cutting usually is seen only in garnet. Figure 6–2 shows side views of the various forms. The girdle edge may be left sharp to be provided with a grooved bezel, grooved to receive a wire for suspension, or the edge may be slightly rounded, in which case the stone is drilled for mounting with a loop or ring.

Transparent or semitransparent stones usually are cut double cabochon. The top of the stone is high or regular cabochon, and the bottom or back is cut as a low cabochon. This form of cutting greatly improves the brilliance and color of the stone. This is caused by its lenticular form which concentrates the light and causes it to be reflected from the back rather than permitting most of it to pass through. That would happen if the stone were cut with a flat back. This form is common in amethyst, moonstone, and tourmaline, and cabochon emeralds, rubies, and sapphires invariably are cut in this manner. Cabochon forms are known from the earliest times (Figs. 6–3 to 6–6).

137

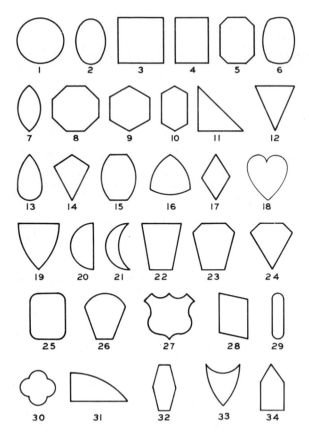

**Fig. 6-1.** Names of various forms of cabochon and faceted stones.

1, Round or circular; 2, oval or elliptical; 3, square; 4, rectangular or cushion; 5, octagon or rectangular cut corner; 6, cushion antique; 7, marquise or navette; 8, octagon; 9, hexagon; 10, oblong hexagon; 11, triangle; 12, wedge or peak triangle; 13, pear shape (cabochon) or pendeloque (faceted with table); 13, drop shape double cabochon, or briolette (faceted circular or oval cross section); 14, kite; 15, tonneau or barrel; 16, triangle cushion; 17, rhombus or diamond; 18, heart; 19, shield; 20, half round or half circular, or half moon; 21, crescent; 22, keystone cut corner; 24, kite or triangle cut corner; 25, oblong; 26, keystone; 27, shield; 28, quadrilateral; 29, oblong; 30, clover; 31, horn; 32, oblong hexagon; 33, shield; 34, bullet (pentagon). Nos. 1 to 7 are standard types.

In general, the principles and techniques used in cutting and polishing specimens are employed in cutting and polishing cabochons.

The worker who has mastered the principles involved in the polishing of specimens will not find the cutting and polishing of cabochons difficult. For the first attempt at cutting a cabochon, a piece of Montana agate about 1 or 1¼ in. long, ¾ in. wide, and about ⅜ in. thick should be selected. A stone of this size is convenient to handle, for it may be firmly held without danger of slipping and grinding the fingers.

The stone should be without flaws, so that the time and effort will not be wasted. Agate is inexpensive and fine perfect pieces are readily obtainable.

Should the stone have a few minor cracks or flaws, these should be removed by grinding. In commercial work, or where a rare specimen is at hand, it is not always possible, necessary, or advisable to remove all cracks and flaws from the stone. Sometimes, when an order is received

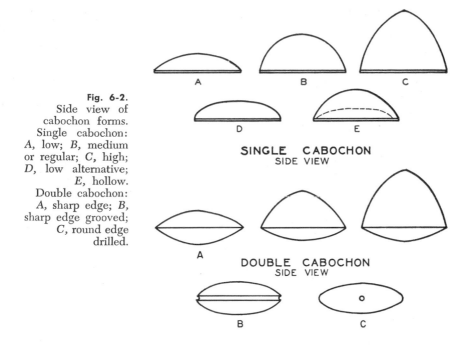

Fig. 6-2.
Side view of
cabochon forms.
Single cabochon:
A, low; B, medium
or regular; C, high;
D, low alternative;
E, hollow.
Double cabochon:
A, sharp edge; B,
sharp edge grooved;
C, round edge
drilled.

SINGLE CABOCHON
SIDE VIEW

DOUBLE CABOCHON
SIDE VIEW

for a stone of a given size but with a limited price stipulation, it is impossible to supply a perfect stone. On many occasions feathered or flawed stones are cut for artistic effect or for use in inexpensive jewelry. Amethyst and tourmaline often are used for this purpose.

Some stones, as labradorite, rose quartz, and pink tourmaline, invari-

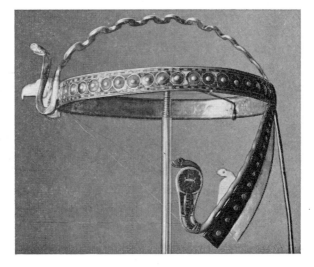

Fig. 6-3.
Gold diadem of
Tut-Ankh-Amen
(XVIII Dynasty, Egypt
1358–1349 B.C.)
inlayed with circles of
carnelian and small
cut stones.

ably are feathered or flawed, and perfect specimens are rare. An emerald without a flaw seldom is found.

When grinding a cabochon, the same care should be exercised as when grinding a specimen. There should be correct wheel speed, an adequate supply of coolant, and moderate pressure of the stone on the wheel. The hand holding the stone, with the thumb and forefinger, is supported and aided by the other (Fig. 5–10).

The forearms should rest on a rigid support, thus affording control of the grinding. When grinding cabochons there will be a tendency to grind in the center of the wheel. The hard agate being ground has many points or edges that require rounding to form the domed top or the rounded outline of the cabochon stone. These points or edges, through pressure on the wheel face, act as dressing tools and, if the pressure is continued

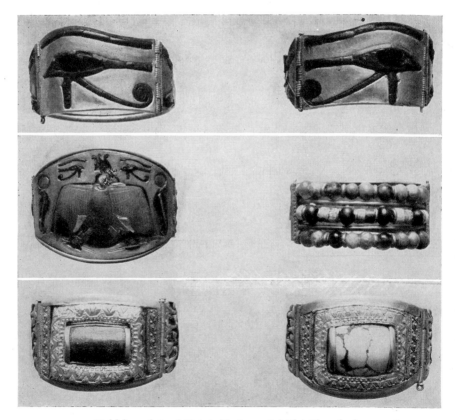

**Fig. 6-4.**  Gold bracelets of Tut-Ankh-Amen inlaid with polychrome glass and various gems, turquoise, carnelian, and lapis lazuli.

**Fig. 6-5.** Gold necklace with stone inserts carnelian and glass paste in imitation of striped agate and bloodstone. Etruscan, fifth and sixth centuries B.C. Found at Vulci about 1832. Stones are approximately 12 by 16 mm.

for a short period, will wear a hollow or groove in the wheel with sharp ridges at its sides (Fig. 6-7). When grinding, the fingers may receive painful cuts from these edges. The greatest grinding efficiency is obtained by altering the point of contact of the stone on the wheel so that grinding is done over the entire face of the wheel. Wheel truing or wheel dressing tools (Figs. 6-8 and 6-9) are rarely required for cabochon work. The diamond truing tool is used for rapid truing of wheels that have become worn out of round or bumpy, or for developing special contours for fancy work. The "Huntington-type" tool generally is used to freshen the periphery of the grinding wheel so that it will cut more freely. If the grinding wheel selected is too hard, "glazing" occurs, and repeated applications of the spur-type dresser may be necessary. Should this occur, a slower wheel speed is advisable, or the selection of a grinding wheel with a softer bond may become necessary. The cost of a grinding wheel is very low compared with the value of the stone being ground and the possible cost incurred through cracking the stone while grinding on a wheel that is too hard. Commercially, also, the time saved by using a fast-cutting soft wheel more than compensates for the extra wheel wear. The best results are obtained when the wheel grit and grade, wheel speed, and proper grinding technique are such that the wheel face is in excellent condition at all times.

A wheel that has become grooved through incorrect grinding may be corrected by concentrating the pressure while grinding a stone toward one edge of the wheel. Thus, a troublesome ridge will be worn down, and by continuing this same procedure on the other side of the wheel, the result will be a crowned wheel trued without waste (Fig. 6–10). This operation will make use of every grain that is ground away instead of wasting it when dressing the wheel with a conventional tool (Fig. 6–11).

If the agate selected has flaws, they should be ground out first. The back of the stone then should be ground from the material remaining, and the most interesting or colorful portion of the stone should be used for the front. The back may be ground flat although it is preferable to

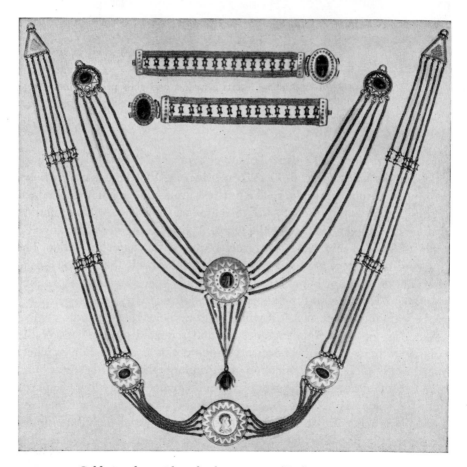

**Fig. 6-6.** Gold jewelry with cabochon stones (Ptolemy III, 247–222 B.C.). Bracelets: gold, garnet, and carnelian. Necklace: gold and amethyst. Girdle: gold, emerald matrix, and carnelian, with coin of Ptolemy III, Butgets I.

grind this surface slightly convex because in this form it is easier to polish. For the first attempt at cabochon cutting, a stone with an elliptical outline should be selected. If the stone selected is a pebble, the grinding of the flat back or a slightly rounded one quickly produces a cabochon form with only a moderate amount of grinding. No attempt should be made at this time to cut stones to definite sizes. Every effort should be exerted to develop co-ordination of the hand and the eye in order to produce stones having well-proportioned forms and true outlines. Templates as shown at 3, Figure 4–25, with holes of the required shape and size, can be used if desired. The outline may be scribed on the specimen with a pointed aluminum rod. The stone then can be ground to the outline marked.

If a slab or an irregular fragment has been used, the humps, corners, and thick edges should be ground away to produce a domed shape. The

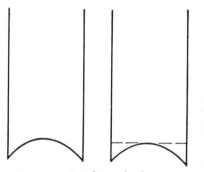

Fig. 6-7. Grinding-wheel contours. Wheel face produced by grinding in center.

domed or convex surface may be produced by holding the stone so that its edge rests on the forefinger with its back against the thumb. At the same time the stone should be held and supported with the other hand. Then, with the fingers the stone should be held against the grinding wheel using a universal motion. Removing corners or thick edges from the stone by grinding near or at the edge of the grinding wheel prevents deep grooves from forming in the face of the wheel. The contour of the convex surface of the cabochon should be uniform because a cross section of the outline of the stone is a parabola (Figs. 6–2 and 6–12). The included angle formed by the back on the stone and the front surface should always be an acute angle to assure the security of the stone when mounted. Rough-grinding may require two minutes or more, depending on the size and type of material being ground and the equipment used.

Fig. 6-8. Wheel truing or dressing tools.

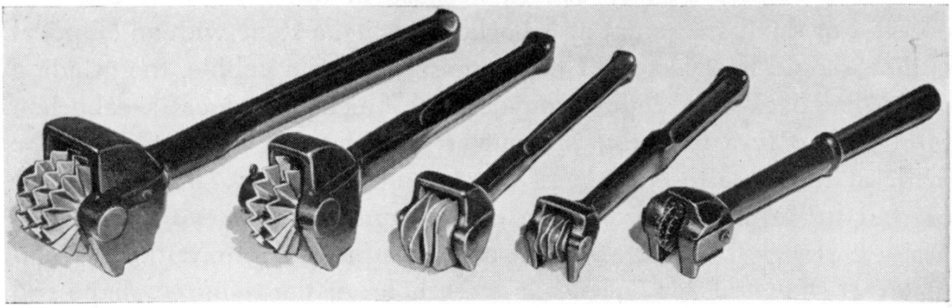

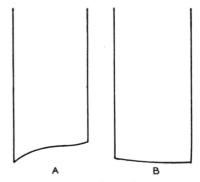

Fig. 6-9. Huntington type wheel dressers.

Having ground the stone to a uniform shape, the next step is to finish-grind the stone. For this purpose, a No. 180 grit wheel is quite satis-factory, although finer wheels composed of Nos. 220 or 240 grit are preferable.

In finish-grinding, the back of the stone is finished first. All coarse grinding marks are removed on the fine wheel, the stone being manipulated in the same manner as specified for rough grinding. By rotating the stone and giving to it a slight oscillating motion, it is quickly trued and ground to a uniform surface. This operation may be performed in two minutes or less. The backs of opaque cabochon

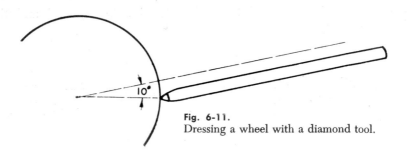

Fig. 6-10. Grinding-wheel contours: A, partly trued by grinding; B, trued face.

stones such as jasper, turquoise, or malachite, are usually ground flat and the surface left unpolished.

Fig. 6-11.
Dressing a wheel with a diamond tool.

Having ground a flat or slightly convex surface, the outline is trued by holding the stone with the back at a right angle to the face of the wheel and parallel to the spindle. Then, by light pressure against the wheel while turning the stone through an arc, the outline may be trued (Fig. 6–13). Some practice is needed to produce perfect results, and proper co-ordination of the hand and the eye is acquired only by practice. The elliptical outline, commonly called oval, is the easiest of the curved outlines to produce. A true circular form is more difficult to develop. Templates are useful in producing true outlines, especially when stones are to be cut to a definite size and shape.

Fig. 6-12. Roughed cabochon with back finish ground.

In truing the outline by finish-grinding, care should be exercised to avoid excessive grinding for this makes the edge of the stone thicker than necessary, and more time will be required to true up the front of the stone (Fig. 6–14).

Having acquired a true outline, the sharp edge forming the back and the sides of the stone should be chamfered or beveled at an angle of 45 deg. with the horizontal (Fig. 6–15). This is done by holding the stone edgewise to the face of the wheel with the back of the stone at an angle of 45 deg. with it. The stone is lightly pressed against the rotating wheel, and at the same time it is turned. The pressure must be applied uniformly so that the edge thus ground is regular. The grinding of this edge is important, the purpose being to protect the stone from chipping in han-

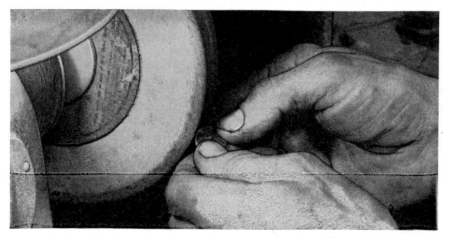

Fig. 6-13.   Shaping and finish grinding on fine-grit (No. 180 or 220) wheel.

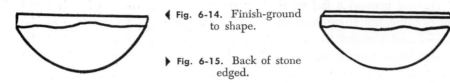

◀ **Fig. 6-14.** Finish-ground to shape.

▶ **Fig. 6-15.** Back of stone edged.

dling or in subsequent setting. Figure 6–15 shows the stone at the present stage of grinding. In order to polish the back of the stone and to facilitate handling during the polishing process the stone is cemented to a lap stick.

CEMENTING. While most specimens may be faced or polished without the use of special holders or fixtures, cabochon stones, because of their small size and regular shape and surface, are difficult to hold with the fingers. To facilitate handling and to exercise complete control during the various operations, the stones, after the finish grinding operation, are cemented to lap sticks. Cement, having pitch, wax, or shellac as a base, is used for this purpose. While many varieties of cement are available for the purpose of cabochon cutting and for general lapidary work, ordinary red commercial sealing wax will give excellent results.

The security of the stone, when cemented, depends upon the cement, the technique used in cementing, as well as the subsequent handling. Stones of small size, no larger than a pinhead, may be finished without trouble provided ordinary care is exercised in handling. Usually, when a stone breaks away from the cement, the cause is improper handling. Some cements with a pitch base will not hold a stone by the polished surface when, during the various operations, it becomes chilled from cold water. This trouble is rare when sealing wax is used. Should it occur, however, it is due to grit having been ground into the cement during the polishing operations. The cement thus becomes hard and loses some of its adhesive quality. This condition can be remedied by adding a small quantity of fresh cement by heating the original bar of cement, then rubbing the melted cement across the end of the lap stick.

All cementing should be done in a certain place in the shop set aside for this purpose. The usual equipment (Fig. 4–24) consists of a Bunsen burner or an alcohol lamp, a steel rolling plate about 1½ in. wide and 6 in. long with one sharp edge and one rounded edge, a tweezer, a knife, a knockoff block, and an alcohol pot. A shelf to the rear of the table usually has a series of holes into which lap sticks are placed after the cement has set, as shown in Figure 4–24. As an alternative a small stand may be provided. Lap sticks should be kept in a separate box having compartments for the various sizes. Three are required for all-round work. These sticks (Fig. 4–20) are about 5½ in. long, and the body diameters are ¼, ⅜, and ½ in. respectively. Sticks such as meat pegs, broom handles, round paint-brush handles, or dowels have been used for this purpose. Penholders with the upper metal portion removed are better, but for ease of handling and greatest efficiency, turned lap sticks made of hard wood, as birch or maple, are essential.

When cementing a new stick or adding cement to one already used, the stick is held in one hand and the bar of cement in the other. The cement is passed through the Bunsen flame until it melts. The melted portion then is transferred to the lap stick by rolling the lap stick and drawing it over the end of the stick of melted sealing wax. With new lap sticks, the best results will be obtained if the end of the stick is heated. The cement then will adhere better. The cement should be heated to a degree that will make it plastic so that it can be easily rolled. Excessive heating should be avoided so that the cement will not burn.

After a quantity of melted cement has been rubbed onto the end of the stick, the mass is rolled on a smoothed steel block. This rolling forms a concentric layer of cement about the stick, and by repeated applications of cement, the necessary amount required for the different sizes of stones is added. During the rolling process, a portion of the plastic cement is drawn or rolled over the end of the lap stick. This cement may be returned to the body of the lap stick by holding the stick vertical and pressing it against the steel block. In this manner it can be quickly determined if there is sufficient cement on the lap stick, for the knoblike end of the cement should be about the size of the stone to be cemented. If all of the lap sticks have been used, and all have cement masses larger than a stone which remains to be worked, the surplus cement may be removed from a lap stick by heating and rubbing it onto the cement stick, thus reversing the cementing process. The cement also may be removed with the fingers after they have been moistened. The small pieces can be kept in a small box for later use.

The position of the cement on the stick may be further controlled by axial movement during the rolling process. In this manner, the cement may be rolled to the point of the stick or away from it, as desired, by a rolling motion away from or toward the steel block. While the cement is being heated or prepared on the lap stick, the stone to be cemented is held securely by the tweezer in the other hand, and is slowly passed back and forth through the Bunsen flame. This gradually warms the stone which should not be heated to a degree where it cannot be comfortably held in the fingers. Excessive heating should be avoided. A temperature range of 100 to 150 deg. F. is ample.

In grasping or holding the stone with the tweezer, the two legs of the tweezer should bear upon opposite or flat portions of the stone. The stone never should be grasped by the girdle or other curved portion, for the stone may snap away from the tweezer and break.

If a large number of stones is to be cemented, they may be heated in a pan or container placed in hot water, or a hot plate with controlled temperature may be used. Unusual care is required in the cementing of some stones, for excessive heat will cause them to crack. Malachite, azurite, coral, smithsonite, apatite, and some types of opal will readily crack, if heated beyond a critical temperature.

Having heated the stone and the cement at the same time, the melted-cement end of the lap stick is brought in contact with the stone on the surface opposite the one which requires polishing. The cement is molded over the surface of the stone with the fingers of one hand while the stick is held with the other hand. Right-handed persons will find it convenient to hold and rotate the stick in the right hand while the cement is molded with the first three fingers of the left hand. The forefinger should rest on the top of the stone pressing the stone against the end of the lap stick while the thumb and third finger mold the cement. The cement should be uniformly molded into a trumpet shape, and the stone should be centered with the stick (A, Fig. 6–16). The rounded edge of the steel plate can be used to advantage in rolling the cement so it will be concentric. The final molding should be done with the fingers.

Before the cement sets, the stone should be firmly pressed to the lap stick. This is important. In the majority of cases where stones have broken off the stick during operation, and cement still adheres to the stone, it will be found that a neck of cement existed between the stone and the end of the stick (A, Fig. 6–17).

Maximum strength and security are obtained when a stone is properly cemented onto the stick. If not enough cement is used, the stone may break off, and if too much is used, a portion of the cement will be ground away and wasted (B and C, Fig. 6–17).

The best results will be obtained when the edge of the stone is entirely exposed for working, when the stone is perfectly centered against the end of the lap stick, and when the plane of the girdle or the back of the stone is at a right angle to the axis of the lap stick (A or B, Fig. 6–16). The cement is molded and the stone is centered at the same time by rotating the stick in the hand and sighting across the top surface of the

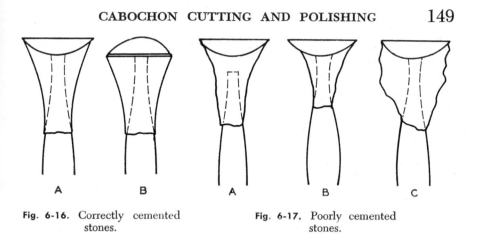

Fig. 6-16. Correctly cemented stones.

Fig. 6-17. Poorly cemented stones.

stone. The stick may be set in one of the holes in the shelf, but this should not be done until the cement has set and the danger of tipping has been eliminated. When the stone has cooled to room temperature. the polishing may be completed.

When a large number of stones of uniform size are to be worked, considerable time is required to cement the stones to sticks, particularly if the stones are large. This work must be done carefully because it is necessary to guard against tipping of the stone while the cement is setting. Special lap sticks designed by the author eliminate this delay. These lap sticks are made of duraluminum rod or tube, spun, turned, or swaged to shape. To the end, an aluminum plate or cap is affixed, the surface of which is faced truly at a right angle to the axis of the stick. This surface is slightly smaller than the outline of the stone to be cemented. To fix the stone, the aluminum lap stick is held in the Bunsen flame until the applied cement has been melted. The stone is warmed, and it is applied to the stick, centered, and set aside on the setting block to cool. The lap stick which provides a base for the stone to rest upon prevents tilting. When the stone is to be removed, the stick is held in the flame and, being a good conductor of heat, the cement is quickly melted and the stone easily removed. Lap sticks of this type are shown in Figures 4–22 and 4–23.

The polishing procedure for cabochon stones is identical with that which applies to the polishing of specimens. Therefore, at this point it is well for those who are beginners in stone polishing to review that data. The fine grinding-wheel scratches are removed by smoothing on No. 220 crystolon or carborundum cloth, by briskly rubbing the stone on a piece of abrasive cloth, or by holding the stone against a rotating disk wheel to which the cloth has been cemented or fastened ( Fig. 6–18 ).

By careful application so as to avoid overheating and the danger of cracking, a stone 1 in. long may be thoroughly smoothed in less than two minutes. The use of two abrasive cloths, one which is fresh and the other worn very smooth, will facilitate the operation. The rough scratches may be quickly smoothed down with the fresh cloth, after which the stone should be applied to the smooth cloth which will finish the surface ready for polishing. The saving in time made possible by this process is evident when a number of stones are being finished at one time, as they may be operated upon in rotation. The rough-grinding marks may be eliminated by the fresh cloth; also, whenever a stone becomes too hot to handle, it may be set aside to cool and the next one may be worked on.

The use of the loupe will enable a close examination of the surface to be made to ascertain if all deep scratches have been removed. If the surface has been properly prepared and smoothed with a worn cloth as a final step, the surface will be glossy, but it will be covered with very fine scratches left by the abrasive cloth. During this operation, the stone

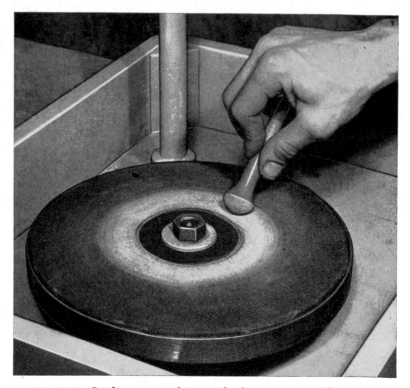

Fig. 6-18. Sanding or smoothing a cabochon stone using drum-type sander, surface, crystolon, or carborundum abrasive cloth.

should be oscillated so that every portion of it is treated uniformly.

At the conclusion of this operation, the stone should be thoroughly scrubbed with soap and water to remove every trace of grit. Grit that remains lodged in crevices in the cement can be removed with a sharp tool. Any adhering grit may be firmly secured by passing the cemented portion through a Bunsen flame.

The next step is that of polishing the surface of the stone on a hard felt wheel (Fig. 5–11). As a polishing medium FFF silicon carbide grain mixed with water to form a thin paste is applied to the surface of the wheel with a flat brush. Excessive pressure or prolonged working on a nearly dry wheel should be avoided, for heat quickly generated at the point of contact with the wheel may crack or ruin the stone. Continuous application of wet abrasive is of the greatest importance. If the preceding operations have been thoroughly performed, the polishing process will not require more than two minutes for the size of the stone under consideration. At the end of this time, if properly handled, the surface of the stone will be smooth and it will possess a dull, glossy polish, free of scratches left from the previous operations. During the polishing operation, if the surface of the stone is periodically examined with a 3x loupe, all scratches and dull spots may be readily detected, and removed by further working. If, during this operation, deep long scratches in distinct contrast to the rest of the surface persist, it is evident that coarse grit is present in the polishing abrasive. If continued operation of the wheel does not remove the grit, it may be necessary to remove the polishing material, clean off the felt wheel with a scraper or turning tool, clean out the entire contents, and start with fresh, clean polishing material.

After the stone has been properly treated and it is again thoroughly clean, it is ready for the final polish.

Best results have been obtained by the use of tin oxide applied to a cowhide- or calfskin-covered leather wheel (Fig. 6–19). However, in polishing hard stones, levigated alumina will give good results. The polishing powder is mixed with water to the consistency of thick cream, and is applied to the surface of the leather with a brush, or the wet brush may be used to apply the dry powder. The stone is pressed firmly against the surface of the wheel and rotated so that all portions are uniformly treated.

This final operation is rapid and should not require more than one or two minutes. If proper care has been given to the treatment of the stone, it will show a brilliant, uniform polish with a high degree of luster.

Fig. 6-19. Polishing cabochon stone on a drum-type leather-covered polishing wheel.

After the back of the stone has been finished, the next step is to remove the stone from the cemented holder, reverse it, and finish the domed surface or front of the stone.

The cement on the stick holding the stone is heated in a flame, during which process the stick is rotated in the hand and passed back and forth through the flame. At the same time, the stone itself is kept outside the flame as much as possible so that too great a temperature change will not crack the stone. With a paring knife, the heated and softened wax is scraped away from the stone and the stone is ready to be removed. No attempt should be made to remove soft, brittle stones until the cement has been completely heated and is plastic. Twisting or otherwise straining the stone to remove it from a cement which is stiff through lack of heating may cause brittle or fragile stones to break.

After the surplus cement has been removed from a stone, the cement on the stick should be thoroughly heated and rolled on the steel block to form a cylinder which is applied to the back surface of the warm stone. The stone is pressed firmly onto the end of the stick, and the plastic cement is molded around the bottom of the stone. Care must be exercised to prevent the cement from running over the edge and hiding the edge from view. Sufficient cement should be on the end of the stick to provide a firm support for the stone throughout the various operations, but the cement should not be bulky and larger than the outline of the stone. The cement should be properly molded into a trumpet shape (*B*, Fig. 6–16). Bulky or irregular masses of cement holding a stone interfere with the proper turning of the stick during operation. At the same time, bulky masses always have hollows or cavities wherein grit may lodge, thereby contributing to the contamination of the polishing material subsequently used.

After sufficient skill has been attained, the grinding of the convex or domed portion of a stone may be done prior to cementing, provided the stone is large enough to be handled easily. However, in developing this convex surface, easier control and a true universal motion can be imparted to the stone only by cementing it to a lap stick as previously described.

In finishing the front of the stone the entire surface should be ground down on the fine grinding wheel to a regular convex form, thus lowering the wall remaining from the shaping (Fig. 6–20). Here it may be noted that excessive finish-grinding, while shaping the stone, produces a thick wall, the removal of which adds considerably to the time required to finish the stone. It is common practice, when rough-grinding a stone of this size, to allow 1 mm. for removal in finish grinding and shaping. Thus, if the required finished size is 18 x 25 mm., the rough stone should be at

Fig. 6-20. Stone finish-ground and edged.

least 19 x 26 mm. In finish-grinding the dome of the stone, a slight wall or border (safety edge) is left at the girdle (Fig. 6–20). This edge should be at least 1 mm. wide for a stone of the size stated, and larger for stones of greater size. This is a protecting border, and it should be of uniform height around the stone. The purpose of this edge is to prevent grinding through the edge of the girdle, thus destroying the outline.

In the next step of sanding, this wall is removed and polished down to the girdle, leaving the protecting bevel edge below. The remaining polishing steps are identical to those previously described.

Although the majority of hard stones may receive a fine polish on the last operation in a short space of time, special treatment must be given to a number of stones, particularly the soft varieties or those possessing a varying degree of harshness. In general, when hard stones in Group 1 are being polished, the dull surface left by the sander is given its first polish by the continued application of wet, creamy polishing material, after which the leather wheel is permitted to dry out until it pulls or drags on the stone thus giving the stone a bright, glossy finish.

In other situations, depending on the type of stone being polished, it is necessary to vary the character of the leather polishing wheel. This may be done by working dry, using light pressure on soft stones or heavy pressure where hard durable stones are at hand. Because of the varying characteristics of stones even in those of the same species, it is possible to give only general recommendations for the polishing of unusual stones. If satisfactory results cannot be obtained by working the stone in the usual manner, the polishing technique should be varied as described herein until a satisfactory method has been found.

Although all of the cabochon stones eight and under on the scale of hardness may be polished by either of the two methods described, certain stones having a granular structure can be polished satisfactorily on a tin lap, in a manner similar to the polishing of cabochon rubies or sapphires. Jadeite, which has a coarse crystalline structure, is typical and the surface finish is greatly improved when treated by polishing on a tin lap with tin oxide.

When the stone has been finished, it may be removed in either of two ways. With hard durable stones, the simplest method is by knocking the stone off with a stick. With a sharp-pointed knife, a small portion of the cement is chipped off near the edge of the stone, care being taken that the stone is not damaged. The lap stick is then placed on a steel block having a straight edge, with the stone overlapping the steel plate. The back of the stone should rest against it (Fig. 6–21). While the stick is held thus with one hand, the thumb supporting the stone, the upper edge of the stone is given a sharp blow with a wooden stick and the stone is quickly and cleanly removed. It is necessary that the back of the stone be placed over the side of the steel plate without resting upon it, otherwise the stone may become chipped or broken.

The alternative method to remove the stone is by heating. This method only should be used when the stone being treated is brittle, fragile, or soft, or when it possesses cleavage planes or other weak structure.

Should a small amount of the cement adhere to the stone, it can be removed; in the case of a hard stone, with a knife; or, from the softer types, by the fingernail. After most of the cement has been removed, the stone is placed in alcohol which quickly dissolves the remaining cement. Soft, porous stones and those upon which alcohol acts as a solvent (such as amber and copal) should be removed at once. They are then rinsed

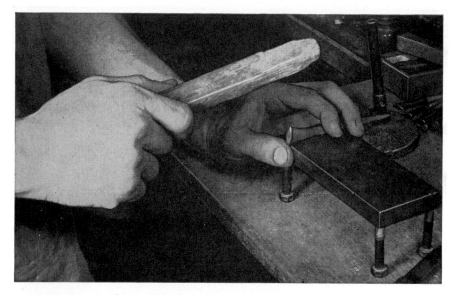

Fig. 6-21. Knocking-off block. Stone is in position for removal from lap stick.

in water and dried, after which the finished gem is added to the collection or mounted in some form of jewelry.

Having mastered the cutting and polishing of an ellipse or oval cabochon, other forms or shapes should be tried (Fig. 6–22). Odd pieces of stone always can be used because they can be finished in any one of a variety of forms and shapes. Practical application of cabochon forms are seen in Figures 6–43 and 6–44.

Next, forms with straight sides should be worked. In this group the rectangular shape is the easiest to cut. In finish-grinding a rectangular shape, the two long sides are ground parallel. Their parallelism may be checked by placing the stone between the jaws of a millimeter gauge (Fig. 6–23), then holding it up to a light source or toward a white card or background upon which light reflects. In this manner a slight degree of taper may be readily detected. By grinding with greater pressure toward the wider end of the stone, the sides may be ground parallel.

After these sides have been ground correctly, one end is finished at a right angle to the sides. Again, the stone may be checked with a millimeter gauge (Fig. 6–23), by comparing the trueness of the end with the blade of a gauge. The fourth side is treated in a similar manner, after which the stone is edged and finished as prescribed previously.

**Fig. 6-22.** Various forms of cabochon stones.

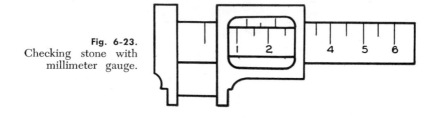

**Fig. 6-23.**
Checking stone with millimeter gauge.

The foregoing technique applies where the apparatus used is of the conventional type; that is, the grinding heads have wheels which rotate in a vertical plane. Where the grinding apparatus has wheels which rotate in a horizontal plane, the grinding and polishing steps follow in a similar manner. However, a little more skill may be required in forming or grinding the stones to shape if the stone is held in the hand and is not cemented to a lap stick.

When grinding is done on wheels which rotate in a horizontal plane, the grinding of the stone is done on the flat side of the wheel and one hand only is used to hold the stone. A stone is shaped by holding it so that any projection on it is in contact with the grinding wheel (Fig. 6–24). This action is continued over the entire surface until the stone roughly assumes a cabochon form. During grinding, the stone is moved across the face of the grinding wheel to prevent grooving of the wheel and to maintain the face of the wheel as true as possible. The back of the stone is readily ground flat by holding the stone to the rotating wheel with the first three fingers. In removing the stone from the wheel, if it is impossible to hold it in the fingers to lift it off the surface of the grinding wheel, the stone may be slid over the face of the wheel and removed at the edge, assisting with the other hand.

The stone is shaped by holding it with its back at a right angle to the face of the wheel and parallel to the spindle, thus giving the stone an oscillating or an arclike motion. For small stones, the best results are obtained by cementing the stone to a lap stick, then grinding in the usual manner. The method used in shaping and sizing a cabochon stone on a horizontal grinding lap, when the stone is cemented to a lap stick, is identical with that used in shaping, sizing or lapping stones for facet work. The only difference is in the type of grinding or lapping medium.

SIZING. Although most gemstones may be roughed out in a similar manner, shaping and sizing or finish-grinding to specific dimensions may be accomplished in a number of ways. With ordinary cabochon stones,

Fig. 6-24.
Grinding large
cabochon stone, using
a Sperisen Jr. lapidary
machine with plate-
mounted grinding wheel
both coarse and fine.

a fine grinding wheel, either a No. 220 or 240 silicon carbide wheel or a
sandstone wheel, may be used. If the stones are sufficiently large, they
may be manipulated readily by hand and accurately shaped and sized.
Small stones that cannot be held readily are cemented to lap sticks, the
pointed end of which is placed in a small hole or depression in a rest, at
a suitable height, so that, when the stone is pressed against the wheel,
the portion of the stone ground will be at a right angle to the back of the
stone. The point of contact on the wheel face should be in such a position
that the grinding operation is in view at all times (Fig. 6–25). Flat stones,
such as onyx, sard, or bloodstone, may be handled readily, even in
small sizes, by using a support made from a flat stick having a shoulder
cut at one end against which the stone rests. The stone is clamped
in position and held securely by the thumb of one hand, the other
hand aiding and supporting the unit (Fig. 6–26). Table-cut stones
(onyx), having single and double bevels, usually are finished in this
manner.

Considerable time may be saved by shaping and sizing in the manner
prescribed. If exceptionally accurate sizing is required, however, such
as fitting stones into formed mountings, shaping and sizing on a horizontal loose abrasive charged pewter lap will give far better results (Figs.
6–27 and 6–28). Sizing on a fine grinding wheel must be done by wet
grinding. This necessitates constant drying for if the wet stone is applied
to the bezel in order to check the size, the bezel or mounting will become
covered with water obscuring the contour and the work will not be
accurately fitted.

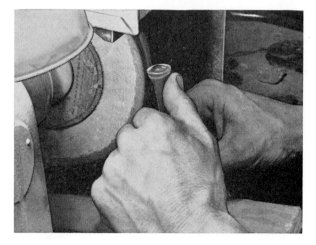

**Fig. 6-25.**
Sizing and shaping gem cemented to lap stick.

Although the stone may become covered with loose wet abrasive, when sizing on the lap, the abrasive is easily wiped away in one stroke on the hand or apron before checking against the mounting. In roughing out stones to be finished to a definite shape and size, it is customary to rough-grind the stone 1 mm. or more larger than the finished size. The first step in finish-grinding to size is to shape the stone truly, removing the rough chipped edge left by the rough-grinding wheel by grinding on the lap, after which the size is checked with a millimeter gauge or template.

If the stone being ground has a circular or elliptical outline, continued grinding and checking should follow the initial truing until the stone has been finish-ground to the size desired. Stones with straight sides, thus having parallel opposite sides, such as the square or rectangular shapes, are treated in a similar manner. First, the rough-ground stone is trued on a fine wheel or lap; the size is checked, and then the opposite parallel sides are lapped to the proper over-all dimension, and finally the remaining sides are finished at a right angle. A toolmaker's square

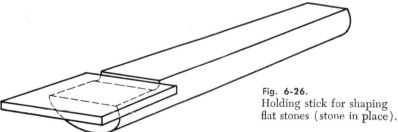

**Fig. 6-26.**
Holding stick for shaping flat stones (stone in place).

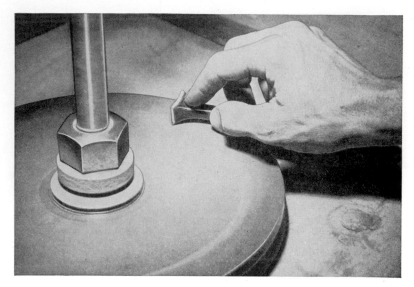

**Fig. 6-27.** Shaping and sizing stone; stone outline is bounded by straight sides.

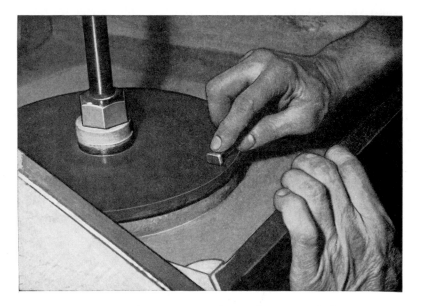

**Fig. 6-28.** Sizing stone on lap — alternate method.

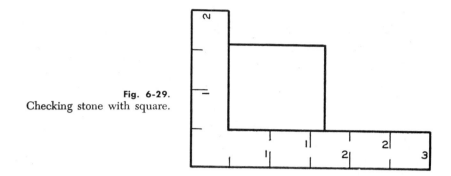

**Fig. 6-29.**
Checking stone with square.

or a contact goniometer is also useful for checking squareness (Figs. 6–29 and 6–30).

Triangular forms, or those that have bounding sides intersecting at angles greater or less than 90 deg., are finished in a similar manner. They require the use of a contact goniometer for checking, however, if accurately formed stones are desired (6–31).

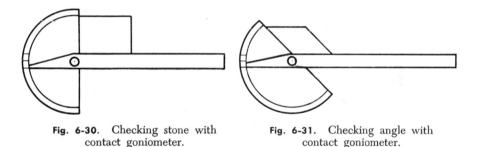

**Fig. 6-30.**   Checking stone with        **Fig. 6-31.**   Checking angle with
contact goniometer.                              contact goniometer.

When cutting stones to fit mountings with numerous prongs, or the common hatband type of bezel, as the stone nears the required size, the sharp edge formed by the back of the stone and the side should be chamfered or beveled to prevent chipping. Invariably a stone is chipped if this precaution is neglected and the stone is forced into the mounting.

In a similar manner, on all stones with sharp corners that are required

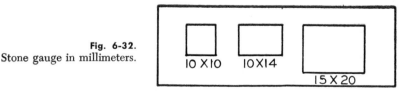

**Fig. 6-32.**
Stone gauge in millimeters.

10 X 10        10 X 14

15 X 20

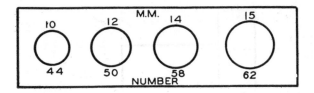

Fig. 6-33.
Stone gauge for round stones.

to fit corresponding bezels, the sharp edges should be rounded slightly for the same reason or to prevent chipping during the setting process.

Whenever stones are cut to mountings, such as cast rings, the stone is cut to fit the filed opening at the top of the ring, and the stone setter later cuts the bearing into which the stone sets.

In mass production, stones may be cut to fit templates (Figs. 6-32, 6-33, and 6-34) having standard shapes and sizes, thus insuring absolute uniformity. During the lapping operation, where the lap passes across the stone and away from it (Fig. 6-27), if the table surface joins the side at a right angle, the grinding action of the loose abrasive causes small chips to break out at the sharp edge. This can be prevented by edging the stone at an angle of 45 deg. from time to time, by removing all loose abrasive grain from the surface of the lap with a wet brush, and using the abrasive charged surface of the lap only.

When sizing faceted stones or stones cut to accurate dimensions, the practice is to use pewter laps charged by the frequent application of wet abrasive grain applied with a brush. A 1½-in. flat varnish brush is most useful for this purpose. The abrasive used is silicon carbide grit No. 220 or 240. In cutting very small stones or facets, excellent results are obtained by using No. 320 grit.

The lap stick is held in the hand with the pointed end of the stick

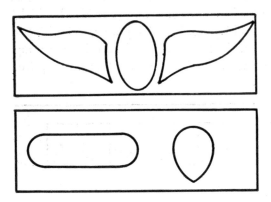

Fig. 6-34.
Templates for special shapes.

TABLE 6.  STANDARD SIZES FOR RING STONES
*(In millimeters)*

| | | | |
|---|---|---|---|
| 4 x 6 | 8 x 10 | 12 x 14 | 15 x 20 |
| 5 x 7 | 9 x 11 | 12 x 16 | 16 x 22 |
| 6 x 8 | 10 x 12 | 13 x 18 | 18 x 25 |
| 7 x 9 | 10 x 14 | 14 x 16 | 20 x 30 |

across the palm of the hand, and the cement end is held and manipulated by the first three fingers (Fig. 6–35). The forefinger is on the side of the stick while the thumb and third finger are on opposite sides adjacent thereto. With the stick held in the hand and placed in grinding position on the lap, the forefinger will be uppermost, and the thumb and third finger on the sides of the stick controlling it will be parallel to the lap. In this manner, the stone may be moved across the lap or grinding wheel without touching the fingers to the face of the wheel (Figs. 6–27 and 6–28). The stone is shaped, if the outline is curved, by means of the three fingers twisting the stick through an arc, while at the same time a uniform pressure is maintained on the grinding wheel. When the outline is irregular, or is not in a true form, and it requires correction, greater pressure or prolonged grinding is given to this area. When the form has been trued after finish-grinding, the protecting bevel edge is placed upon the stone by holding the stick at an angle of 45 deg. with the face of the lap, and the stick is rotated with the stone in contact with the lap, if the stone has a curved outline. A uniform pressure must be maintained so

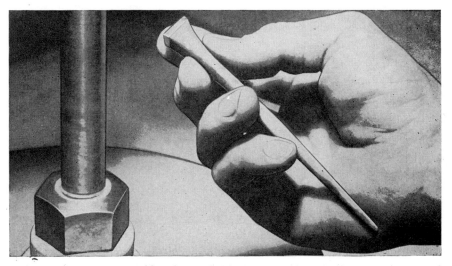

**Fig. 6-35.**  Holding lap stick for shaping and sizing of stone.

## TABLE 7.  STONE GAUGES

*Sizes in number and diameter in millimeters*

| No. | mm. | No. | mm. | No. | mm. | No. | mm. |
|---|---|---|---|---|---|---|---|
| 1 | 1.2 | 17 | 4.0 | 33 | 7.0 | 49 | 11.6 |
| 2 | 1.3 | 18 | 4.1 | 34 | 7.2 | 50 | 12.0 |
| 3 | 1.4 | 19 | 4.3 | 35 | 7.4 | 51 | 12.3 |
| 4 | 1.5 | 20 | 4.5 | 36 | 7.6 | 52 | 12.5 |
| 5 | 1.7 | 21 | 4.6 | 37 | 7.8 | 53 | 12.8 |
| 6 | 2.0 | 22 | 4.8 | 38 | 8.0 | 54 | 13.0 |
| 7 | 2.2 | 23 | 5.0 | 39 | 8.2 | 55 | 13.2 |
| 8 | 2.3 | 24 | 5.2 | 40 | 8.3 | 56 | 13.5 |
| 9 | 2.5 | 25 | 5.5 | 41 | 8.8 | 57 | 13.8 |
| 10 | 2.7 | 26 | 5.7 | 42 | 9.2 | 58 | 14.0 |
| 11 | 2.9 | 27 | 5.9 | 43 | 9.6 | 59 | 14.2 |
| 12 | 3.0 | 28 | 6.0 | 44 | 10.0 | 60 | 14.4 |
| 13 | 3.2 | 29 | 6.3 | 45 | 10.3 | 61 | 14.6 |
| 14 | 3.4 | 30 | 6.4 | 46 | 10.7 | 62 | 15.0 |
| 15 | 3.6 | 31 | 6.6 | 47 | 11.0 | | |
| 16 | 3.8 | 32 | 6.8 | 48 | 11.3 | | |

## TABLE 8. COMPARATIVE STONE SIZES TO DIAMOND SIZES

*Sizes in number, diameter in millimeters, and approximate weight of round brilliant-cut diamonds*

| No. | mm. | Dia. wt. | No. | mm. | Dia. wt. | No. | mm. | Dia. wt. |
|---|---|---|---|---|---|---|---|---|
| 2 | 1.3 | .01 Ct. | 19 | 4.3 | .30 Ct. | 36 | 7.6 | 1.75 Ct. |
| 3 | 1.4 | .015 | 20 | 4.5 | .35 | 37 | 7.8 | 1.87 |
| 4 | 1.5 | .023 | 21 | 4.6 | .37 | 38 | 8.0 | 2.00 |
| 5 | 1.7 | .03 | 22 | 4.8 | .42 | 39 | 8.2 | 2.25 |
| 6 | 2.0 | .04 | 23 | 5.0 | .46 | 40 | 8.3 | 2.50 |
| 7 | 2.2 | .05 | 24 | 5.2 | .50 | 41 | 8.8 | 2.75 |
| 8 | 2.3 | .062 | 25 | 5.5 | .55 | 42 | 9.2 | 3.00 |
| 9 | 2.5 | .08 | 26 | 5.7 | .62 | 43 | 9.6 | 3.25 |
| 10 | 2.7 | .10 | 27 | 5.9 | .75 | 44 | 10.0 | 3.50 |
| 11 | 2.9 | .11 | 28 | 6.0 | .83 | 45 | 10.3 | 3.75 |
| 12 | 3.0 | .12 | 29 | 6.3 | .92 | 46 | 10.7 | 4.00 |
| 13 | 3.2 | .16 | 30 | 6.4 | 1.00 | 47 | 11.0 | 4.25 |
| 14 | 3.4 | .18 | 31 | 6.6 | 1.12 | 48 | 11.3 | 4.50 |
| 15 | 3.6 | .20 | 32 | 6.8 | 1.25 | 49 | 11.6 | 4.75 |
| 16 | 3.8 | .22 | 33 | 7.0 | 1.37 | 50 | 12.0 | 5.00 |
| 17 | 4.0 | .24 | 34 | 7.2 | 1.50 | | | |
| 18 | 4.1 | .25 | 35 | 7.4 | 1.62 | | | |

as to form an edge of uniform width. This edge should not be over ½ mm. wide for the average stone.

The uniform shaping, grinding, or edging of the stones listed in Group 1 sometimes is difficult because of the uneven structure and varying degrees of hardness in some of the stones. Stones like turquoise matrix and variscite often contain portions which differ greatly in hardness. Fibrous stones also require care, skill, and patience to finish properly.

The finishing and polishing operations to follow are identical to those previously described.

LAPPING.   For general lapidary use, laps are made of iron and pewter, each of which has its specific use. For the best results the use of the laps are not interchangeable. The iron lap is excellent for lapping flat surfaces (Figs. 6–36 and 6–37); it may also be used for rough-grinding stones to shape, in which case it replaces the regular grinding wheel. The wet abrasive is applied with a brush. During the late war, when grinding wheels were scarce, the iron lap was often used in this manner, and, except for a few ground fingernails, results achieved were excellent.

The iron lap offers considerable resistance to the abrasive grain and the grain passing under the stone being lapped grinds or cuts a groove, about the size of the grain, across the stone face. The cutting action is rapid, particularly where large size abrasive grain is used.

For rapid lapping and for rough work, or where a large amount of material must be removed, abrasive grain Nos. 100 to 150 is used. For moderate lapping, abrasive grain No. 220 will give satisfactory results. For finishing before polishing, abrasive grain or powder No. FFF is used. Finer grains or powders up to No. 600 are available, but for finish lapping before polishing, FFF will give satisfactory results. In lapping stones, silicon carbide grain is used. A uniform grain No. 600 may be used, although this is usually reserved for special technical work.

A small stone may be lapped easily if held with one hand, while the moist abrasive grain is applied by means of a brush with the other hand (Fig. 6–36). However, in lapping large specimens or slabs, both hands

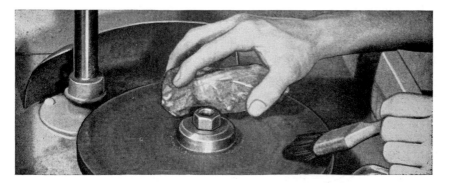

Fig. 6-36.  Lapping a large stone flat on a cast-iron lap.

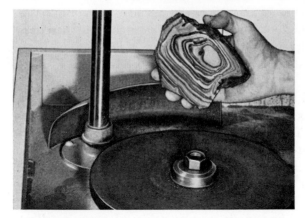

Fig. 6-37.
Lapping a large stone flat
on a cast-iron lap.

may be required to hold the stone securely. The abrasive grain then
may be applied to the lap by suspending a small trough above the
center of the lap and placing therein a quantity of abrasive grain. Water
dripping from the spout of a container fastened directly above the
trough carries the abrasive grain along and, dripping to the lap near
the center of the wheel, keeps it fed, permitting free handling of the
stone being lapped (Fig. 6–38).

When lapping flat surfaces, the stone should be held securely and
moved across the face of the lap with uniform pressure, so that the
surface of the stone will be flat and not crowned. To obtain a truly flat
surface, considerable skill is required, for the tendency of the stone is
to heel over caused by the drag of the lap, thus removing material more

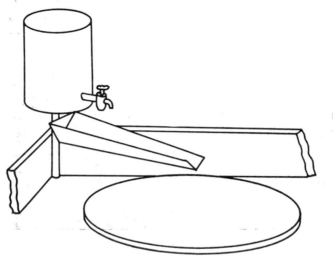

Fig. 6-38.
Automatic lap feed.

rapidly at the leading edge. The lap having more lapping surface per revolution at the periphery also will grind faster at or near its edge, and if the stone is held stationary, it will be ground more rapidly toward the edge which is nearest the edge of the lap. This tendency to grind more rapidly on the outer edge of the lap may be counteracted by constantly rotating the stone being lapped or by exerting greater pressure on the stone where the lapping action is less.

The stone being ground should not extend beyond the edge of the lap for, if the stone is tilted over the edge, the lap will grind a groove in the stone that may require lengthy grinding to remove. If the stone being ground is a rough slab with a slight taper, and it is desired to obtain a parallel slab, the stone is held on the lap with the thickest portion being used as the leading edge; that is, this portion intercepts the cutting action of the lap for at this point the grinding or lapping action is the greatest.

From time to time the slab is examined and checked with a millimeter gauge for uniform thickness and with a straightedge for flatness. By holding the stone up to a light source and placing a straightedge on the side ground, light between the straightedge and the surface of the stone will reveal inequalities such as convex or concave portions. If the surface becomes concaved after prolonged lapping, it is an indication that the lap is crowned. To grind the surface flat, it will be necessary to face the lap truly.

More often the surface of the stone may become convex, in which case, if the lap is true and flat, the fault lies with the operator. To obtain a true flat surface, practice is the remedy. However, unless the surface of the stone is to be polished on a tin lap, a slight crown to the surface is easier to polish. For a 10-in. lap the speed for rapid working should be from 400 to 500 r.p.m. In some instances, the surface of the lap may be scored or grooves may be cut across it, forming a grill pattern. These grooves catch and retain the abrasive grain, materially improving the lapping action. If, on the other hand, the material to be lapped has been previously sawed and the surface is flat and fairly accurate, satisfactory work can be done with a normal lap with a smooth turned face.

Steel or thin sheet-iron laps, supported by wood disks, also may be used, but it will be found by comparison of respective performances that the cast-iron lap gives superior results. As these laps do not take a charge (only a very slight amount of abrasive enters the metal), they may be thoroughly cleaned by washing and by removing all traces of grit from the surface. The lap may be used with fine grit, thus eliminating the necessity for a number of laps, or, by using the reverse side, one lap may serve equally well.

When lapping with finer grits, in particular the fine powders, constant attention should be exercised for, if the abrasive on the surface of the lap should become too dry, the pull of the lap may wrench the stone away, resulting in possible damage to the stone, to the operator, or to both. In lapping large flats, or bulky objects such as book ends, better control of the object can be had by erecting a fence across the lap surfaces against which the object will rest.

In shaping and sizing a thin slab upon an iron lap, the slab should be properly supported or cemented to another slab, such as a thin piece of agate, otherwise the chattering which may result from improper handling may cause the thin slab to break. This rule applies to freehand grinding and lapping. If the slab is cemented to a lap stick, this trouble will be avoided.

A special holder, a "T" shaped metal unit, is shown in Figure 6–39. As the cementing face of the unit is machined to a definite thickness, parallelism of the slab may be readily checked by means of a millimeter gauge by observing the over-all thickness of the slab and the metal plate. An aluminum plate ¼ in. thick and of suitable size may also be used.

Pewter laps also may be used for lapping flat surfaces, but the action is not so rapid as when a cast-iron lap is used. A pewter lap has certain advantages which make it ideal for the lapping and sizing of stones for faceting. As pewter is softer than iron, it permits the abrasive grain to enter and thus the lap becomes charged. By controlling the amount of abrasive on the lap, the cutting action as well as the type of finish of the stone can be varied. Thus, by the continual application of fresh abrasive, a coarse cut can be made. If, however, the surplus abrasive is cleaned off, if a wet brush only is used, and if the surface of the lap is kept wet, the charged lap will make a fine cut with considerable gloss. The reason is that only the tips of the embedded abrasive grain do the cutting, because the bulk of the grain is below the surface of the lap. The grains entering the lap usually are smaller, thus the edges of the stone being

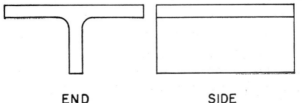

Fig. 6-39.
"Tee" section metal cementing plate.

END            SIDE

ground will be quite smooth and free from chips. The lapping action of an iron lap is so harsh that if that type of lap were used for sizing and cutting stones with facets, all facet edges would be chipped. Then, too, as an iron lap will not take a deep charge, the abrasive must be applied constantly, resulting in coarse ground surfaces.

The lapping of a stone should not be concentrated in one zone, but the action should be distributed over the entire face of a lap, thus prolonging its true surface and flatness. It is customary in lapidary shops to reserve one lap for the sole purpose of flat lapping. Some laps are used for sizing or faceting while others are used for finishing cabochon stones instead of using the fine grinding wheel. After a time the surface of a lap becomes worn and it will be necessary to true it by facing. This should be done in a lathe, but it is often done in the shop on the regular lap spindle by hand turning. Soft-metal laps may be faced and trued with little difficulty. With ordinary skill, a reasonable degree of accuracy may be attained without the use of elaborate turning equipment.

TRUING LAPS. Laps should be trued in a lathe, however if this is not possible, soft metal or wood laps may be trued by hand in a satisfactory manner. Several sharp-pointed turning tools or chisels are required for truing laps. Lacking these, old files about 10 in. long will serve. The ends of such files should be ground to a fine, sharp point (A, Fig. 6-40). A tool rest or stop is required. This consists of a board placed above the lap, parallel to its surface, clearing the lap by ⅛ in., and wedged or clamped securely between the box walls.

The turning tool is firmly held in one hand in a vertical position and is guided by the other hand which rests against the edge of the tool-rest board. The motion of the tool is controlled by the fingers, and the tool is guided along the board rest (Fig. 6-41). The tool is brought downward in contact with the surface of the lap, and an initial cut is made near the center or spindle portion of the lap for this portion usually is almost free of an abrasive charge. The tool then is moved outward, and the turning progresses in easy stages. To face the lap perfectly, the charged surface of the lap must be completely removed. The charge in a well-used pewter lap usually penetrates about 1/32 in.

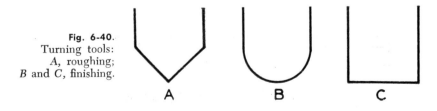

Fig. 6-40.
Turning tools:
A, roughing;
B and C, finishing.

A        B        C

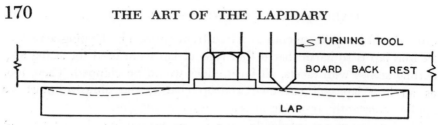

**Fig. 6-41.** Turning or facing lap with hand tool.

After the abrasive-loaded surface has been removed, high spots or raised portions of the lap are turned down until the surface is practically uniform. If the lap has been badly worn with a deep hollow, it is more economical to flatten the adjacent surfaces and continue to use the lap, concentrating further lapping of stones on these trued surfaces until they are also worn down, after which the entire lap surface is trued (Fig. 6–42). After the high portions of the surface of the lap have been removed, it will be necessary to lower the tool rest so that the turning tool will have proper support. This is done to prevent the tool from digging into the lap and grooving the surface which is bound to happen if the tool support is too far above the surface of the lap. A round-nose, flat, or straight-edged chisel (B and C, Fig. 6–40) now is substituted for the pointed tool, and by careful application the surface of the lap is gradually trued flat. The surface is checked from time to time with a straight-edge which, when placed on the surface of the lap, shows irregularities. Hand turning or truing of a lap surface may require from ½ to 1 hour according to the size and condition of the lap and the skill of the operator.

Occasionally other laps and abrasives are used in lapping. These, however, are specialized operations, and in the lapidary shop they are rarely used with but one exception, the diamond-charged lap.

Diamond laps vary considerably; thus, they may be made of cast iron, mild steel, copper, bronze, zinc, tin, boxwood, or ivory. Diamond-charged laps most frequently used are made of cast iron and copper or bronze. Cast-iron laps are universally used in polishing diamonds, and the copper, bronze, or tin laps charged with diamond dust are in regular use in lapidary shops for cutting corundum gems.

TRUING OUTER RIM ONLY

**Fig. 6-42.** Truing the lap surface.

**Fig. 6-43.**
Cabochon stones, Nevada opals in gold
set with diamonds (from
author's workshop).

SPECIAL TREATMENT.   Although the majority of gems can be polished
by both of the methods described, a few gems require special treatment.
These are the cabochon forms of the various corundum gems, such as
cabochon ruby and sapphire, asteriated or star ruby and sapphire, and
the oriental cat's-eye, a variety of chrysoberyl.

These stones are rough-ground in the usual manner. During grinding,
careful attention is exercised to assure proper orientation of the stone
to secure the best effect. In the regular cabochon corundum gems, the
base of the stone should be at a right angle or normal to the $c$ axis of
the stone (Fig. 6–45). If the original form of the rough gem retains a
distinct hexagonal outline, orientation of the back of the stone, or of the
table facet in the case of faceted gems, is done by simply grinding a flat

**Fig. 6-44.** Application of cabochon stones: 1. green Wyoming
jade; 2. Chinese jade; 3. lapis lazuli; 4. turquoise; 5. New Zealand
jade; 6. lapis lazuli; 7. Wyoming jade; 8. Black Wyoming jade
(from author's workshop).

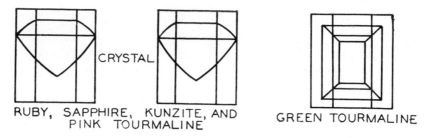

**Fig. 6-45.** Orientation of crystals for cutting of gems.

surface on the gem at a right angle to the plane of the prism faces. Correct orientation of the stone is of great importance because the majority of corundum gems possess distinct dichroism, and the finest color is observed when the stone is viewed by transmitted light along the $c$ or longitudinal axis.

The property of dichroism is utilized in the proper orientation of the stone when the rough material is devoid of a definite hexagonal form. This is the result when crystal faces have been completely removed by the abrading action of river streams or when a gem is to be cut from a broken fragment of a larger crystal. When the stone is examined by transmitted light, and it is held in different positions, different tones of color are observed. In the blue sapphire a fine blue is seen in one position, and at a right angle to this, the color is a greenish blue or gray blue. In the ruby, the color observed, when viewed along the principal axis, is a crimson, usually with a slight shade of purple, and at a right angle thereto the color has a slight brownish cast. When a stone is oriented so that the finest color is observed, the transmitted light travels along the main or $c$ axis. By grinding a flat surface at a right angle to this axis, or to the line of sight, the stone will be properly oriented.

After rough-grinding, the stone is cemented to a lap stick. Sometimes, when a stone is very small or, through lack of grinding experience, holding is difficult, the stone may be cemented to the lap stick for rough-grinding.

Finish-grinding, shaping, and sizing is done on a pewter lap with an abrasive No. 220 silicon carbide grain. Diamond-charged laps may also be used if preferred; this practice is recommended when cutting corundum gemstones. In the absence of a lap of this kind, the standard pewter lap utilizing silicon carbide will suffice. The abrasive moistened with water is applied to the lap by means of a brush. The back of the

stone is cut first, the lap stick is held in a vertical position and, as it is rotated, the stone with its surface in contact with the lap is automatically
ground with a slight convex surface. When all rough-grinding marks have
been removed from the surface, the outline of the stone is ground (Fig.
6–46). Considerable skill and experience are necessary to develop true
symmetrical outlines, for the corundum gems possess distinct grain with
hard knots or zones of greater hardness than the rest of the material.
When grinding a stone on a lap to shape the outline, the softer portions
naturally are ground more rapidly, which results in an irregular outline.
By carefully controlling the positions of the stone on the lap, the hard
portions are ground and rounded to conform to a true outline, after
which the stone is edged.

The stone is then sanded with silicon carbide cloth, and is further
smoothened on a wooden wheel with silicon carbide grain FFF which is
applied wet with a brush. Superior results, however, are obtained by
polishing the stone on a tin lap using fine diamond powder No. 6. This
finish is smooth and possesses a considerable degree of polish. During
this process the diamond powder mixed with oil is wiped on the lap
with the finger or with a small leather wiper, the diamond and oil mixture
being contained in a small pot. The pressure of the stone on the lap
forces the diamond powder into it, thus charging the lap and at the same
time results in gradually polishing the stone.

Some difficulty may be experienced in polishing due to the grain or
hard spots in the stone. By changing the position of the stone so that the

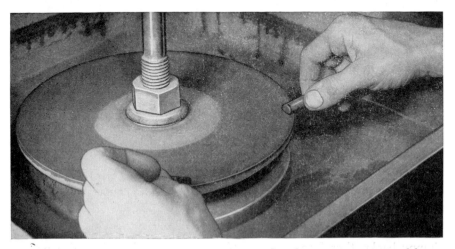

**Fig. 6-46.** Shaping and sizing stone with curved outline on a conventional lap
made of metal (pewter), to which abrasive has been applied with a flat brush.

wheel travels across the surface of the stone from a different direction, a position will be found where the surface of the stone becomes uniformly polished. The hard knotty portions of the stone usually are the first to receive a polish. Final polishing is obtained by using fine tripoli on a tin lap in a manner similar to the foregoing procedure. When polishing materials of this type are used, the wheel should be scored so as to retain this material for a long time. After the back has been polished in a satisfactory manner, the stone is reset on the lap stick with the front of the stone uppermost. The same procedure then is repeated which finally results in a cabochon ruby or sapphire. The polishing time can be lessened considerably by turning grooves in the tin lap and working the stone in the grooves which should have radii slightly greater than the maximum radius of the stone. Final polish also may be developed by finishing on a boxwood or maple wheel with No. 6 diamond powder.

Asteriated stones, rubies, and sapphires are treated in a similar manner. However, considerable skill may be required to properly orient the stone so that the center of the star is in the center of the stone when it has been completed. In the Orient where the majority of the asteriated stones are cut, it is the custom of the lapidary to produce as large a stone as possible. The results usually are poorly shaped stones with irregular, unsymmetrical tops, bulky backs, indistinct girdles, and off-centered stars. On numerous occasions, stones have been received that had off-centered stars, but they were readily centralized by tilting. This was accomplished by grinding and truing the bottom of the stone, thus lapping off the required amount of material necessary to tilt the stone and centralize the star (Fig. 6–47). In most cases, the im-

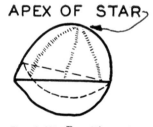

Fig. 6-47. Recutting star sapphire to centralize star.

provement was effected with a small reduction of size when the apex or center of the star did not diverge over 15 deg. from the vertical. The loss of weight in recutting lopsided stones of this type is not important in spite of the fact that these stones are sold by the carat, because the appearance of the stone resulting from recutting is so much improved. The back of star rubies or sapphires is rarely polished, and in the majority of the stones, this portion is thick and lumpy. The asterism is an optical effect caused by the action of light at or near the surface of the stone and not from reflection from the back of the stone. Deep, thick, lumpy backs, therefore, are not only unnecessary but they also present difficulties in setting because of the rounded edge. Some stones as received from the Indian lapidary were almost as round as a ball. All stones can be improved in form, and as the value of the stone is in its optical effect, the removal of the excess weight from the back without reducing the size of the outline, does not detract from its value. On a number of occasions, star sapphires with thick backs have been recut and finished into a thick double cabochon form or polished into spheres. When mounted as mobile units in modern type jewelry the effect is unique.

Cat's-eyes also require special care in roughing out, for the eye effect is caused by light reflecting from the fibrous, tubular, or lamellar structure in the stone, the light rays being concentrated at the convex surface of the stone. When cut cabochon, all fibrous stones exhibit this phenomenon (Fig. 6–48). To obtain the best effect in the common varieties, the stone, if oblong, should be cut so that the fibrous structure that produces the eye will be at a right angle to the longitudinal structure, the back of the stone being perpendicular or normal to the line of sight. True cat's-eye, which is called oriental cat's-eye, is a variety of chrysoberyl. The eye effect in the cut stone is caused by the action of light on a similar structure, although the parallel lamellae are much finer.

Fig. 6-48. Proper orientation for oval cat's-eye.

Asteriated stones and cat's-eyes are invariably cut in elliptical or circular forms. The best effect usually is obtained when the stone is cut as a round cabochon having the thickness of the stone from the plane of the girdle edge slightly greater than one half (about two-thirds) the diameter. Proper proportion is important. Flat stones should be avoided, for, with a low dome, the effect is poor, the star or eye in the respective species being diffused.

The common varieties of quartz cat's-eye, tourmaline cat's-eye, etc., are made by cutting cabochon stones from fibrous material.

Other phenomenal stones which require special treatment are the chatoyant varieties of feldspar including sunstone, moonstone, plagioclase, and labradorite. The best effect is obtained by orientating the stone by reflected light, observing the position in which the chatoyant property is best exhibited, and then grinding the flat or back of the stone at a right angle to the line of sight. When these stones are cut

cabochon, the chatoyance is exhibited in a
zone about the apex or top surface of the
stone. Stones of this type, cut with a flat top
and steeply sloped or curved sides, exhibit
this chatoyance over the entire flat surface.

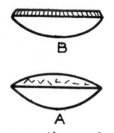

Some varieties of opals require special
treatment in order to develop the greatest
value and beauty in cutting. These are the
black opal, boulder opal, in which the color
or opal portion is in thin veins, and the

Fig. 6-49.  Alternate forms
of black opal.

white opal (Fig. 6–49), which has a horizontally laid structure (Figs.
6–50 A and B). In the true black opal, the color invariable is in thin
layers between a friable sandstone and black or gray common opal, commonly called potch. In the majority of cases, the fire layer is so thin that a
portion of the black or gray back is cut with it to form a stone sufficiently
thick to be durable. On rare occasions, fine black opal is found in nodular
form in which case it is cut as an ordinary cabochon. When the average
stone is cut, the sandstone layer is removed by grinding on a fine wheel
with No. 180 or 220 grit silicon carbide, although the majority of lapidaries who cut opals exclusively use sandstone grindstones. The removal
of the sandstone coating on the opal exposes the fire. Should this layer be
uniform and unmarred by pit holes, sand or matrix spots, the surface
should be trued so that it will be symmetrical and parallel to the black
or gray portion which will be the back of the stone.

These stones are treated in a manner opposite to regular cabochon
cutting; that is, the front of the stone is finished first and the back last.
The reason for this procedure is that the fire-opal portion often includes
spots, or imperfections, which must be removed first before the outline
of the stone can be determined. On occasion, beautiful patterns or pictures are disclosed which might be lost if any other treatment were used.
After all blemishes have been removed or eliminated as far as possible,
the outline is decided upon and the stone is ground to the desired shape.
While the most common form is the ellipse, black opals, because of their
unusual beauty, are not limited to regular geometrical forms or outlines.
They may be cut to any shape governed by the piece in the rough, such
as pear shape, triangular, wedge, kite, half-moon, or crescent. An article
of jewelry may be designed around the stone; thus, the opal may serve
as the body or wing of a bird, butterfly, or any other type of beautifully
colored organism. After the outline has been determined upon, the surface or front of the stone is rounded slightly if the fire opal is of sufficient

thickness. It also may be left flat and the edge beveled or rounded down to the girdle, the girdle edge being the plane formed by the junction of the fire opal and the black or gray back. The back of the stone is then finished and, when cut, it resembles a low cabochon stone (Fig. 6–49).

Few stones require such good judgment and skill in cutting as do the black opals, each stone being an individual study. Often the removal of the sandstone coating discloses pit holes, sand spots, or matrix spots in the surface. In that case, the stone should be sawed into two or more pieces for their presence in a finished stone, if they are of large size, detracts considerably from the appearance and value of the stone. One or more small pin-point spots which are not removable are not seriously detrimental, and their removal might easily require the reduction of the stone to a size where it might not be readily salable. Black matrix spots in dark or black opals are not so noticeable; sand spots or pits, however, are always a source of trouble.

In some stones the color or fire is arranged in parallel layers alternating with the black potch or fireless common opal. Stones of this type often are deceiving for one surface exposed by fine grinding might not appear as brilliant as another some distance below it, the edge of which shows brilliant color. This condition is often provoking and induces the cutter to remove the surface of the stone that might be acceptable, in the hope of disclosing the hidden layer as being phenomenal. Sometimes the cutter is successful in producing an exceptional stone, but more often the result is a mediocre stone or none at all. Some stones have greater color play or fire when the opal is viewed from the side, but as the front of the stone is viewed at a right angle, this play of color is not as prominent, consequently the stone lacks the same fire. It sometimes happens that a lower strata of color may lack fire in the very center owing to a penetrating gray or black potch, which causes a ring or circle of color about the stone. Thus, in an effort to produce a better stone, the lapidary sometimes loses one which may be good.

Boulder opal is found in two types. The spider-web type has veins of color that penetrate the brown ironstone matrix (sandstone colored by iron oxide) in all directions. This type is cut with the matrix in the usual cabochon forms. The other type is similar to the black opal having the fire opal arranged in thin seams or in veins, which cut the iron stone in different directions. They often have a checkered appearance, the veins being from a fraction to several inches apart and varying in thickness from a few hundredths to several millimeters. When the matrix is broken out, the pieces usually part along the veins of opal. This pro-

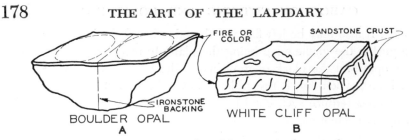

**Fig. 6-50.** Sawing on dotted lines to give best results.

duces blocks of ironstone having one or more parting faces covered with a thin layer of brilliant flaming opal, the pattern of which is of infinite variety. In parting, it is common for the opal to break in or near the center of the vein, thus leaving a coating of fire opal on each piece of ironstone (A, Fig. 6–50).

These stones make fascinating sets for mounting. The cutting technique applied is identical to that of the black opal. If the opal surface is thick enough and the broken surface is fairly uniform or flat, the process of cutting is simple, requiring the removal of only a slight amount of material to finish the stone. Should the broken surface be irregular or have a curved face, the irregular fractured surface may be smoothened and polished, following the curved contour. This is a form of cutting of great interest to those who develop artistic jewelry. It often happens that the vein material is too thin to even permit of following the slight irregularities by polishing. If the opal is sufficiently bright or brilliant, the surface is left in the rough condition, and only the outline is cut and polished as already stated. After cutting and polishing the front, the back of the stone is finished as a low cabochon stone, and a slight bevel edge is left on the front surface so that the stone can be set (B, Fig. 6–49). Thus, in one type of opal, several different treatments are possible which afford a wide variety of interesting gem stones.

The regular type of white opal often has a horizontally laid pattern which exhibits a fine degree of color and fire when viewed from the side. This invariably is the thinnest part. Thus, in order to cut the finest stone, the rough stone should be sawed into strips across this layer so that one side of the sawed slice becomes the back of the stone (B, Fig. 6–50). Unfortunately, most of this type of fine material is rarely found over 8 mm. thick which limits the size of the stone if best results are desired. Large stones made of this material must be cut with the back parallel to the horizontal layer and these rarely exhibit the fire and beauty to be obtained when cut as previously set forth.

Translucent as well as opaque stones that should always be cut in the cabochon style are those gems that exhibit a play of color or an unusual optical effect, as the opal, moonstone, sunstone, or oriental cat's-eye, and stones which exhibit asterism, as the star ruby, or star sapphire. Labradorite may be cut with a flat top to show broad flashes of color, or cabochon to show an effect like a moonstone.

ROUGHING, SPECIAL TREATMENT. A number of gemstones, with well-defined planes of cleavage, such as the spodumene gems, hiddenite and kunzite, require special treatment in roughing because of their pronounced tendency to cleave when subjected to shock. If sawing is necessary in order to cut to a special size or to remove imperfections, the saw should be perfect so that chatter or vibration is eliminated. In sawing gemstones of this type, a true-running diamond saw is the best to use; and for this purpose the resinoid bonded diamond saw is ideal. These saw blades are used in small trim saws (Fig. 4–42), many types of which are available. By proper control of the position of the gemstone in sawing, practically all of the tedious operation of hand lapping (roughing out) can be avoided and the danger of splitting eliminated.

Although the roughing out is customarily performed as described above, better results can be achieved after sawing, by using a diamond charged copper lap. Because of its soft grinding action, a resinoid bonded diamond impregnated lap is the best to use.

An iron lap with No. 220 silicon carbide grain may be used for roughing to approximate size and shape, and the stone is held in such a position that the grinding action is at a right angle (across) to the plane of cleavage. After cementing the stone to a lap stick, the stone is shaped and sized on a pewter lap and faceted in the usual manner. By placing the stone being faceted on the lap in such a manner that the cutting action crosses the cleavage planes as much as possible at an angle, and not parallel thereto, the tendency to split can be avoided (Fig. 7–83).

All stones having one or more pronounced cleavage planes should be removed from the cemented position on the lap stick by carefully heating the cement.

When grinding long, slender stones where the length of the stone is many times the width, as for example, long cabochon forms that are used for bar pins, the grinding wheel should be true so that vibration and chatter are avoided, and the pressure on the stone being ground should be carefully controlled to prevent breakage. The stone should be supported at a point opposite the point of contact upon the wheel, and for best results the long axis of the stone should be in the plane of the grinding wheel.

The same principle should be utilized when it may be necessary to grind thin slabs. Full support should be given to the stone so that the thumb presses the stone squarely onto the grinding-wheel face. Lack of proper support, or any tendency to exert a leverage upon the stone while it is being ground, may result in breaking the slab. Soft-bond grinding wheels are invaluable in work of this type.

While most cabochon and faceted stones may be roughed out in offhand grinding (Fig. 5–10), the roughing of large stones requires the use of a grinding or steady rest upon which the stone is supported during grinding. The purpose of the rest is not only to support the stone, but also to prevent abnormal wear upon the grinding wheel. Because of the weight and bulk of large masses of rock, it is impossible to grind in the normal manner. The vibration and chattering cause bouncing on the wheel face which rapidly develops flats, the hammering action of which may readily cause damage to the stone or to the equipment.

The rest or support should be at a height that will permit grinding the stone at a point on the face of the wheel directly opposite the spindle and generally at a point horizontal to the table or bench. During the grinding operation, the stone is set on the rest and the portion to be ground is brought in contact with the wheel by a firm forward motion. By the necessary turning motion, the stone may be ground to the shape desired and, because of the steady pressure, the wheel face will be kept true and circular. Care should be exercised to prevent jamming the stone between the grinding wheel and the rest, by altering the position of the latter when necessary as the diameter of the wheel becomes smaller through wear. The steady rest should just clear the face of the grinding wheel.

SPHERES. The formation of spheres or balls for beads or for ornamental purposes is not difficult in sizes under 2 in. in diameter. If the stone desired to be cut into a sphere requires sawing from a large mass or from a slab previously sawed, the piece chosen is cut out in the form of a cube slightly larger than the finished size. This tolerance may vary from one to several millimeters according to the size of the finished piece. If size is not important — and for the first attempt a definite size should be disregarded — a stone, preferably agate, should be selected that will produce a sphere about ½ to ¾ in. in diameter. If an irregular pebble is chosen, the excess material may be sawed off. Having selected a suitable stone, the grinding or roughing proceeds in a manner similar to that followed in the roughing of cabochon stones; that is, all points, edges, or projecting portions that extend beyond a true

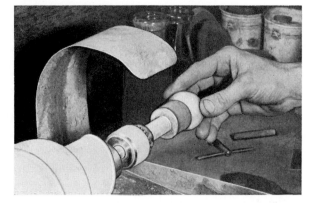

Fig. 6-51.
Rounding a sphere
on a lathe.

spherical outline are ground off. With a little practice, this grinding may be accomplished without difficulty, the co-ordination of the hand and eye resulting in a ball with a fair degree of spherical accuracy.

To obtain a smooth, uniform surface on the rough-ground sphere, the stone is trued by grinding in a metal tube with wet abrasive grain (Fig. 6–51). The metal tube, in various sizes under 2 in. in diameter, may be made of iron, steel, or brass pipe or tubing. Larger sizes should be made in the form of tubular iron laps (Fig. 6–52), but all sizes should be accurately turned or mounted.

For the greatest efficiency, tubes having wall thickness corresponding to standard pipe sizes should be used. These heavy-walled tubes retain their shape over a greater length of time and, because of the larger area of grinding surface, perform the rounding operation with the least expenditure of time. The outer diameter of the tube should be slightly less than the diameter of the finished sphere. This dimension may vary

Fig. 6-52.
Grinding and polishing
a crystal ball.

from 10 to 25 per cent, according to the size of the ball. Thus, for grinding a sphere 1 in. in diameter, a tube ¾ in. in diameter is large enough; whereas, to grind a sphere ⁵⁄₁₆ in. in diameter, a tube ¼ in. in diameter should be used. Tubes with a diameter of ½ in. or less may be held in a regular drill chuck, but larger sizes of tubes, to be held in this manner, require fitted shanks which in turn fit the chuck (Fig. 6–51).

These tubes usually are operated in a horizontal position with the chuck mounted on a polishing head or a grinding spindle; however, a vertical mounting possesses superior advantages and for this purpose a chuck adapter is required to fit the usual vertical spindle.

Regardless of the type of equipment used, the operation of grinding is the same. The speed for tubes up to 1 in. in diameter should not exceed 1750 to 1800 r.p.m. Tubes with larger diameters should be operated proportionally slower. Cylindrical lap for grinding a 3-in. crystal ball gave satisfactory service at 500 r.p.m.

Grinding with wet abrasive grain, No. 180 grit silicon carbide is excellent for the first operation on a large sphere, and No. 220 grit for the smaller ones. A small quantity of the abrasive is gathered about the rough sphere which is held by the first three fingers of the hand. With the tube rotating accurately at the specified speed, the ball with the mass of wet abrasive is placed in the opening of the tube and rolled with a universal motion which is imparted to the ball by a back and forward movement of the fingers. Additional abrasive is added from time to time by means of a brush or by the fingers of the other hand, and the sphere is kept in constant pressure against the rotating end of the tube. In a short space of time, varying according to the size of the sphere and to the accuracy of the previously rough-ground ball, the sphere will be rounded; all of the high spots will have been removed and the surface should show a uniform finish resulting from the finer abrasive. Rough spots, that might remain from the original grinding, will be easily seen if the sphere is washed free of the loose abrasive and dried. Grinding is continued until all rough-grinding marks have been removed. To completely round a rough-ground ball with a ½-in. diameter, by this method, should not require longer than five minutes.

In working on spheres over one inch in diameter, after the initial rounding has been completed, and before finish grinding proceeds, the sphere should be coated with thin, colored lacquer. Marking-out dye or a lacquer spray is excellent for this purpose. This coating serves as a guide in the finish grinding as every scratch, gouge, nick, or hollow portion remaining from the first grinding remains and after a trial grinding with finer grit, these blemishes immediately become visible. These faults are particularly noticeable when making spheres from rock crystal or smoky quartz. Unless all scratches and blemishes are removed in the finish grinding, they are readily seen in the finished sphere especially if the latter is made from one of the transparent gem stones.

For best results in grinding and in order to avoid contamination another tube should be used with a finer grit, usually FFF. If the initial grinding has been done correctly No. 600 grit may be used to produce a finer ground surface and hasten the polishing process.

If only one tube is available, completely remove all of the coarser abrasive by thoroughly scrubbing the tube in water, then proceed with the fine grinding.

After this process, which requires a few minutes, has been completed satisfactorily, the sphere is ready for polishing. The stone is cemented to a lap stick with a little more than one half of the sphere free of cement. After cooling the cement, the selection of the proper polishing technique depends upon the type of stone being worked. The smoothly ground sphere is treated in the same manner as a regular cabochon stone. If the stone chosen is an agate, polishing technique No. 2 follows. If the stone is a jasper or a soft stone, the method prescribed for polishing these stones should be followed. In either case, one side is polished first, after which the sphere is reversed upon the cement stick and the remaining rough side is polished. In the first

INITIAL POLISHING

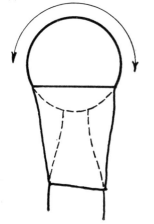

**Fig. 6-53.** Cementing sphere for polishing. Initial polishing.

setting and polishing, if more than half of the sphere has been polished (Fig. 6-53), the unfinished portion can be polished easily without leaving a ridge or mark around the stone which would show that it had been polished in two operations. The stone also may be polished by substituting wooden tubes for the metal tubes used in rounding. This would dispense with the necessity of cementing the stone to the lap stick.

Abrasive grain FFF or No. 600 is used for polishing, which produces a surface with considerable gloss, particularly in stones like agate. Final polishing is done with a clean wooden tube and tin oxide or other suitable polishing material. The wooden tube is simple to make. A hardwood dowel is securely fastened in a chuck and the projecting end is faced truly and then concaved the desired amount. Lacking suitable turning tools, an ordinary flat file may be quickly ground to the desired shape as shown in Figure 6–40.

Large spheres may be held by the hand making it unnecessary to cement the stone to a stick. After finish grinding, the smoothing and polishing may be done in tubular laps. Abrasive cloth cemented in a cup lap will quickly bring the finely ground surface of the sphere to a dull gloss. The remaining operation of polishing may be done with a leather-lined cup wheel, a felt wheel, or with a muslin buff, using tin oxide or levigated alumina for polishing.

In grinding a ball in the tube to produce a sphere, the action of the abrasive not only grinds the stone but grinds the tube as well and, if continued, the periphery of the tube will be ground to a sharp knife edge (Fig. 6–54A). The tube never should be allowed to reach this condition for the fingers can be very seriously cut by the rapidly rotating knifelike edge of the tube. To prevent this, the edge of the tube should be rounded off from time to time with a few strokes of a flat file (Fig. 6–54B).

CUBES often are cut for ornamental pieces. To fashion this form accurately requires considerable skill. The simplest method is to saw the stone as near to the desired size as possible, and to follow with carefully controlled lapping. In commercial work, cubes less than 1 in. in size, if accurately sawed, need not be more than 1 mm. oversize. With average skill, this will allow sufficient stock for truing. When lapping the faces, the same procedure is used as for lapping specimens. A flat cast-iron lap should be used with silicon carbide abrasive grain No. 220.

Two adjacent sides are lapped flat and the interfacial angle is checked with a square (Fig. 6–29). For this purpose, a toolmaker's

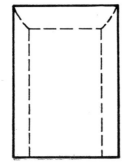

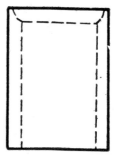

◀ Fig. 6-54A.  Tube ground to sharp edge.

▶ Fig. 6-54B.  Tube edge trimmed.

square, protractor, or caliper square may be used (Figs. 6–23, 6–29, and 6–30). After two sides have been lapped as accurately as possible, a third side at a right angle to either of these two faces should be lapped and trued. The accuracy of this third face with respect to the other two is checked with a gauge, so that, when finished, the third face is at a right angle to the two previously ground. These are ground in the order shown in Figure 6–55A. The fourth rough face, regardless of the one chosen, will be opposite to one of those which have been ground true, thus any side opposite those numbered 1, 2, 3, may be chosen for lapping. Using the trued sides as reference faces, the fourth side is ground flat and at a right angle to its two adjacent faces.

At this point a new factor must be considered, and that is the size or distance between the two parallel faces now existing. If a definite size has been decided upon, the dimension or distance between the two parallel faces is carefully measured, and a slight amount in excess of the size desired is left as this material is removed in polishing. In small cubes this amount need not exceed .2 mm.

In a similar manner, sides 5 and 6 are finished, care being exercised to lap all sides in a uniform manner, maintaining squareness, flatness, and accuracy. In lapping the remaining sides, the caliper square should be used for checking (Fig. 6–23). The finished parallel sides should be grasped between the jaws of the tool, and the right-angle side should be checked against the body of the tool. After the cube has been lapped to size, a slight bevel edge is given to each of the twelve boundary edges so that these will not chip off in polishing. A choice of two methods is available for polishing the six sides. One method is to smooth and polish on flat wheels as prescribed for specimen polishing, according to the type of stone selected; and the other method is to polish on a tin lap with the proper polishing medium such as tin oxide.

If a number of cubes of one size are desired, they may be finished at one time by cementing them together (Fig. 6–55B) or to a plate. They are then finished by lapping and polishing in the prescribed manner. For proper handling, a number of methods are possible and the choice depends upon the number of cubes to be made. Five or six cubes, up to 1 in. in size, may be treated by cementing them together to form a rod (Fig. 6–55B). Sealing wax, such as that used for cementing stones to lap sticks, will serve perfectly. To simplify cementing, all of the cubes should be heated at one time. A hot plate or a small double boiler may be used, after which the melted cement is applied to opposite faces of the rough cubes to form a rod. Before the cemented cubes

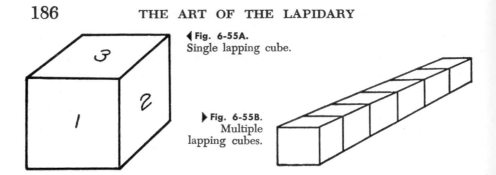

◀ Fig. 6-55A.
Single lapping cube.

▶ Fig. 6-55B.
Multiple
lapping cubes.

have set and the cement has become hardened, the rod is placed on a flat plate and the cubes are correctly aligned.

After cooling, two opposite sides are lapped parallel and to the required dimension. The third and fourth sides then are carefully lapped parallel and at right angles to the first two, a small protecting edge is ground on the four long edges, after which the bar is smoothed and polished. After polishing, the square rod is heated to separate the cubes, and then the cubes are cemented again with the finished or polished faces together, in such a manner as to have the two unfinished faces of the cubes in the same planes.

To finish the set, one of the remaining rough sides is lapped square with the finished sides. The opposite rough side then is lapped to the desired dimension, followed by edging and polishing in the same manner as specified in the first operation. Finally, the finished cubes are heated so as to separate them, and the remaining cement is removed with alcohol. If it is desired to finish a large number of cubes at one time they can be cemented to a flat plate, and the sides can be finished in a manner similar to a large flat surface. By recementing and resetting each set of faces successively, the lot is finished.

Stones cut in rectangular shapes are treated in a similar manner regardless of the size or proportion. Thus, a stone may be cut into small tiles, many of which are used for bar pins or brooch stones. In larger sizes, they may be used for paperweights, boxes, or book ends.

CYLINDERS. As articles of ornament or utility, cylindrical shapes have long been used from ancient Babylon to the present day. Short, stout forms are not difficult to grind and polish, because the same principles as used in grinding and polishing cabochon stones are followed. The stone is ground to the size and shape desired. It is then cemented to the end of a lap stick and the cylindrical surface is lapped to a true surface on a flat lap or grinding wheel. Considerable skill is required to form a true cylindrical shape free from taper. Unless the axis of the lap

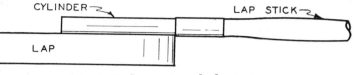

Fig. 6-56. Lapping a cylinder to size.

stick is held parallel to the lap surface, the grinding will cause the stone to be tapered (Fig. 6-56).

It frequently happens that both ends may become tapered so that their diameter is smaller than the middle of the cylinder. By roughing out the stone long enough to allow the ends to be trimmed down truly, the rounded or tapered portion may be eliminated. When small cylinders are lapped or when stones are required which have a length many times their diameter, the difficulty in handling increases. When a number of stones were ground to a finish size of 6 x 40 mm., to be used for bar pins, the stones were roughed out about 5 or 6 mm. longer than the size required. A square strip was first sawed from the stone, and then it was carefully ground as true as possible by holding it in the hand. Special lap sticks with metal tubular ends were used for holding (Fig. 6-57), and the projecting cylinder was then truly ground on a flat lap (Fig. 6-56).

While the lap stick is held and rotated by one hand, the cylinder may be supported on the lap by the other hand. By cementing the

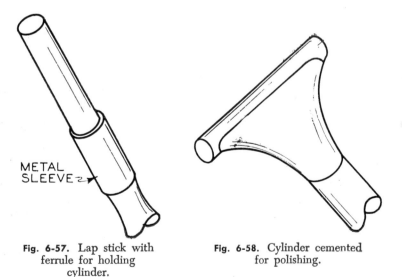

Fig. 6-57. Lap stick with ferrule for holding cylinder.

Fig. 6-58. Cylinder cemented for polishing.

cylinder into the tubular end of the lap stick, the difficulty of holding is overcome. After the stone has been finish-ground and removed from the holder, the portion that was cemented is ground to correspond with the rest of the cylinder. In polishing, the cylinder is cemented to a lap stick at a right angle (Fig. 6–58), and the surface of the cylinder is polished on a flat lap, being kept in motion constantly in order to prevent flats forming on the surface. After the exposed surface has been completely polished, the stone is removed from the stick, and the other side is finished in a similar manner. All that remains to be done is to finish-grind and polish the ends of the cylinder. If the ends are to be rounded, the finishing can be done freehand. To grind the ends square, however, is more difficult and, without experience and skill, this can be done only by arranging a V block at a right angle to the lap. Then, with the block as a guide and a support for the cylinder to rest upon, the ends of the latter may be ground true (Fig. 6–59). After edging to prevent chipping, the ends are polished, using the same method as before.

CONICAL FORMS, like cylinders, are among the oldest forms known and were extensively used for beads and seals thousands of years ago (Fig. 6–60). Identical forms have been used continuously to the present time. As a general rule, the cross section or base portion is circular, but other shaped outlines, as a hexagon or octagon, also are used. A conventional cone form is similar to a high cabochon because it has a circular out-

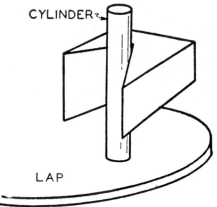

CYLINDER

LAP

Fig. 6-59. V block rest to square ends.

line. However, the majority of conical forms used for beads are like double cabochon stones, with equally developed ends, but the length of the stones usually is more than twice the diameter. The chief use of this form is as a bead and has a hole drilled lengthwise (Fig. 6–61).

Variations of conical forms are numerous; thus, by flattening to form opposite sides and by shortening the stone, it may be converted into a glandular, lenticular, or lozenge form (Fig. 6–62).

Disklike forms, polished all over and drilled through the thinnest

**Fig. 6-60.** Agate bead necklace of Queen Shub-ad. Ur, 3500 B.C.

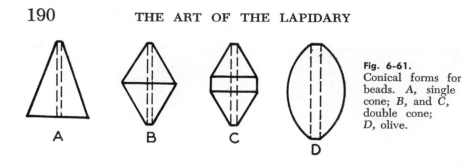

Fig. 6-61.
Conical forms for
beads. *A*, single
cone; *B*, and *C*,
double cone;
*D*, olive.

portion, are commonly used for beads. When these disks are very small,
they are known as rondells (Fig. 6–63).

DROP FORMS (Fig. 6–64) are similar to conical forms having one end
flattened or rounded. Most of the forms in use have a circular cross
section, but on occasion this may be elliptical. In matched pairs, circular
drops may be used for eardrops or for articles of jewelry, such as
ornamental handles for small coffee spoons (Fig. 6–65).

In fashioning the drop form, the regular grinding operations are
followed. Particular care is required in making a number of equal size,
to carefully grind to shape, size, and contour. After the stone has been
finish-ground, it is cemented in a metal tube-ended lap stick to facilitate
handling, the pointed end of the drop being upward. Ordinary lap sticks
may be used, but with their use, the stones often break off the cement
because of the leverage exerted in the finishing operations. After the
pointed end has been finished, the stone is removed and recemented.
Finishing the back or rounded end requires care to obtain a smooth,
even junction where the two surfaces meet. After final polishing, the
drop is removed from the cement, and the pointed end is either drilled
or grooved for fastening in the cup-shaped mounting.

One of the finest examples of jewelry from ancient times, the necklace
of which is composed of round and drop-formed beads, is illustrated

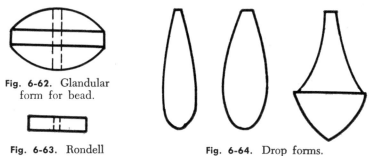

Fig. 6-62. Glandular
form for bead.

Fig. 6-63. Rondell
form for bead.

Fig. 6-64. Drop forms.

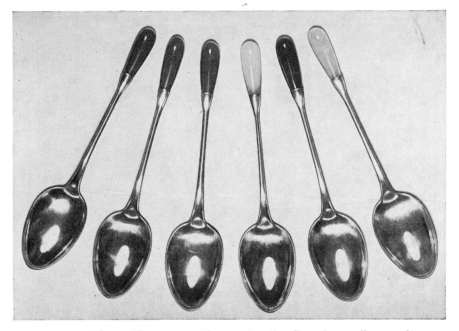

Fig. 6-65. Silver coffee spoons with gem stone handles; chrysocolla, carnelian, chrysoprase, rock crystal, black onyx, and rose quartz.

in Figure 6–66. Beads of various types have been used by all peoples all over the world. The jade beads of Mayan workmanship produced in pre-Columbian times, illustrated in Figure 6–67 are typical. When it is considered that the Mayan lapidary did not possess metal tools and that the drilling of holes through cylinders of jadeite over 2 in. in length was accomplished by means of abrasion using bird bones with quartz sand, the results achieved are remarkable.

Drops with an elliptical cross section are carefully roughed out and finish-ground to size, and the broad surface is cemented to the lap stick. The stone is then treated in a manner similar to the treatment given to double cabochon stones (Fig. 6–68).

HEART SHAPES are among the most interesting forms to cut, and these are used in all kinds of jewelry. In the smaller sizes, they may be used singly or in matched pairs for rings, pins or brooches, bracelets, charms, or wristlets (Figs. 6–69 and 6–70). The larger sizes have always been popular as pendants. Heart shapes are cut in single as well as double cabochon types. The single cabochon cut is used when the stone is mounted in a permanent position in a piece of jewelry where one side only is observed.

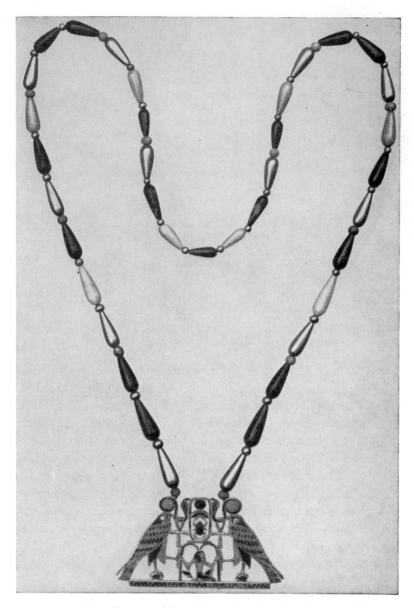

**Fig. 6-66.** Magnificent necklace of carnelian, lapis lazuli, green feldspar, and gold (Egyptian Princess Sit-Hat-Hor Yunet, 1906–1887 B.C.).

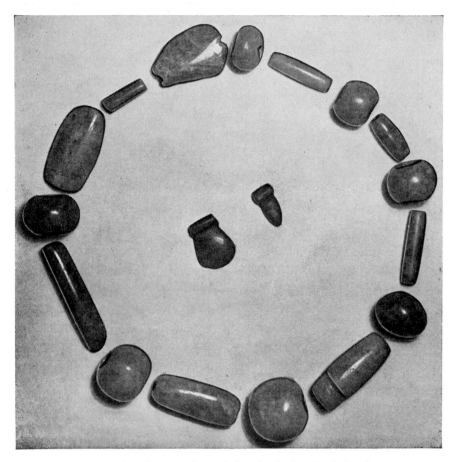

**Fig. 6-67.** Author's collection of rounded and cylindrical jade beads of Mayan workmanship. Two objects in center are miniature adzes.

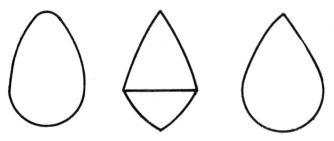

**Fig. 6-68.** Pendant forms.

**Fig. 6-69.** Necklace of hearts, 13 by 13.5 mm. Stones are amethyst, carnelian, chrysocolla, tourmaline, chrysoprase, carnelian, and black onyx.

Double cabochon forms are invariably used as pendants. These may be cut with a sharp girdle edge about which a bezel is placed. Some are grooved to be suspended by a wire, while others have rounded edges and are drilled for suspension by a peg having a loop (Fig. 6–71).

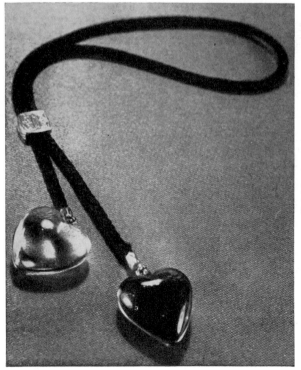

**Fig. 6-70.**
Wristlet with rock crystal and amethyst hearts, 14 by 15 mm., and white-gold mounting.

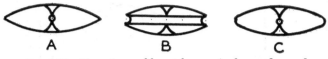

Fig. 6-71. Top views of heart forms: A, sharp edge and drilled; B, grooved; C, round edge and drilled.

In the single cabochon form, the stone is roughed out in the manner prescribed for regular cabochon forms, and it is ground as true as possible. The crotch is ground on the sharp edge of the grinding wheel (Fig. 6–72) or on a special contour wheel (Fig. 6–73), and, as the crevice extends from the back of the stone to a distance about one quarter the width of the stone forming an arc, it is important that this crevice accurately divides the stone into two equal sections and that it is in line with the point opposite. Finish-grinding follows in like manner, and care must be exercised to grind a true perfect form. After the stone has been completely ground, it is polished in the usual manner. To finish the stone correctly and make a well-formed heart requires care and patience. Two points which require special attention are the crotch which should be well shaped and polished, and the point opposite which should not be rounded off. To smooth the crotch before polishing, a piece of abrasive cloth is doubled over a knife blade or any sharp-edged straight tool, and this smoothing lap is briskly rubbed along the crevice of the stone until the surface is smooth and the grinding marks have been removed.

This portion of the stone may be polished on a sharp-edged leather or wooden wheel using tin oxide or levigated alumina. The polishing face of the wheel should be turned to a form which will correspond to the shape of the crevice. In polishing stones of this type, it is customary

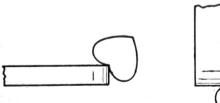

Fig. 6-72. Grinding fancy-shaped stone on edge of lap.

Fig. 6-73. Grinding fancy-shaped stone.

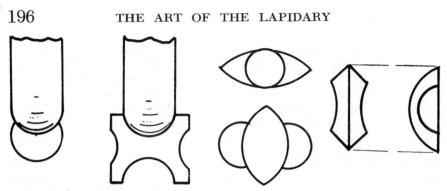

**Fig. 6-74.** Grinding fancy-shaped stones on formed contour wheels.

**Fig. 6-75.** Crescents applied.

to finish the irregular or hollow portion in each step first. Thus, the crevice portion is smoothed first and then the remainder of the stone is similarly treated; the crevice is polished, and finally the rest of the surface is finished. If polishing proceeds in this manner, any tendency to scratch a previously polished surface will be eliminated.

In cutting double cabochon heart shapes, the same principles apply. However, as the outline of the stone becomes the girdle edge, care and skill are required to finish-grind both sides of equal thickness. This can be done by careful grinding and by continually checking results with the eye. The manner in which the heart is to be suspended determines the type of edge to be cut. If the stone is to be suspended from a peg and loop, the edge of the heart may be either rounded or sharp, although the latter is generally used when a band is placed around the stone. If a wire is to be the suspending medium, then the girdle edge is flattened to a width of at least 2 mm., and a groove is ground around the stone. It is well to place the groove around the stone before it is polished, for the polishing not only removes small chips which may have been formed in the grooving process, but it also smooths the groove and thus lessens the danger of chipping when setting the wire. The stone is grooved with a round-edged lap of mild steel charged with diamond powder, although a wheel with a formed edge and other abrasives also may be used.

Other fancy shapes, such as the clover leaf (Fig. 6–73), which has multiple segments, are treated in like manner. The stone may be divided into segments by approximation, using the eye as a guide; or, if greater accuracy is desired, the stone may be cemented to a template having the desired number of faces to correspond with the number of segments to be cut. The division into segments is made with the use of a

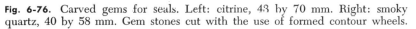

**Fig. 6-76.** Carved gems for seals. Left: citrine, 43 by 70 mm. Right: smoky quartz, 40 by 58 mm. Gem stones cut with the use of formed contour wheels.

guide rest plate on a lathe. The template with its cemented stone is brought in contact with the guide rest plate and the stone is moved to the rotating diamond-charged wheel held in the spindle of the lathe.

Crescents and fancy-cut cabochon stones with recurved faces require the grinding and polishing of one or more faces in a hollow curve. While this may be done on the edge of a grinding wheel, if the degree of accuracy required is not too great, the best results are obtained by grinding the curve with a properly formed grinding wheel (Figs. 6–73 and 6–74). By dressing the face of the grinding wheel to the desired radius, the recurved surface is ground without difficulty (Figs. 6–75 and 6–76).

When the curved surface is ground, the stone is first held so that its back surface is square and parallel with the grinding spindle. Then, as the grinding progresses, the stone, which is held in contact with the wheel face, is drawn upward and the back is tilted away from the wheel in a radial manner. Thus, the surface not only is curved but it is also convex. Smoothing and polishing follow in a similar manner.

When grinding fancy shapes, care should be used to prevent the points from breaking off. No other great difficulty will be experienced in cutting and finishing these pieces. The recurved surfaces of the stones outlined may be smoothed with an abrasive cloth rolled around or cemented to a round stick which has the desired curvature. To smooth the stone, the abrasive lap stick is briskly rubbed in the curved surfaces of the stone in a manner similar to filing; that is, the smoothing lap is given a backward and forward motion over the surface of the stone. Only a few strokes of the smoothing lap are necessary to prepare the surface for polishing.

Fig. 6-77.
Concaved stones for
cuff links.

CONCAVED STONES are of a great variety and size. The same principles
of grinding and polishing are used for all stones from the smallest size
cup or bearing jewels to the largest bowls, but there is a difference in
the size of the wheels used. Stones with cut concaves may be used for
many kinds of jewelry, such as rings, cuff links, or brooch stones. For
ornamental use, ash and pin trays are familiar to all. The simple, circular
flat-back stone, concaved and drilled, is widely used for buttons, dress
sets, cuff links, and shirt stud sets (Fig. 6–77). Although these sets may
be made in all geometrical or fancy shapes, the circular or disk form is
the easiest to make. The circular shape is cut from flat slabs about 2½ mm.
thick, and the finished size of the stone is from 12 to 14 mm. in diameter.
The usual procedure is to rough- and finish-grind to shape and size, then
edge both sides, and finally cement the stone top up for grinding the
concave.

For grinding small concaves, an assortment of silicon-carbide abrasive
wheels are desirable, although turned and formed iron laps will serve
as well. Abrasive wheels are convenient to use, however, as they may
be furnished with lead-bushed holes which permit their use on a tapered
spindle of a polishing head (Fig. 6–78). These wheels, as received, have
a straight parallel hole, and initial mounting requires some care to wring

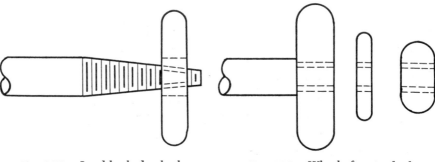

Fig. 6-78.   Lead-bushed wheel on          Fig. 6-79.   Wheels for standard
          tapered spindle.                              thread.

them onto the tapered spindle so that they will run true. Once they are accurately mounted and, if necessary, trued with a diamond dressing tool, they may be removed and remounted at will, and they will continue to run true.

Small iron laps, if used, should be fitted with individual arbors which may be held in a chuck; or, a polishing head with a special screwed and shouldered spindle may be used, in which case all of the wheels are tapped with thread to fit (Fig. 6–79). A suitable rectangular-shaped pan of rustless metal, with a splash guard, is used in connection with these wheels. The splash guard may be bent to suit wheels of different diameters, and the lip of the guard should extend a trifle below the top of the wheel, so that the abrasive grain applied to the rotating wheel will not be thrown into the face of the operator (Fig. 6–80). Abrasive wheels for grinding concaves should be of the vitrified silicon-carbide type, medium-hard, No. 220 grit. Abrasive grain of the same size, namely No. 220, also is used with the wheel and is applied to the wheel face by a brush or with the fingers, which usually is quicker. Spindle speeds, ranging from 1750 to 2000 r.p.m., are satisfactory for this class of work. Faster speeds are dangerous to the work.

After the shape of the stone has been duly prepared for grinding a

**Fig. 6-80.** Correct position when grinding concave.

round concave, a wheel with a diameter of 1¼ to 1⅝₁₆ in. should be selected. This will have the required curvature to grind the concave. For the first attempt, the spindle speed should not exceed 1750 r.p.m. This will enable the operator to become familiar with the slight difference in grinding from that already experienced. For best results, the operator should be seated before the grinding head, the normal position of the forearms should be horizontal with the elbows close to the body, thus affording complete control of the grinding (Fig. 6–80).

With a quantity of wet abrasive in the pan and a surplus of water with it, a small quantity of the wet abrasive is held to the rotating wheel. The lap stick, together with the stone to be concaved cemented to it, is held firmly in one hand, aided and supported by the other. The stick then is held to the wheel so that contact is made in the center of the stone, the normal position of the lap stick being at an angle of approximately 45 deg. with the horizontal (Fig. 6–81). Care should be used when starting the concave, to centralize it, and after a few seconds of grinding, the work should be examined. If it is centralized properly, work should be continued; if it is off center, the stick should be rotated so that the off-center portion of the stone to be removed is the lower portion away from the wheel, because the tendency is to grind on the surface nearer the operator. This is caused by the pull of the wheel and the tendency for the stone to go in the direction of the wheel rotation. A gentle pressure against the wheel to counteract this pull will keep the stone in position and at the same time centralize the concave.

After a depression of reasonable size has been made, so that there is little danger that the stone will slip off the wheel, rotating the stone

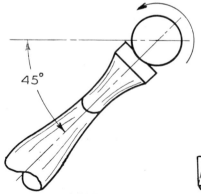

45°

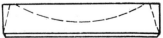

Fig. 6-81. Grinding concave.          Fig. 6-82. Properly ground
                                                  concave.

should be continued so that the concave will be uniformly ground. During the entire grinding process, wet abrasive is continually placed on the wheel. The concave should be ground until only an edge remains on the stone, about 2 mm. wide. This edge is allowed to remain so that, when the bevel edge of the stone is ground, the concave edge will almost meet it (Fig. 6–82).

When the concave has been properly ground, the edge will be concentric with the edge of the stone and the concave will have a uniform surface with its curvature matching that of the grinding wheel (Fig. 6–81). If a number of stones for a set are to be worked, the concaves of all matched pieces should be of equal size. After grinding, the stones are carefully washed to remove all adhering abrasive particles.

In polishing the concaves, the previously described principles or steps are followed. As the majority of stones used for concaved pieces have a fine texture and are listed in the second class, polishing of this class will be treated first. The initial polishing or smoothing is done with small wooden wheels, which have been turned to the same form and slightly smaller in diameter than the grinding wheels. The best wood to be used for this purpose is southern gum. Poplar also may be used, but wheels made of poplar will wear out of round more quickly.

By using wheels of slightly smaller diameter for smoothing, the center of the concave is readily polished. This would not be the case if the polishing wheel were the same size as the grinding wheel. Abrasive grain 1–F, FF, or No. 320 is applied wet in a similar manner to the No. 220 used for grinding the concave. After a few moments of lapping, the concave loses its rough appearance and takes a dull gloss. The operation is continued until all coarse rough-grinding marks have been removed. The time required to smooth a concave about 12 mm. in diameter is approximately two minutes. The stone as well as the operator's hands are then washed to remove all abrasive. The next step is to polish with a small felt wheel of the same size as the wooden wheel, using abrasive grain FFF silicon carbide. After a few moments of work, the concave will have a glossy finish with a slight dullness. For smoothing or polishing stones softer than glass, 2–0 pumice may be used to replace the silicon carbide. This abrasive is less costly than the silicon carbide, and is satisfactory for the softer stones. During the grinding and polishing operations the concave must be examined periodically to check the progress. The abrasive may be cleared away by simply wiping with the finger.

Final polishing of the stone, using tin oxide and a small felt, or wooden wheel, follows washing and cleaning as previously outlined.

In a minute or two, the finish should be bright with a uniform polish over the entire concave. During the grinding and polishing operations, the operator is cautioned in the following:

GRINDING. During this operation, the stone may be dislodged from the wheel face, causing the wheel to grind or chip the edge of the stone as it rubs over this edge. For this reason the bevel edge is ground last; otherwise the stone may be chipped and ruined.

In slipping off the face of the grinding wheel, the stone may come in violent contact with the rotating spindle or other metal portion of the polishing head, resulting in a chipped or broken stone.

POLISHING. Cleanliness is of the utmost importance. When proceeding from a grinding stage to the use of finer grits, the stone should be thoroughly cleaned and all particles of abrasive should be removed. If coarse scratches appear in the work, they usually are caused by contamination of coarser grit mixed with the finer grain.

The chief source of contamination is in the dislodging of particles of coarse grit that remain in crevices in the cement that holds the stone or that remain lodged between the stone and the cement fastened to it. All of this should be removed by scraping with a sharp pointed tool.

When polishing with the felt wheels, excessive pressure should be avoided, and the stone being worked should be wet and be supplied with wet abrasive at all times. Should the concave of the stone become dry from lack of wet abrasive, heat would be quickly generated from the friction which could easily crack or burn the stone.

After the concave has been finished, the bevel edge is cut. This should be done on a fine grit wheel or preferably a pewter lap to which silicon-carbide abrasive grain No. 280 or 1–F is applied wet. The bevel edge may be ground in a freehand manner or, if a true job is desired, a back rest or jamb peg is required. This may be an ordinary board or post fastened in an upright manner near the lap. Small indentations having been previously placed in the rest, arranged in a vertical position to receive the pointed end of the lap stick which is placed therein, and the end to which the stone is affixed is touched to the lap. In place of a special rest, the side wall of the lapidary bench with a series of holes similarly arranged, will serve, provided the wall is near enough to the lap. The angle of the lap stick to the lap should be about 10 to 15 deg. according to the amount of bevel desired and, as a rule, the stone should be placed on the lap so that the direction of rotation of the lap is away from the stone and not toward it. This is of great importance when the lap stick is at a greater angle to the lap.

In grinding the bevel on a circular stone, a firm, uniform pressure against the lap is essential while the stone is rotated in contact with the lap surface. The stone is examined from time to time to ascertain the condition of the ground surface. If the bevel edge is slightly irregular or uneven, the portion from which the most material must be removed is placed on the lap and carefully ground to produce a uniform edge. After this edge has been uniformly ground, a small protective edge is ground at the top of the stone to prevent chipping. The bevel edge then is polished on a felt wheel in the manner already prescribed for cabochon stones, or it may be polished on a tin lap with tin oxide. The latter method will produce a flatter facet and sharper edge. The top flat surface is finally polished on the tin lap. This will finish the stone and at the same time define the concave edge which should be concentric with the bevel edge of the round stone.

Larger round concaves are ground in a similar manner by using larger wheels. Ash trays or receptacles of various types may be made in this manner. Grinding wheels that have been used for other grinding purposes and that have been reduced to a diameter of four inches are excellent for this purpose. A variation of the spherical concave is seen in some cylindrical forms where the depression is deeper and the walls of the hollow portion are vertical. This form is common in cylindrical boxes. If the depression is not too deep, it may be started in the usual manner with grinding wheels, using the largest size wheel first, followed with smaller wheels (Figs. 6–83 and 6–84A).

Iron laps are handy for this purpose and they are used with silicon carbide grain No. 220. The time required varies according to the depth as well as the size of the depression. To finish, a cylindrical lap is used which is slightly smaller in diameter than the aperture (Fig. 6–84B). This last operation in lapping can be done with a horizontal rotating tool,

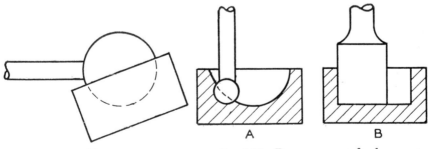

Fig. 6-83. Deep concave.        Fig. 6-84. Deep concaves for boxes.

HARDWOOD PLATE, BRONZE BUSHINGS.
ANGLE PLATE WITH ADJUSTING SCREW.

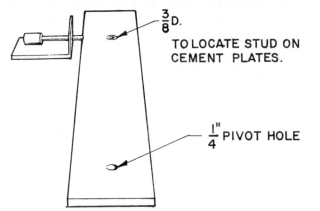

$\frac{3}{8}$D.

TO LOCATE STUD ON
CEMENT PLATES.

Fig. 6-84C.
Simple drilling and
counterboring jig.

$\frac{1}{4}$" PIVOT HOLE

but greater ease of operation and efficiency are possible with the use of a drill press to hold the tool. The tool is lifted from time to time and fresh abrasive is constantly brushed against it. At the same time, the stone is rotated so that the lap rubs over the entire surface of the hollow being ground. To grind a true cylindrical cavity, a simple fixture is required (Fig. 6–84 C). The stone is cemented to a plate or disk to which a centralized boss ⅜ in. in diameter is fixed. The boss fits into a base plate pinned at one end to the drill press table and this fixture is adjusted on the drill press table so that the concave of the stone to be ground is in axial alignment with the spindle of the drill press.

By means of a feed screw fastened to the table and abutting the fixture, lateral motion is imparted thereto and the grinding wheel or lap is thus enabled to remove small amounts from the cavity formed till the

Fig. 6-85.
Rock-crystal watchcase
23 x 24 mm.
(author's creation).

Fig. 6-86.   Small gemstone trays in preparation.

desired size is reached. The downward travel of the spindle is controlled by stops on the machine, thereby controlling the depth of the cavity. (Fig. 6–84B). Diamond-charged tools may also be used in this operation. After the depression has been ground to the depth desired, it may be polished by following the same principles described for polishing spherical concaves; the smoothing and polishing laps, however, must be of a cylindrical shape. When grinding in this manner with the use of a drill press, the article ground should be placed in a shallow or oblong box to prevent the abrasive from splashing over the apparatus. The watchcase in Figure 6–85 is made in this manner.

The four items in Figure 6–86 are shown completed in Figure 6–87.

Figure 6–88 illustrates three stages in the preparation of the small coupeés shown in Figure 6–89, (1) the block sawed from the rough

Fig. 6-87.   A. Monterey jade (Calif.), 68 mm.; B. Venus hairstone, Brazil, 65 mm. o.d., 50 mm. i.d. Spoon with chrysoprase handle; C. Orbicular jasper (Calif.) 54 x 84 mm.; D. Venus hairstone, Brazil, 52 x 59 mm.; E. Rhodonite (Calif.) 59 mm. diameter (author's creation).

**Fig. 6-88.** Small cups and vases in preparation. Stages 1, 2, and 3.

**Fig. 6-89.** Cordial coupeés 46 mm. dia., 117 mm. high; forged sterling silver stands (author's creation). Upper (left to right): Rosequartz, Brazil; Botryoidal amethystine chalcedony, Nevada; Phantom amethyst, Africa; Blue chalcedony, Arizona. Lower (left to right): Nephrite jade, Alaska; Carnelian, Mexico, Green moss agate, India; Red plume agate, Oregon.

**Fig. 6-90.** Phantom amethyst coupeé, 46 mm. dia., finish ground.
Mounted to cement chuck.

mass, (2) additional sawing to reduce time in roughing, and (3) the completely roughed out unit ready for finish grinding. The finish ground coupeé is shown in Figure 6–90.

Oval concaves (Fig. 6–91) are fashioned in a manner similar to round concaves. After the concave has been started, a slight lateral pressure will cause the stone to be ground more on one side or the other according to the direction of pressure. By carefully controlling the lap stick, a true ellipse may be ground without difficulty. For this work, the grinding wheel should run true, and the face of it should be turned to the curvature necessary to produce a satisfactory concave. For turning and truing small abrasive wheels, a small diamond wheel-truing tool serves best

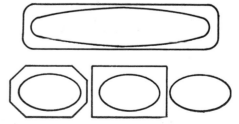

**Fig. 6-91.**
Various forms of concaved stones.

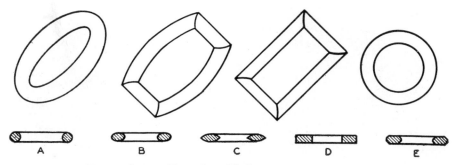

**Fig. 6-92.** Various forms of brooch and link stones. Cross sections: *A*, circular; *B*, oval; *C*, marquise; *D*, rectangular; *E*, octagonal.

although the dressing can be done by using a very hard abrasive stick. As a general rule, concaves ground in stones used for rings or other jewelry pieces, have a flat border on the top surface of the stone; for this reason the concave must be properly centered and accurately ground. In certain cases, as for example in watch crystals cut from rock crystal, having fancy shapes, oblong, rectangular or octagonal concaves extend to the edge of the stone regardless of the shape. This is done to prevent the joining line (concave edge and the flat back) from showing when viewed from the front of the stone. To form a concave of this type, the grinding is done in the usual manner, and the concave is gradually ground until it extends to each corner of the stone. A grinding wheel of the necessary diameter is selected and, after grinding the main portions, the stone is drawn forward so that the wheel grinds to this corner, easing up on the grinding pressure. After all corners have been

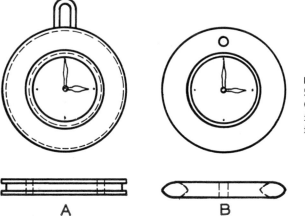

**Fig. 6-93.**
Stone frames for watches. Cross sections: *A*, grooved for band; *B*, drilled for cord.

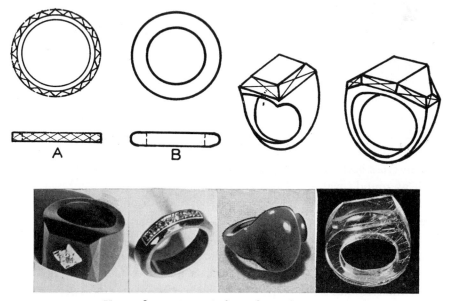

**Fig. 6-94.** Upper, finger rings: *A*, faceted; *B*, plain. Lower: Jade rings made by the author. First and second, black jade set with diamonds. Owner, James McGrath, Piedmont, Calif. Fourth, abstract ring. V.H.S. (Richard L. Sperisen creation).

finished, the concave is smoothed in which process all irregularities should be eliminated. Polishing follows in the usual manner.

Small grinding wheels or laps also may be used for drilling (actually grinding) holes in thin stones or for various purposes such as making simple or fancy-shaped links or frames in stone (Fig. 6–92), for use in bracelets, brooches, pendants, or watchcases (Fig. 6–93), as well as finger rings (Fig. 6–94). After a slab of stone has been roughed and finish cut to the desired shape and size and it has been cemented to a lap stick, grinding proceeds as outlined for grinding concaves. If the stone

## TABLE 9. RING-SIZE DIMENSIONS

| Ring size | Dia. inches | Ring size | Dia. inches |
|---|---|---|---|
| 0. | .453 | 7. | .683 |
| 1. | .486 | 8. | .716 |
| 2. | .520 | 9. | .748 |
| 3. | .552 | 10. | .781 |
| 4. | .585 | 11. | .814 |
| 5. | .618 | 12. | .845 |
| 6. | .650 | 13. | .879 |

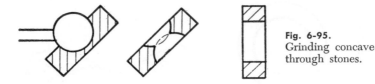

Fig. 6-95.
Grinding concave
through stones.

is not too thick, the concave may be ground through it (Fig. 6–95), after which the stone is reversed and the concave on the opposite side is ground in a similar manner.

The cross section of the piece to be ground may be of varying form, such as round, oval, elliptical, square, rectangular, or a combination of these. Round and elliptical forms are commonly used. After the hole has been ground, it is lapped to size with cylindrical laps and abrasive grain No. 220. Circular links are the easiest to make. The difficulty of fabrication increases as the form and section of the link become more elaborate. The inner portion of the circle or link is the most difficult to produce. After the hole has been lapped to size, the curved portion is formed by drawing the stone over the lap, grinding those edges or portions which project beyond the true form.

Formed laps shaped similar to those shown in Figure 4–5 are excellent for this purpose. These are readily made from mild steel or iron and, when used with abrasive grain No. 220, they enable the operator to quickly grind or lap the contour to the desired size. Smoothing is done by using abrasive cloth wrapped about a round stick held in the chuck of a polishing machine. The abrasive cloth may be cemented to the stick or it may be secured by grasping the rolled cloth with the stick in the chuck of the polishing head. Further smoothing is done with cylindrical wooden laps, using FFF silicon carbide grain. Later, a felt wheel may be used with FFF grain to polish a glossy finish and to remove any irregularities. Final polishing is done by felt wheels, using levigated alumina or tin oxide.

The outer surface then is finished in the usual manner. Final polishing is with a muslin buff and tin oxide. Because this wheel is flexible, it produces a uniform bright finish over the entire curved surface.

Fancy-shaped links with a rectangular cross section are the most difficult to produce (D, Fig. 6–92). The inner corners of the square and rectangular forms are broached out, using flat steel laps and abrasive grain. The action is similar to filing. While the majority of colored stones used for links are polished, an attractive frosted finish often is used for rock crystal and onyx. This is produced by finish-grinding and smoothing in the usual manner, after which the stone is carefully rubbed with a flat steel lap, using 1-F abrasive grain wet. The entire surface is rubbed with a universal motion. The curved inner portion may be finished in a similar manner, substituting round laps or rods for the flat ones.

Blasting by compressed air and dry abrasive grain also will serve. Although this process is rapid, it is not recommended for frosting articles with fine detail. Such finishes may be obtained by using FF or FFF grit.

A glossy finish intermediate between a frosted and a polished surface may be produced by using medium-hard rubber wheels bonded with abrasive. Cratex wheels made in several grits are excellent for this purpose. With proper equipment a large number of concaved articles for ornamental or decorative use may be made.

CROSSES always are popular for pendant pieces. These usually are made flat with a rectangular cross section, although round, elliptical, or fancy forms and shapes are occasionally seen. The flat type is carefully sawed from slabs to the size desired, after which the arms are lapped to size and polished. Although reasonable accuracy may be attained with the equipment in use in most shops, the work may be facilitated by the use of special tools or jigs.

To produce work of this type a milling machine is ideal. The work can be cemented to another flat stone (a piece of flat agate will serve) which is held securely in a vise or is clamped to an angle plate. Diamond-charged laps, properly lubricated, quickly lap the stone to size.

In this manner a number of crosses may be made at one time. After lapping to size, each arm is polished in the usual manner, and the cemented pieces are separated and the flat sides polished; or, if preferred, this polishing may be done prior to grinding the arms. Without a milling machine, the lapidary is forced to use whatever equipment is available

Fig. 6-96.
Grinding and lapping a cross.

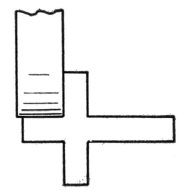

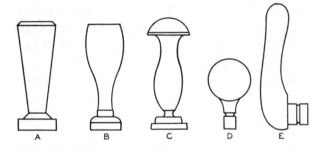

Fig. 6-97.   A, B, and C, seal handles; D, knob; E, cane handle.

to him. With true running wheels and laps, the lapping of the arms of the cross may be done on the corner edge (Fig. 6–96). A support should be fixed at a height so that the center line of the spindle is in the same plane as the center line of the stone. The slight curvature resulting from grinding on the face of the wheel or lap may be removed by lapping on the side and polishing in a similar manner.

Knobs and handles of various types (Fig. 6–97) are not difficult to produce, because these are ordinary grinding and polishing jobs. The end where the handle is fastened into the object usually is shouldered or reduced in diameter and grooved so that it may be fastened securely. A tinned copper or brass wire is wrapped in the groove and soldered, after which the handle is placed in its metal socket and gently heated. With soft solder and a suitable flux, gentle heating secures the article in place. The objects also may be secured with cement, usually shellac or sealing wax, but this method is not as durable or permanent. Occasionally drilling is preferred so that a pin may be pushed through and riveted.

Shouldering (Fig. 6–98) and grooving are similar. Shouldering consists of grinding or lapping an end of the stone to a smaller diameter so that it may be fastened into a receptacle. This may be done freehand on the wheel or lap, which must have a sharp edge, the stone being rotated without axial movement so that the shoulder edge is uniform. The reduced

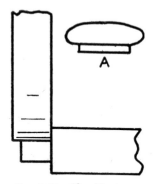

Fig. 6-98.   Shouldering a stone; A, the stone shouldered.

portion should be concentric. Accurate shouldering can be done only with a proper rest set parallel to the grinding wheel and placed at the required distance from it, so that the end of the stone will bear against the rest. This will limit or fix the portion to be lapped. The stone, which is held parallel to the lap spindle, is rotated in contact with the revolving

**Fig. 6-99.**
Grinding a shoulder
(grooving) on an onyx
bar with a diamond-
charged wheel in a
small lathe.

lap; thus the end is ground down the desired amount (Fig. 6–98).

Grooving is done in a similar manner (Fig. 6–99), with the narrow grooving wheel replacing the grinding wheel. Shouldering and grooving may be performed by using grinding wheels or laps to which abrasive grain is applied wet. However, for accuracy, long life, and ease of operation, as well as cleanliness, it is preferable to use wheels or laps made of mild steel or iron, charged with Nos. 3 or 4 diamond powder and lubricated with oil. In some cases where oil may have a detrimental effect, water may be substituted with success. On hard, tough structure, stones such as jade, water as a coolant will give better results than oil.

THREADING. The cutting of standard threads, in stone, both inside and outside, is sometimes necessary. Diamond-charged steel tools are used for this purpose. The tools, which are in the form of small wheels, are mounted in suitable equipment, usually in the form of a universal grinding spindle clamped to the saddle of a lathe or other threading tool. The work to be threaded is mounted on the faceplate or chuck, and the small threading tool is brought in contact with the carefully trued, revolving work. The diamond tool is well lubricated with oil and, through the thread-cutting gears and lead screw, the diamond tool grinds the thread in the object according to the pitch of the screw thread selected.

Chasing internal threads is somewhat delicate, for the wheel must be smaller than the diameter of the hole. Light cuts should be made and the work should be fed by hand, otherwise the tool will quickly wear away and the work may be ruined. Chasing outside threads is done with large diamond-charged wheels that are much more durable and capable of taking heavier cuts.

# CHAPTER 7

# *Faceted Stones*

## STYLES OF CUTTING

THE majority of gem minerals may be found in beautiful prismatic crystals, some of which exhibit a marked degree of regularity with uniform brilliant faces. They are rarely mounted in their natural state but require the art of the lapidary to develop their true beauty, brilliance, and fire or play of color. As most faceted gems are transparent, the function of the polished facets is to increase the brilliance of the stone by taking advantage of the optical properties of the mineral to develop to a maximum its intrinsic beauty. As a result, faceted stones may be seen in an infinite variety of styles of cutting, from the simplest form to the most complex. Like cabochon stones, they may possess any geometrical outline having a girdle edge which is bounded on both sides by planes of varying sizes called facets.

To achieve the best results, the stone should be perfect, free from flaws and inclusions of any kind. Opaque stones also are cut with facets to obtain special effects, the simplest and most common form of which is the table-cut onyx, sard, or bloodstone commonly used for rings (Figs. 7–1 to 7–4). This form consists of a flat top and back having single or double bevel edges. The stone may have any geometrical outline as circular, elliptical, square, or rectangular. In the single-bevel table cut, the slant bevel edge extends from the table or top of the stone to the back, the included angle of the girdle edge with the back being 80 deg. or less. In the double-bevel table cut, two bevel facets are cut, extending from the front and back of the stone respectively. Both bevels meet at the girdle edge, the included angle being approximately 160 deg. or less. The upper facet may vary in size from one quarter to one half the thickness of the stone. In the majority of cases, the back portion of the stone is about twice the thickness of the front portion.

As a general rule, opaque stones faceted in the table cut are polished on one surface only, which is always the front of the stone. The double

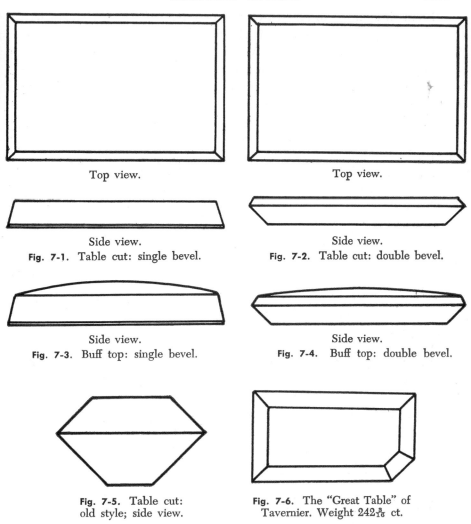

Top view.

Top view.

Side view.

Side view.

**Fig. 7-1.** Table cut: single bevel.

**Fig. 7-2.** Table cut: double bevel.

Side view.

Side view.

**Fig. 7-3.** Buff top: single bevel.

**Fig. 7-4.** Buff top: double bevel.

**Fig. 7-5.** Table cut: old style; side view.

**Fig. 7-6.** The "Great Table" of Tavernier. Weight 242$\frac{3}{16}$ ct.

bevel or table cut is the basic form from which all faceted stones having a girdle are developed. The form is old, having been developed from the octahedron, two opposite points of which were ground and polished (Fig. 7–5), the upper to a flat broad facet normal to the vertical axis of the crystal, the lower to a much smaller facet. Occasionally, flattened octahedrons or cleavages were found which, when polished, produced double-beveled forms of large size. The "Great Table" of Tavernier, a diamond cut in this form, is a notable example. The weight of this stone was 242$\frac{3}{16}$ ct. (Fig. 7–6).

From this simple form, two classes or groups of faceted stones have been developed. The one series is characterized by forms having straight-line girdle edges, the outline of which is some simple geometrical form, as square, rectangular, or octagon. The second series is characterized by forms often complex, having rounded or conical surfaces, upon which are polished series or rows of facets. The girdle edge usually is circular or curved. Thus, throughout the two series, it is a simple matter to trace the development of faceted stones.

In the majority of cases, where table-cut stones of small size are in use today, the back facet meets in a point if the stone has a square form, or in a ridge if the stone is rectangular (Fig. 7–7). The point also may be flattened slightly to form a small facet. This point, ridge, or flat facet, which is called the *culet* in a properly cut stone, should be seen directly opposite the center of the table when the stone is viewed with transmitted light. Table-cut stones usually are square or rectangular in shape.

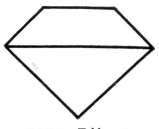

**Fig. 7-7.** Table cut: modern; side view.

In Figure 7–8, the different parts of a faceted stone are named. The large plane surface on the front of the stone is called the *table*, the facets sloping from the table to the girdle edge are the *main facets*, and the entire front of the stone is the *crown*. The girdle edge or widest part of the stone divides it into two portions. The back facets extending from the girdle edge also are called *main facets*, the small facet or flattened point is called the *culet*, and the entire back portion of the stone is the *pavilion*.

With the double-bevel table cut as the basic form, many simple-faceted

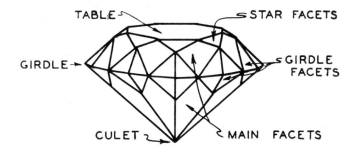

**Fig. 7-8.** Names applied to facets on a gem.

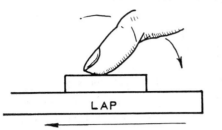

Fig. 7-53.
Taper cause by poor
control in lapping.

ducing flat surfaces is somewhat more difficult than lapping surfaces of large area, for the small size increases the difficulty of holding. In the lapping process, the tendency is to produce a slightly convex surface, and considerable practice is required to be able to correct this fault.

While the stone is being lapped, it should be turned from time to time so that the lapping action on the stone is uniform from all directions. If the stone were held in one position, a greater amount would be ground off on that portion of the stone which received the initial grinding action of the lap, as shown in Figure 7–53. The result would be a wedge-shaped stone. This can be prevented by turning as previously stated or by exerting greater pressure on the stone at a point farthest away from the point of initial grinding. This method, however, requires considerable practice and experience, parallel lapping being more difficult to produce. After one surface has been lapped flat, the stone is removed, and the opposite side is lapped flat and parallel to the first side. Although some difficulty might be experienced, every effort should be exerted to lap the stone as flat as possible so that both sides are parallel. The stone should be properly held on the lap and carefully controlled so that the necessary accuracy is secured. The parallel jaws of a caliper square may be used to check the accuracy of the lapped surfaces (Fig. 6–23).

Obviously, if a flat, accurately sawed slab is to be lapped, little difficulty is experienced in producing flat surfaces ready for polishing. For fast lapping, fresh abrasive grain is constantly applied to the lap, and finish lapping is done with the lap cleared of surplus grain and used wet only.

After the flat stone has been lapped in a satisfactory manner, it is cemented to a lap stick for convenience in further handling. The lap sticks used for faceting are similar to those used in cabochon work, but they usually are made of a harder, close-grained wood. Lap sticks for faceting, made of "Mexican Rosewood" (cocobolo) are ideal. Cement used for holding stones in facet work should be harder and tougher

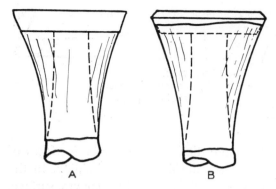

Fig. 7-54.
Table-cut stones
cemented for shaping and
sizing: A, single bevel back
up; B, double bevel front up.

than that used for cabochon cuts, as the stone must be firmly secured
so that it will not bend on the stick if it becomes warmed by friction
in the polishing process.

As a general rule, faceted stones are cemented front up and the top
of the stones are finished first. The only exceptions to this rule are
table-cut stones that have a single bevel, and faceted stones with irregular forms, if it is necessary to fit these into bezels where the shape or
form of the stone would be reversed if the front were finished first. In
such cases, the back of the stone is uppermost and the stone is cut to
fit the bezel. The stone then is reversed and finished in the usual manner.

Both types of table cuts, single and double, should be tried, preferably
together. The stones, when properly roughed out and cemented to the
lap sticks, will appear as shown in Figure 7–54. The steps outlined for
cementing should be observed.

Sizing stones on the lap is a simple grinding process. The operator
should be seated before the lap bench in a comfortable position (Fig.
4–26) and at a suitable height so that the forearms may rest on the edge
of the lap bench without strain or fatigue. The lap stick is held by the
first three fingers of the hand which grasp the stick near the cemented
stone. The pointed end of the stick rests on the fleshy part of the palm
of the hand adjacent to and opposite the thumb (Fig. 7–55).

The first and third fingers are opposite each other holding the stick
and, during the lapping of the stone, they are in a position parallel to the
lap surface. The index or second finger should be on top of the stick to
control the pressure. In lapping very small stones, the index finger should
rest on the stone itself in order to counteract the leverage exerted in
lapping for, if too great pressure is exerted, the small stone may break
off the lap stick (Fig. 7–55).

When the lap stick is held in the proper position, the facet being

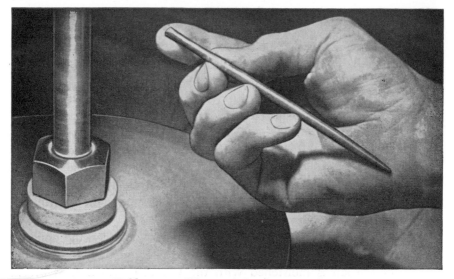

Fig. 7-55. Holding a small lap stick for shaping and sizing a stone.

ground is directly opposite the index finger and in the same plane as the first and third fingers. This position is of the greatest importance for, through the correct holding of the stone, facets may be placed at any point upon the surface of the stone, at the will of the operator. The same method of holding is used in faceting, and the operator should learn to hold the lap stick in such a manner that when the stone is touched on the lap, the required facet is ground at will.

In placing the stone upon the lap, the girdle of the stone should be as near as possible at a right angle to the direction of the lap travel at the point of contact with the lap. That is, it should be at a position on the lap where the pull or lapping action is directly away from the stone (as near as possible) and in line with the lap stick, the latter being held so that its center line is parallel to the lap surface (Fig. 6–27).

Should the stone be placed on the lap in any other position, difficulty will be experienced in maintaining a true lapped surface, for the tendency will be for the stone to tilt or turn on the surface of the lap. Holding the stick parallel to the lap surface also will cause the edge of the stone to be lapped square with the surface of the stone, which is important if the stone is to be cut to a definite size (Fig. 7–56). The lap stick should not be tilted so that its surface becomes ground from contact with the lap.

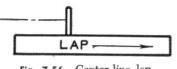

Fig. 7-56. Center-line lap stick parallel to lap.

During lapping, the stone should be passed over the surface of the lap so that all portions of the lap surface are brought into use, maintaining the trueness of the surface as long as possible. Lapping on one section of the lap will develop a hollow surface, and ultimately the lap will require truing as prescribed. An alternative method of lapping to size or shaping is to alter the position of the lap stick by 90 deg. to that described so that the girdle edge of the stone is in the plane of the operator and the spindle (Fig. 6–28). Although this method is more cumbersome, the operator is able to observe the grinding or lapping action by tilting his head to one side and by observing the point of contact with the lap surface. Thus, the stone may be accurately shaped although a greater amount of reliance is placed upon sight control and less upon the sense of touch.

Having ground one edge or side in a satisfactory manner, the opposite side is placed on the lap and ground similarly. From time to time, the surface of the lap is moistened with the wet abrasive-charged brush, using a moderate supply. With each application, the stone should be lifted, or else the surplus abrasive, which is thrown off the wheel, will strike the hand and cover it with grit which may cause discomfort and loss of control in the lapping.

The second side of the stone is then ground parallel to the first one, and the accuracy is checked with the parallel jaws of the caliper square (Fig. 6–23). Should the two sides be slightly out of parallel, the stone is placed on the lap and greater pressure is exerted toward the portion of the stone of greater thickness (Fig. 7–57). The tendency for the lap to grind a stone tapered is one that has caused some confusion and difficulty to lapidaries. This action is caused by the different surface speeds across the surface of the lap, by the position of the stone on the surface of the lap, by the turning action of the lap on the stone itself, and by the unequal pressure on the stone through the lap stick.

To correct a tapered stone, greater pressure should be exerted radially

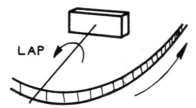

**Fig. 7-57.** Twisting effort to correct taper.

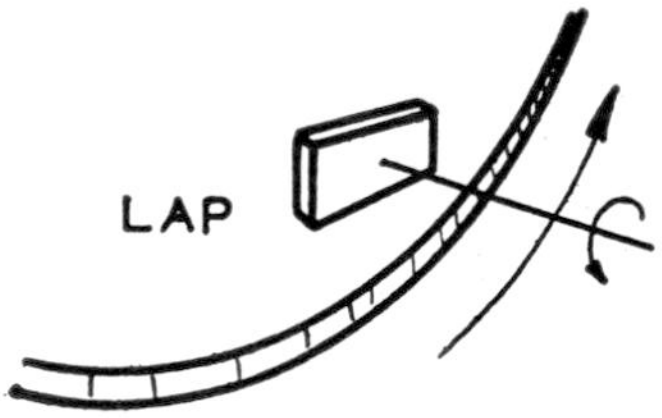

**Fig. 7-58.** Alternate method correcting taper.

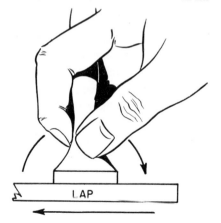

**Fig. 7-59.**
Lapping stone cemented to lap
stick. Pull of lap causes tilting of
stock resulting in tapered stone.

on the lap stick (Fig. 7–57), the direction of the lap rotation being away from the stone or in line with the lap stick. This same control may be attained by placing the stone on the lap in different positions. Thus, the stone in Figure 7–57, if placed on the lap in the position shown in Figure 7–58, will tend to turn in the direction indicated and a greater amount of material will be removed from the left portion or thick side. Cemented stones that require lapping are treated in a similar manner (Fig. 7–59). In lapping to a definite size, greater care is necessary, and the size and shape of the stone are checked every few moments.

After both sides have been lapped parallel, one end (the third side) is finished at a right angle. A square is used to check (Fig. 6–29, or millimeter gauge, Fig. 6–23), after which the fourth side is similarly lapped. All sides then will be square. After a little practice, a number of stones may be lapped to size within close limits without difficulty, the usual tolerance being .1 mm.

Lapping and sizing of the double table-cut stone is similar in every respect to that of the single-bevel table cut. After the latter has been sized correctly, the sharp edge formed by the side and the back is beveled slightly at an angle of 45 deg. as a safety edge, as prescribed for cabochon stones. This edge, however, should be very slight.

The stone then is reversed on the lap stick. Care must be exercised to set the stone square with the stick, after which the front side is finished. In its present setup (front of the stone uppermost), it is now similar to the double-bevel table-cut stone.

The next step is to cut the bevel edge or facet. While it is possible to lap or grind a single facet with a fair degree of accuracy freehand and without a mechanical support, precision and the correct facet angle can be attained only through the use of a rest or lap-stick holder.

For this purpose the simple back rest or jamb peg will serve admirably although, if preferred, the lap stick may be held in a mechanical holder. In using the back rest, the radial position of the facets is controlled by the hand, and the angular position, slope, or inclination of the facets is controlled by means of the back rest. The pointed end of the lap stick is placed in a hole near the bottom of the back rest to produce facets having steep inclination with respect to the table. By inserting the end of the lap stick in higher series of holes, the resulting facets become less steeply inclined (Fig. 7–60).

Thus, through proper holding of the lap stick radially and with respect to the pointed end, vertically, facets may be placed at any point or position on the surface of the stone. In faceting by hand, the lap stick, which is first properly oriented (A, Fig. 7–60), is held in the same manner as described in lapping and sizing. When the stone is placed upon the lap, the point or surface being ground is always opposite the forefinger. Furthermore, with respect to lapping the facets, the stone should be placed on the lap at a point where the lap travel is directly away from the stone, the direction of rotation of the lap also being away from the stone (Figs. 7–60 and 7–61). The same rules apply in faceting as in sizing. Departing from this rule in faceting will cause difficulty in controlling the action of the lap upon the stone, for the pull of the wheel will cause the stone to tilt or turn. As far as possible, the stone should describe a small arc on the surface of the lap, and it should not be held constantly in one position because this would result in grinding a hollow in the surface

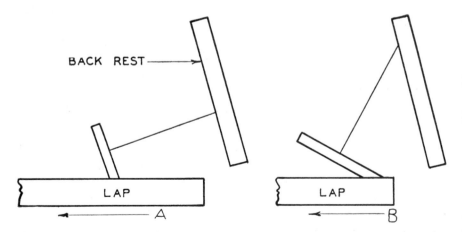

BACK REST

LAP     A

LAP     B

**Fig. 7-60.** Angularity of bevel edge or facet controlled by position of lap stick.

Fig. 7-61. Faceting a large stone on a pewter lap.

of the lap. The same rules apply to faceting with a mechanical head.

A fresh charge of grit is applied to the surface of the lap to grind away the bulk of the facet. As the facet approaches maximum development, the charge is brushed off the wheel using a wet brush, and the final cutting is done with the embedded charge in the lap which results in a smooth flat facet. From time to time, the development of the facet is observed after a few seconds of grinding, depending on the size of the facet. Should the facet tend to become ground tapered, this error is corrected by a gentle pressure toward the higher point. While the facet is being lapped, the operator's undivided attention should be given to the work. If one of the facets should become overdeveloped through careless handling, it may be necessary to recut the entire series or even reshape the stone. Mechanical heads, if accurately made, require little attention after the stone has been correctly set up. Should the stone become ground tapered, the error may be corrected as shown in Figure 7–57 by a slight radial movement or adjustment of the lap stick in the facet head, or through a compensating device integral with it. After the first facet has been fully and evenly developed, a small edge is left on the side near the girdle to protect the stone, so that its size and shape will not become altered during cutting and polishing, and to prevent the forming of a thin knife edge which is always subject to the danger of chipping, during the setting process (Figs. 7–1 and 7–62).

**Fig. 7-62.**
Side view of single-bevel table cut.

During faceting, the lap stick should be held firmly in position in the hole in the back rest so that the pull of the lap upon the stone will not drag the stick out of position.

Following the completion of the initial facet, the rest of the facets which surround the stone are finished in like manner. On stones which are bounded by long, straight lines, square, or rectangular, the facets are lapped successively until the series has been completed. Irregular octagon forms, commonly seen, are best treated by lapping the long facets first. The usual procedure is to lap opposite facets — first the sides and then to finish the corners. On stones bounded by a circular or curved girdle, a single facet may bound the stone (Fig. 7–49). Sometimes the border is divided into a number of facets, in which case the stone is treated like a brilliant-cut stone (Figs. 7–50 and 7–51).

Faceting of the double table-cut stone is done in a similar manner. However, the front or crown facet as a general rule extends only one third of the thickness of the stone, and this forms a girdle edge which divides the stone into two portions, the lower portion or pavilion being twice the depth or thickness of the upper portion or crown. Occasionally, the girdle edge may divide the stone into two equal portions, the facet development on both sides being equal.

The facets on the front of the double-bevel table cut should be cut the required width and uniformity. The facets then are polished, the stone is reversed, and the back facets are cut with the same degree of inclination, leaving a slight edge (Fig. 7–2). In regular commercial work, the back facets of opaque or semitranslucent stones are rarely polished. On translucent varieties of quartz, however, the back facets should be polished for this greatly increases the brilliancy of the stone. The back facets of the double-bevel table cut may be extended to meet in a point at the culet and sometimes may have two or more rows according to the size of the stone. Table-cut stones, polished in this manner, are popular as ring stones. As the broad table surface sometimes is used for engraving, these stones occasionally are referred to as seal stones. This type of stone is roughed out, shaped, and treated in the same manner as the double-bevel cut and, if the stone is transparent, the back of the stone is not ground flat but it is developed into a pointed dome. After the stone has been sized and the front finished, the stone is reversed upon the lap stick and the back facets are cut. The large facet adjoining the girdle edge is cut as previously described, being careful not to cut through the edge. All facets about the stone are cut in a uniform manner, after which they are polished (Fig. 7–7).

The step cut (Fig. 7–9), which is a simple modification of the table cut, differs only in the number of step facets placed on the stone. This form usually is applied to transparent gemstones, but on occasion, to obtain artistic effects, opaque stones also may be cut in this manner. In cutting and polishing step-cut forms, the beginner and the experienced lapidary become acquainted with the importance of proportion and its effect upon the brilliance and beauty of the stone.

Through long experience, the lapidary has learned that, to obtain the best results in a faceted stone, to obtain maximum brilliancy, and to develop its full beauty, the stone must be properly proportioned so that light entering the front of the stone is reflected from the back facets.

As a general rule, faceted transparent stones are cut to definite proportions as to length, width, and thickness, and the slope or inclination of the main facets varies slightly for stones of different species. Correct proportion and the proper inclination of the facets are of the greatest importance in stones having circular girdles. In general, a properly proportioned, transparent, faceted stone has about one third of its total thickness above the girdle edge and about two thirds of its total thickness below it. Thus, the back portion or pavilion is twice the thickness of the front portion or crown. The total thickness of the stone, from the table to the culet, is approximately four fifths of the width of the stone. The top flat surface, called the table, usually is from 40 to 50 per cent of the width of the stone. In rectangular or oblong stones, the table is elongated.

In the step cut, there is no fixed rule for the number of facets used. The usual practice, in stones weighing three carats or less, is to apply two rows of facets on the front of the stone and from two to three rows of facets on the back portion (Fig. 7–9). Stones weighing over three carats usually have a greater number of step facets, particularly on the back where four or more rows of step facets may be placed.

In cutting stones of this type, the same technique is used as that described in the cutting of table-cut stones. However, the stone must be roughed out to conform to the specifications prescribed.

For the first attempt at faceting a transparent stone, rock crystal is particularly suitable; it is hard and fairly durable, and when finished and properly cut and polished, it possesses a fine degree of brilliance. As the material is inexpensive, errors and mistakes which are bound to occur will not be costly. A piece of rock crystal, free of flaws, that will cut into a stone about 12 by 16 mm., should be used. This will enable the operator to exercise greater control over the cutting of the facets than if a smaller stone were used. The flat table surface is ground first, after which the stone is roughed to shape and near the size desired, and the crown or front, as well as the pavilion or back of the stone, is given a slightly curved shape as shown in Figure 7–63. The table of the stone then is lapped flat on a pewter lap with abrasive and, by removing the surplus grain and wetting the lap only, a fine finish is readily attained.

The stone then is cemented to a lap stick, with the table uppermost. The position of the stone is controlled by molding the cement with the fingers as described in cementing, and the stone is mounted squarely and truly on the stick. While the skilled lapidary is able to mount these stones squarely and truly without any trouble and with a minimum expenditure of time, the beginner may experience some difficulty. To facilitate accurate mounting, a mounting jig designed by the writer may be used, as shown in Figure 7–64. This unit consists of a hollow chucking member into which the lap stick is placed and secured. A column parallel to the chucking member, having a graduated right-angle sliding unit, is used to check the accuracy and truth of the setting.

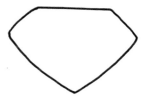

Fig. 7-63. Cross section of step cut roughed out.

The lap stick, secured in the chucking member by means of a split chuck at the upper end and centered by the point in the lower end, may be rotated in the chucking member column support. Thus, the squareness may be checked from all positions.

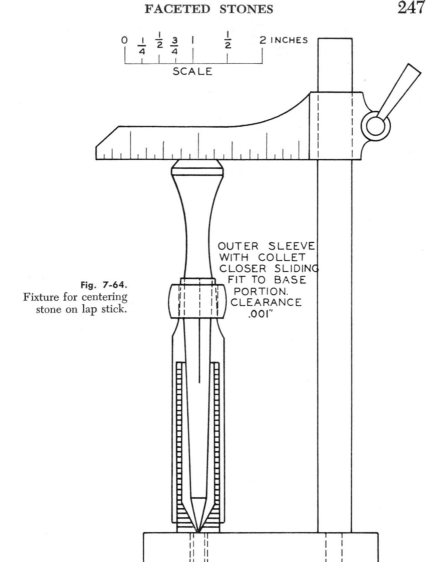

0 $\frac{1}{4}$ $\frac{1}{2}$ $\frac{3}{4}$ 1 $\frac{1}{2}$ 2 INCHES

SCALE

OUTER SLEEVE
WITH COLLET
CLOSER SLIDING
FIT TO BASE
PORTION.
CLEARANCE
.001"

**Fig. 7-64.**
Fixture for centering
stone on lap stick.

After the cement has cooled and set, the stone is sized and the facets are lapped as previously described under table-cut stones. In small, step-cut stones, as a rule, only two steps are cut, the main facet or larger step being cut at the required angle. A trial cut is made with the lap stick held at an angle approximately correct, the inclination being judged by the eye. The matching facet opposite then is developed in a similar manner. Both facets are checked with a contact goniometer and, if necessary, proper adjustment is made by raising or lowering the pointed end of the lap stick until the facet being cut corresponds to the correct angle. Care is necessary to prevent overcutting, which would develop the facets so large that the table would be too narrow. The proper proportion is attained when the table is just a little over half the width of the stone. The end facets are cut next, in a manner similar to the side facets. The appearance of the stone at this stage resembles a regular table-cut stone (Fig. 7–7). Although the stone chosen for the first attempt at step cutting is large for this style of cutting, and would ordinarily be cut with three steps, two steps only should be cut. The final step is cut by raising the pointed end of the lap stick to a higher position (Fig. 7–60) and lapping in the customary manner. As a general rule, this second step facet is about one half the width of the first step or main facet and, when fully developed, the table is a little less than one half the width of the stone. It is important to maintain the greatest degree of accuracy in the lapping of the main facets in round stones (circular girdles) to the correct angle or inclination, depending upon the refractive index of the stone. But, with the step-cut stone having a number of facets in series, three or more less steeply inclined, it is impossible to conform to this rule, and a special treatment is followed. Thus, in light-tinted stones, the first or main facet which extends from the girdle may be lapped at an angle greater than that recommended; the second facet less steeply inclined is lapped to the correct angle, and the third facet adjoining the table is lapped at an angle less than normal. Thus, for light-colored stones, the plane from the girdle edge to the table edge is at the angle prescribed.

On medium-colored or tinted stones, the main facet is cut at the prescribed angle, and successive facets are less steeply inclined, while on dark stones, by reason of the absorption of light, the facets are lapped at an angle less than that recommended. This practice, to a lesser degree, is followed as well in lapping the back facets of the stone. Although it is of greater importance to maintain the back facets at the proper angles, less divergence from the ideal is permissible. The front of the stone is cut and polished, and then the stone is reversed upon the lap stick and the back is treated in like manner. The proper inclination of the facet is maintained by the position of the pointed end of the lap stick in the back rest or jamb peg, if the stones are hand cut, and by the position of the yoke on the column if a faceting machine is used. Inclination of the facets may be checked quickly and accurately by a contact goniometer.

After the beginner has finished several stones in this manner, other forms, such as the emerald cut (octagon-shaped step cut, Fig. 7–10), should be attempted and, with increasing skill, other varieties of stones should be tried. Few stones can equal in quality the various types of beryl for this work. It is hard and durable and possesses a fine uniform grain, and it is one of the easiest stones to polish.

In the emerald cut (Fig. 7–10), the long side facets are cut first; these are followed by the end facets; and finally the corner facets complete the series. As a general rule, opposite steps in the same series of facets are cut about the stone and, if two steps or series of facets are used, the main or girdle-edge facet is broader than the facet next to the table. In large stones, where three or more series of facets are lapped, the width of the facets may be equal for all series, or they may be progressively narrower from the girdle to the table. As a general rule, the facet adjoining the table is the narrowest.

The French cut (Fig. 7–13) is similar to the faceted-back table cut, but it has a slight modification which consists of an additional series of facets placed about the table, and the stone is treated as prescribed for the table cut. For the first attempt, a square stone should be cut, for the corner facets will then be equally spaced about the axis of the stone. After roughing and sizing, the main facet is cut at the prescribed angle. Now, by raising the pointed end of the lap stick to a higher point in the back rest, and by rotating the lap stick, and holding it so that the pointed corner, formed by the table surface and two adjacent main facets, comes in contact with the lap, the top series of facets, four in number, are ground as indicated. The angle of inclination should be such that the newly developed triangular facet will meet the corner of the stone at the girdle edge in a point, and that the base opposite will cut the corner of the table equally (Fig. 7–13). When finished, the table surface will be square, and with respect to its original position, it will have been rotated on the axis of the stone 45 deg. The remaining facets are cut successively in 2-3-4 order, after which they are polished. The back facets are step cut and usually there are two or three rows or series of facets. Other shapes are shown in Figure 7–14.

A simple modification of the French cut is sometimes seen in which the table forms an octagon (Fig. 7–15), and the corner facets are less prominently developed. The base or table side, opposite the corner at the girdle, is developed to a length equal to the length of the side facet where it joins the table, thus forming an octagon-shaped table. This type of cutting is frequently seen in small square diamonds.

The Cardinal cut (Fig. 7–16) is similar to the French cut, but the top series of facets, eight in number, produce an eight-sided table. After the main facets have been lapped, the eight corner facets are cut in a manner similar to the French cut. Two facets, however, are cut in place of the single corner facet in the former case; otherwise the stone is finished in a similar manner. The Cardinal cut is commonly applied to small square diamonds and only infrequently in colored stones. The French cut is almost exclusively used for caliber stones.

The crosscut (Fig. 7–17) is a common form, with straight sides, and it is used on a great variety of stones. To produce this form, the stone is faceted with two series of facets in step form (A, Fig. 7–65). The angle of the lap stick then is altered to a point midway between the position required to lap the two steps. By a slight radial movement, the lap stick then is held in this position, and the corner, which is formed by the inter-section of the four side facets, is held to the lap and a triangular facet is developed (B, Fig. 7–65). Considerable care and delicacy of

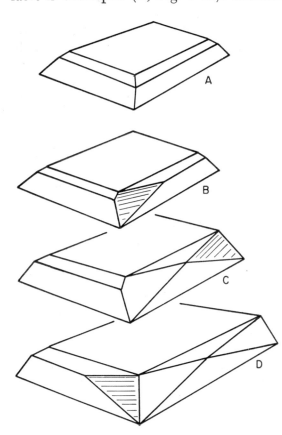

Fig. 7-65.
Progressive stages in cutting crosscut. First is the step cut followed by cutting corner facets.

touch are required to develop the facet in the correct position, by giving the lap stick enough radial movement to develop each triangular facet evenly. One side of this facet extends from the girdle to the table, and the point opposite this side divides the two step facets into equal parts. All four triangular facets may be lapped in a similar manner, the angularity of all being equal in a square stone. After completion of the four corner facets, the adjoining or mating facets are lapped in a similar manner, taking care to obtain the correct amount of angularity.

In a correctly cut stone, all of the triangular-shaped facets in the same series will be of equal size and the corners will meet in points.

The shapes most commonly used for the crosscut are the rectangle and the octagon (rectangular-cut corner). In the latter shape the position of the facets shows a Maltese cross (Fig. 7–19). In the elongated octagon shape, the corner may be treated in various ways. A single triangular-shaped facet produces a rectangular-shaped table (Fig. 7–19); two triangular facets in step form, with their apexes joined, form a table having an octagon shape (Fig. 7–20); and the side cross facets are not triangular but become quadrilateral. Another alternative is to apply the same style

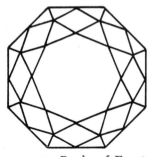

of cutting to the corners as appears at the sides (Fig. 7–21). Thus, the crosscut in an octagon shape may have 32 facets disposed about it between table and girdle. In the regular hexagon or octagon shape having equally developed sides, this is an interesting example of lapidary work. One large diamond of octagon form, the Pascha of Egypt (Fig. 7–66), which weighs 48 ct., has been cut in a similar manner.

**Fig. 7-66.** Pascha of Egypt.

The same principle of crosscut facets may be applied to larger stones and these may have three or four series or rows of facets (Fig. 7–18). The procedure in every case is the same; the required number of steps are cut in series about the stone and the crosscutting or lapping of the corner facet progresses from row to row. The back facets of all crosscut stones may be cut in the usual step cut, or a modification similar to the front facets may be applied (Fig. 7–17). In the modification, additional diagonal facets less steeply inclined are cut in place of the step facets, gradually reducing in size and in number until they meet in a point or edge at the culet. The main facets adjoining the girdle edge are lapped first, with care to develop all uniformly so that the girdle edge is of the same thickness about the stone. The large cross facets then are cut (Fig. 7–17) by turning the lap stick slightly, holding it in this position and holding the lap stick at a steeper angle. Facets of a similar type or position on the stone opposite mates may be cut in regular order which is the best procedure to follow if a mechanical holder is used. Or, if the hand method is used, the lapping of right- and left-hand facets in the same series may be preferred. The remaining series of facets, less steeply inclined, are cut in like manner and are either parallel to or at an angle to the main facets.

The lens cut (Fig. 7–22) is effective and is usually applied to rectangular-shaped stones. The stone is roughed out in the usual manner, the top surface is ground in a cylindrical form, and the ends are almost straight. After truing and sizing on the lap, the facets adjoining the girdle at the ends of the stone are usually cut at an angle not less than 80 deg. with the plane of the girdle. Sometimes the end facets are not beveled.

The remaining long facets, extending from side to side, are less steeply inclined and they are cut in a manner similar to the regular step cut. Considerable skill is necessary to develop the top facets evenly and at the same time to maintain proper symmetry. The facets near the top of the stone are the most difficult to cut because of the nearly vertical position of the lap stick. After the front of the stone has been finished, the back facets are step cut in the usual manner. The lens cut sometimes is applied to cylindrical forms on which facets are uniformly disposed around the surface. The stone is drilled lengthwise for suspension as a bead or as a drop, or it may be partly drilled on the ends and suspended from a swivel. Stones of this type are ground and lapped to a true cylinder, and the facets then are lapped as already prescribed. It will be necessary to reset the stone several times in order to develop the facets evenly about the cylindrical surface. Stones of this type usually have the ends faceted, in which case the cylinder is set concentric on the lap stick. The end facets then may be lapped in the manner prescribed for round stones.

There are many modifications or combinations of the conventional forms and in every case the principle of cutting is similar.

The single cut (Fig. 7–25), which is the simplest form of the round (circular) faceted stone, that is, a faceted stone having a circular girdle, has one series of facets which extend from the girdle to the table and a matching series directly opposite which extends from the girdle edge to meet in a point at the culet. This latter facet is absent in all small stones.

Although single-cut stones usually are small, for the first attempt at faceting a round stone of this type, the diameter of the stone should not be less than 10 mm. This will enable the operator to develop the facets to better advantage, for the facets will be of moderate size and a greater degree of control may be possible. A suitable material should be selected, and for this purpose rock crystal is excellent. A low-grade aquamarine or beryl is even better, and the slight additional cost is negligible. The aquamarine has a fine uniform grain and it is one of the easiest stones to polish. In a first attempt at polishing, this factor is of great importance to success. In roughing out the stone, it is customary to grind a flat surface for the table. The stone should be ground as circular as possible, and then, opposite the flat side, a conical form should be ground, leaving a slight wall adjacent to the flat surface between the flat table and the cone (Fig. 7–67), or, if desired, the slight wall may be beveled as shown at A, Figure 7–68. The included angle of the cone should be approximately 100 deg. The flat surface then is lapped on a pewter lap with fine abrasive or with a wetted lap charged with abrasive. The stone then is cleaned and mounted accurately on a lap stick. The circular contour is rounded or lapped on the horizontal lap (Fig. 6–46). An alternative method, using a vertical rotating lap and working on the lap face, permits the operator to view the work being ground (Fig. 6–25) requires less skill and is somewhat more rapid.

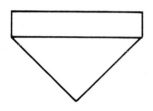

**Fig. 7-67.** Cross section of single cut roughed out for small stones.

If a large number of stones having circular girdles are to be cut at one time, a rounding jig will facilitate handling and at the same time produce true, accurately formed pieces in a minimum of time. A fixture of this type (Fig. 7–69), designed and built by the author, consists of a chucking unit into which the lap stick may be placed and held securely. A circular template on the body of the tool serves as a guide, and an adjustable stop enables the operator to fix the tool so that any desired diameter may be lapped. In using this tool, the stone must be cemented concentric with the lap stick in order to avoid excessive grinding and loss of material.

In like manner, all mechanical faceting tools in which the quill or dividing unit is permanently fastened to the yoke permit the ready shaping and sizing of the gemstone by properly adjusting the height of the unit with respect to the lap surface. Gemstones having circular girdles are readily formed, and by proper indexing any geometrical outline permitted by the number of divisions in the index may be accu-

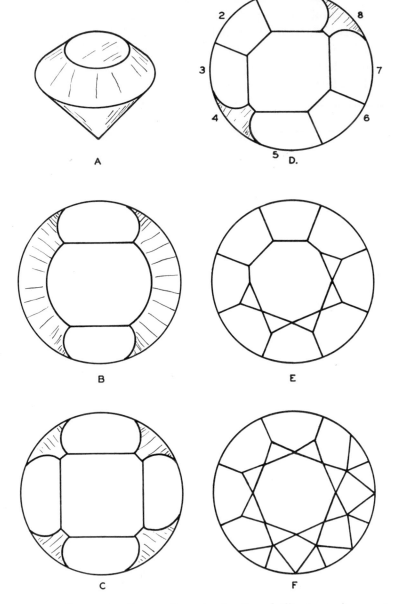

**Fig. 7-68.** Sequence of operations in faceting brilliant-cut forms: A, roughed-table lapped flat. Top views: B, opposite main facets cut parallel; C, four main facets with table squared; D, two diagonal main facets cut; E, cutting star facets; F, cutting girdle facets.

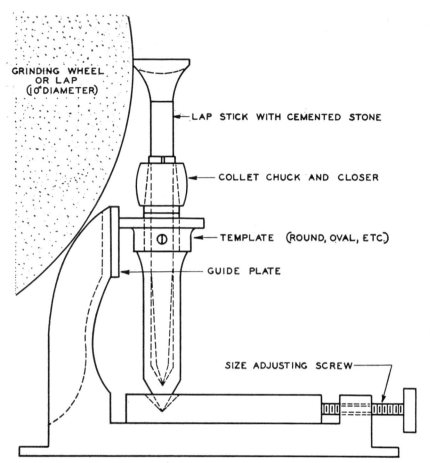

GRINDING WHEEL
OR LAP
(10" DIAMETER)

LAP STICK WITH CEMENTED STONE

COLLET CHUCK AND CLOSER

TEMPLATE (ROUND, OVAL, ETC.)

GUIDE PLATE

SIZE ADJUSTING SCREW

**Fig. 7-69.** Design of adjustable fixture for holding lap stick in the sizing and shaping of stones. Removable template permits use in grinding various outlines.

rately formed. Stones having oval and elliptical outlines, however, must be shaped by hand unless a fixture as illustrated in Figure 7–69 is used.

Templates of other shapes — square, rectangular, oval — also may be used in place of the round one. Stone shapes thus will be produced to match the template used. In rounding or shaping and sizing small stones of any type, 3 mm. diameter or less, care in handling is necessary in order to prevent the small stones from breaking off the lap stick. By a delicacy of touch and by being properly supported, the stone may be lapped in an efficient manner. In sizing very small stones on a horizontal lap, the forefinger should rest upon the stone, and the lap stick should be manipulated by the thumb and third finger. When sizing, shaping, and lapping on a wheel rotating in a vertical plane, the stone is pressed against the face of the wheel, and is supported by the thumb (Fig. 6–25).

After the stone has been rounded, the crown facets are lapped at the proper angle which varies several degrees according to the refractive index of the stone. Elaborate calculations have been made to ascertain the angle at which the front and back slopes should be cut to develop the maximum brilliance in a stone. Although authorities differ widely, the following figures, determined from practice, will give excellent results. It must be remembered, however, that these figures apply only to light-hued or tinted stones for it is common practice to cut all dark-colored stones with facets less steeply inclined. The angle noted is formed by the plane of the main facet with the plan of the girdle.

### TABLE 10.   INCLINATION OF THE MAIN FACETS ON GEM STONES ACCORDING TO THE REFRACTIVE INDEX

| Refractive index | Crown | Pavilion |
| --- | --- | --- |
| 1.50 to 1.60 | 42° | 43° |
| 1.61 to 1.70 | 40° | 43° |
| 1.71 to 1.80 | 37° | 42° |
| 1.81 to 1.92 | 43° | 40° |
| 2.42 | 35° | 41° |
| 2.62 to 2.90 | 32° | 41° |

The specifications apply to stones that are colorless or of medium tint, and to stones having single facets which extend from the girdle edge to the table. These stones have circular girdles, or they may have a regular geometrical outline — square, octagonal, hexagonal. On stones of ir-regular shape, with two or more series of facets and of dark hue, the crown facets may vary considerably. The degree of variance is largely a matter of personal opinion. Many dark-hued stones, such as almandine, ruby, sapphire, etc., have been checked where the crown facets were cut at angles less than 20 and sometimes 15 deg. A few degrees variance of the crown angle is less important than the angles on the pavilion.

On small stones, like those upon which the single cut is used, the facets usually are lapped on the stone directly after rounding, while on larger stones the surplus material on the crown may be ground off in the form of a truncated cone before the facets have been cut.

To cut the facets on a stone, the lap stick is held in the hand as pre-viously described (Fig. 7–70). With the pointed end of the lap stick in a hole in the back rest, the stone is brought in contact with the surface of the rotating lap, and a facet is ground (Fig. 7–61). If a mechanical head

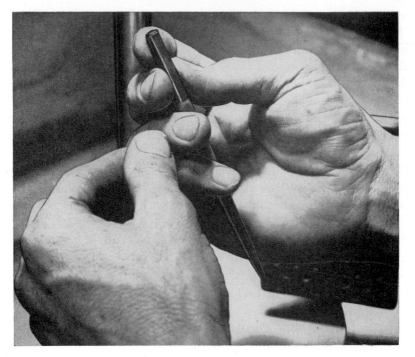

Fig. 7-70. Lap stick properly held.

is used, the lap stick is held in the chuck or other holding unit provided for this purpose and is fixed at the proper angle to cut the crown facets.

The angularity of the top facets is checked with a gauge or a contact goniometer after a trial cut has been made (Figs. 6–31 and 11–15). If the slope or inclination of the facet is too little or too great, the necessary vertical adjustment of the lap stick is made, the pointed end of which is either raised or lowered to give the desired slope. Similar adjustments are made in using mechanical faceting tools.

Facets are numbered in a clockwise manner. After the correct angle has been attained and facet No. 1 is well developed, the facet directly opposite, or No. 5, is cut so that it is equally developed and the edge at the table is parallel to the facet edge opposite. Both facets should be developed so that the table surface between them is about 50 per cent of the width of the stone (B, Fig. 7–68). Facets 3 and 7 then are cut. Care should be taken to develop them in a uniform manner so that all of the facets are equal in size. At this stage the table will be nearly square (C, Fig. 7–68). The four corner edges which are to be cut into facets are

treated in like manner, and opposite pairs of facets are cut. Thus, in
D, Figure 7–68, facets 2 and 6 are finished (in counterclockwise direction), and these are followed by 4 and 8. In faceting by hand, care and
skill are required to space the facets correctly so that when finished all
eight facets will be of equal size and shape, and in radial position they
will be equally disposed about the axis. When finished, each facet will be
spaced at regular intervals of 45 deg. In using a faceting head or a mechanical device for controlling the radial position of the facets, the only
attention required is to be certain of proper indexing and to prevent overcutting the facets. After the front of the stone has been finished and polished, the stone is reversed upon the lap stick and the back facets are
finished. Before cementing the stone for cutting the back facets, the joining edges of the crown facets are marked on the girdle edge (Fig. 7–71).
A diamond point or scriber will serve admirably for marking, and the
light mark left by the point will not rub off. After the stone has been
cemented, these reference lines will show where the facets on the back
of the stone must be cut, for in good work, it is necessary that these
facets be properly positioned.

In cementing the stone for cutting the back facets, every effort should
be made to accurately center the stone on the lap stick and to see that
the girdle edge left exposed is square with the axis of the stick. Where
round stones only are to be cut, the lap stick may be made of metal
having a conical depression turned in the end, which will accurately
locate the stone when cemented. A number of sizes of sticks to correspond to the various sizes of stones will be required, for it is necessary
that the girdle edge be exposed at all times. Accurate centering is of the
greatest importance for, if the stone is off centered or inaccurately
mounted, the facets, when cut, will not be equally inclined and the
brilliance of the stone will suffer.

The back of the stone is treated in the same manner as the front. Two
opposite facets are cut and these are spaced so that the flat surface developed lies squarely between the lightly scribed lines on the girdle edge
(Fig. 7–71). Proper radial spacing is not difficult to attain in the hand
method and, if a mechanical faceting head is used, radial adjustment
should be provided for in the instrument. Should this refinement be
lacking, the necessary adjustment must be made manually. A trial cut
should be made on the pair of opposite facets and the included angle
checked with a gauge. The angle is readily determined, for the sum of
the three angles on the back of the stone — the two angles formed by
the plane of the girdle edge and the included angle at the culet — is

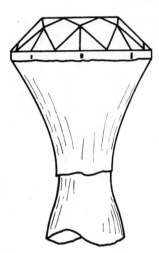

**Fig. 7-71.** Position of facets marked on edge of stone for accurate placing of back facets.

equal to 180 deg. Thus, if the back angle of the stone is to be 40 deg., the included angle of the culet will be $180 - (2 \times 40) = 100$ deg.

Having cut the pair of opposite facets so that they are properly spaced with reference to the scribed lines on the girdle edge (A, Fig. 7–72), and so that they are cut with the proper slope, leaving a slight wall or edge about one half mm., at the girdle edge, the remaining facets are cut in a similar manner (B and C, Fig. 7–72). When these facets have been finished, if the stone has been properly centered and truly mounted, the culet will be in the apex of the stone and all of the facets will be of equal size.

If the culet has been lapped to a sharp point, it is advisable to lap the small flat facet by holding the lap stick in a vertical position, touching the pointed end of the stone to the lap, thus developing the true culet facet. The purpose of this facet is to prevent the stone from chipping

**Fig. 7-72.**
Back views of sequence of operations in faceting brilliant cut: A, opposite main facets cut parallel; B, four main facets cut at 90 deg.; C, two diagonal main facets cut; D, cutting girdle facets.

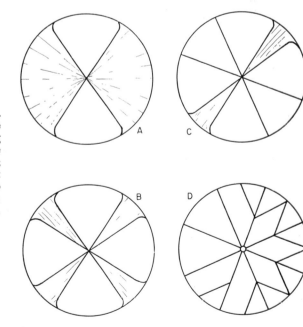

during polishing. Careless handling, the use of too coarse an abrasive, an improper lap or one which is neither true nor properly balanced, will also cause the facet edges or points to chip. Should serious chipping occur, it may be necessary to recut the stone. This can be prevented by using only moderate pressure as the facet nears maximum development, and by using the wet-charged lap, free of loose abrasive. This is not only advisable but necessary as well, for small stones are very rapidly cut away and constant attention to the work is necessary in order to control the cutting of the stone. The time required to lap to size a facet on a small stone may be only two or three seconds. Larger stones require a proportionally greater amount of time, particularly in lapping the main facets, and this depends on the closeness to size that the stone had been roughed out. As a rule, a greater amount of time is required to lap the back main facets because of the greater amount of material left for removal after the stone has been cut to size.

A style of cutting that may be readily developed from the single cut may be seen in the star cut (Fig. 7–26), sometimes called the English double cut. This style is frequently seen on small rubies and sapphires having circular or elliptical outlines. The stone is prepared in a manner similar to the single cut. Roughing, cementing, and finally lapping the first row of main facets to the prescribed angle follow in regular order. The second row of facets, more steeply inclined with respect to the plane of the girdle, is formed by executing a slight radial displacement. By placing the pointed end of the lap stick in one of a lower series of holes on the back rest, the stone is gently touched to the rotating lap so that a facet is developed at the point where two main facets join the girdle edge. The triangular girdle facet, thus formed, lies equidistant between the two adjoining main facets, the radial displacement of each of the 16 facets being 22½ deg. When a mechanical head is used, having a division plate containing 32 holes, the main facets are cut on the eighths, and the triangular facets, bisecting the edge of two main facets, are lapped by indexing the 16ths on the plate or index. Care should be exercised to develop the facets uniformly so that the triangles formed will meet in points at the girdle and at the table. When finished, the crown exclusive of the table will consist of two rows of triangular facets extending from the table to the girdle of the stone, each row facing in opposite directions. After the front of the stone has been polished, the index marks are lightly scribed on the girdle edge, and the stone is cemented on the lap stick truly, with the back surface upward for cutting. The back main facets are lapped as described under the single-cut stone. The eight main facets, which have been cut to the proper angle, meet in a point at the culet. The second row of girdle facets, more steeply inclined, are formed in an identical manner to the girdle facets on the front of the stone.

These triangular girdle facets are developed from the girdle edge to a point midway from the girdle to the culet, and they are spaced equidistant between two main facets, being directly opposite the mating girdle-edge facets on the front of the stone. An alternative method of faceting is to cut the back main facets in the usual manner and, instead of lapping girdle facets, a series of facets less steeply inclined are lapped, extending from the culet to a point on the main facets midway between the culet and the girdle (Fig. 7–26). The facets thus formed are equidistant from adjoining facets and they are cut in a manner similar to the eight-crown girdle facets. When finished, the stone exhibits a starlike arrangement of facets.

The double-cut stone (Fig. 7–27) is another simple modification which is readily developed from the single cut. The stone is prepared in a manner similar to the single cut. Roughing, cementing, sizing, and cutting of the eight main facets follow in regular order. After the completion of the main crown facets, the small triangular girdle facets are lapped. These facets are more steeply inclined. They are formed by a slight radial displacement and by inserting the pointed end of the lap stick in a lower series of holes in the back rest. The stone is gently pressed on the rotating lap and a trial cut is made. Upon examination, should the radial displacement be either too little or too great, the position of the stone is altered so that the facet, when fully developed, extends from the girdle edge, at a point midway between two main facets, to a point on the main-facet edge, which is about 66 per cent (or ⅔) distant from the girdle to the table (Fig. 7–27). The usual practice is to cut the girdle facets in rotation, first on one side of each main facet, then on the other side, continuing around the stone in a clockwise manner, until the series has been completed. When completed, the crown of the stone, exclusive of the table, will consist of eight pentagonal main facets and sixteen triangular girdle facets. From the two series or double row of facets on the crown as well as the pavilion, this style of cutting derives its name, double cut.

When a mechanical dividing head is used, these facets are spaced in like manner. In the head, with a division plate having 32 holes or notches, these girdle facets are referred to as the thirty seconds, because that hole or notch in the division plate is used. To cut the girdle facets the radial displacement is 11¼ deg.

After the crown facets have been polished, the position of the main facets is marked or scribed on the girdle edge so that the back facets, when cut, will be accurately spaced behind the corresponding front facets.

The stone then is cemented squarely on the lap stick, and the back facets are cut in a similar manner. First, the eight main facets are cut to the prescribed angle, as described for the single cut after which the back girdle facets, more steeply inclined, are lapped. In lapping the back facets (D, Fig. 7–72), care and attention should be exercised so that the facets will be equally developed, correctly inclined, accurately spaced with reference to the front facets, and that the girdle edge is not cut through. In small stones, the edge should be about ¼ mm. thick, for a certain amount of material is removed in polishing the back facets, and thus when completed a faint edge is perceptible.

The brilliant cut (Fig. 7–28), which is the most popular style for round-faceted stones, is prepared in a manner similar to the double cut. The stone is roughed and faceted in a similar manner, the eight main facets being lapped to the correct size and at an angle which is correct for the stone in work. Eight triangular table facets, also called *star facets*, less steeply inclined, are developed by raising the pointed end of the lap stick to one of the higher series of holes in the back rest, and by a slight radial displacement, the point formed by the joining of two main facets with the table is carefully lapped away (E, Fig. 7–68).

The flat triangular facet, thus formed, lies midway between two of the adjoining main facets. The base of this triangular facet now forms one side of the table facet, and the apex opposite extends to a point on the adjoining edge of the two main facets, a distance approximating 40 per cent from the table edge to the girdle.

Having completed the series of eight star facets, the sixteen girdle facets more steeply inclined are next finished in the same manner as that prescribed in cutting the regular double-cut form. The pointed end of the lap stick is set in one of a lower series of holes in the back rest, so that the facet when completed will extend from the girdle edge at a point midway between two main facets to the point formed by the intersection of two main facet edges and the apex of the triangular star facet (F, Fig. 7–68). The girdle facets are cut consecutively. When completed, the front or crown will consist of one octagon-shaped table facet, one series of eight triangular star facets, one series of eight kite-shaped or quadri-lateral-shaped main facets, and a third series of triangular girdle facets. In using a mechanical faceting apparatus having 32 divisions, the main facets are indexed on the eighths, the star facets on the sixteenths, and the girdle facets on the thirty-seconds. With the conventional type of mobile facet head, opposite main facets are lapped until all eight are equally developed, taking care during the cutting to check the slope or included angle formed by the table and the main facet. The eight star facets are cut consecutively, with especial care not to overdevelop them. The girdle facets, if properly developed in size and angularity, may be cut in pairs, one opposite the other, affording quicker indexing operations because of similar radial displacement. Faceting devices having notched index plates held in place by a latch, or heads operating through a worm-and-gear unit, are used in a similar manner.

Every effort should be exerted to develop the facets evenly so that all corners meet in points. Overdeveloped facets require a longer time to correct in polishing, and in some cases it is quicker to recut the stone rather than to laboriously polish the facets to the correct size or shape.

After the front of the stone has been polished, the index lines are scribed on the girdle edge and the stone is then reversed on the lap stick for finishing the back facets. These are lapped exactly as described under the double-cut stone, the back of which is identical with the back of a full brilliant cut. The triangular girdle-edge facets should extend to a point on the back main facet midway between the girdle and the culet (D, Fig. 7–72). Modern practice is to extend these facets to a point on the back main facet two-thirds distant from the girdle edge.

Variations of the brilliant cut are numerous, a simple modification of which is referred to as three-quarter brilliant cut. In this style, the girdle facets are reduced in number, eight only being cut on the front and a matching series of eight on the back (Fig. 7–31). This style of cutting is most frequently seen on inexpensive stones or on small round stones. When finished, the crown of the stone consists of a table, eight triangular star facets, eight pentagonal main facets, and eight triangular girdle facets. On the pavilion, there are the culet, eight triangular girdle facets, and eight pentagonal main facets. Because of the lesser number of girdle facets, the girdle edge is somewhat thicker than usual.

Another slight modification may consist of adding four and sometimes eight star facets about the culet, which is reduced to a point and when viewed from the table shows a starlike effect (Figs. 7–26 and 7–40).

The mixed brilliant style of cutting often is used for colored stones (Fig. 7–30). The front is cut in the usual full brilliant style, and the back is faceted with a series of steps less steeply inclined from the girdle to the culet. These facets are spaced exactly as if the stone were to be cut in the usual manner, the several steps lying in the same plane directly in back of the main front facets. The steps are cut as in a regular step-cut stone. The first series is cut at the proper angle so that the facets are accurately spaced with reference to the index lines scribed on the girdle. The remaining series, two or more in number, less steeply inclined, are lapped in a similar manner, care being taken to develop all equally. The several rows will then be respectively equidistant from the girdle. The triangular girdle facets are usually cut last, and these may equal in number the front girdle facets, or half the number may be applied.

The double brilliant cut (Fig. 7–32) is an interesting modification of the regular full brilliant cut, and it is formed by doubling the main facets. This style is rarely applied to small stones and to those having a circular outline, the most popular type of outline for this style of cutting being the antique cushion. The main facets are developed in the usual manner but two steps are made. The second step less steeply inclined adjoins the table. In cutting these steps, the same rules apply as those governing the cutting of step-cut stones. Thus, the inclination or angularity of the lower portion of the main facet may be greater than, equal to, or less than the angle required for the refractive index of the stone in hand, provided that the stone being cut is of a light hue. The upper main facet is cut so that in length it is about 40 per cent of the distance from the table to the girdle. The regular proportions of diameter and thickness are the same as that of the brilliant cut. After the main facets have been accurately and uniformly cut, the triangular star facets are carefully lapped so that, when fully developed, the base opposite the girdle forms one side of the table and the apex of the triangle meets in a point with the upper edge of two adjoining bottom main facets. Thus, the top portion of the main facet is transformed into a triangle. By cutting the 16-girdle facets as prescribed in the double cut or the regular brilliant cut, the series is completed. The crown now consists of one table and four series or rows of triangular facets, each series less steeply inclined, extending from the girdle to the table.

After the front of the stone has been polished, the back of the stone is finished in the manner prescribed for the brilliant cut, the sole difference being that the back main facets are cut in two steps similar to the front main facets. The two steps usually are equal in length, although the lower portion extending to the culet is sometimes cut longer. After the bottom girdle facets have been cut, the pavilion of the stone consists of three series or rows of triangular facets, each series less steeply inclined, extending to and including the culet.

The brilliant cut as well as the double brilliant cut may be applied to a wide variety of shapes, such as elliptical, cushion, or marquise, as shown under forms of cutting (Fig. 6–1). While the facets in the round shape may be started at any point, special care is required in properly placing the facets on stones having two dimensional outlines — length and width. Two side main facets, Nos. 1 and 5, are lapped first so that they are parallel to the longitudinal axis of the stone, and these are followed by the two end main facets, 3 and 7, which are lapped at a right angle to the sides. In lapping these facets by hand, the greatest degree of accuracy is required to space the facets correctly so that the table will be symmetrical with the outline. Careful checking in the lapping of the two side main facets, adjusting the position of the lap stick radially, if necessary, so that the facets are correctly aligned, will enable the operator to "block out" the remaining facets in their correct position (Fig. 7–73).

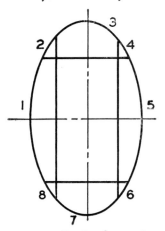

**Fig. 7-73.** Cutting four main facets on oval stone parallel to cross axes.

After the four main facets have been spaced, the four corner facets, 2 and 6, 4 and 8, are lapped in turn (Fig. 7–73). First one corner is cut, then the corner diagonally opposite it is finished. The accuracy may be checked by comparing the table edges of opposite facets which should be parallel. The remaining pair of corner facets follow in like manner.

Special care is necessary to lap these last two facets so that they are placed with the same degree of angularity from the longitudinal axis. Failure to exercise this care will result in a misshapen or distorted table.

Some difficulty may be experienced in faceting oblong stones with the aid of a mechanical head because of the rapid change of angularity of the spacing of the facets radially. For example, in faceting a pear shape (Fig. 7–48), the facets spaced around the circular portion will be regularly disposed and, like the regular brilliant cut, the individual spacing from facet to facet will be 11¼ deg. However, as the facets approach the pointed end, the degree of arc spacing becomes gradually less, becoming only a fraction of the opposite or circular portion. With the conventional facet head, which has a 32-hole index plate, a compensating device is necessary in order to obtain the necessary degree of angularity lying between the 11¼-deg. facet-to-facet spacing. When stones with irregular outlines are being worked, care, skill, and patience are necessary in order to obtain satisfactory results. Similar conditions prevail in elongated shapes, such as the outline in Figure 7–74, which is hexagonal in form having crosscut facets. In this style, it is best to cut matched pairs at the ends and follow by cutting the pairs at the middle of the stone in the order noted. Facets marked 1 and 2 are cut in opposite pairs, and these are followed by those marked 3 and 4, the latter being the most difficult to cut. The facets on the ends are the easiest of the cross series to finish. The usual practice in cutting the main facets is to develop all to equal length so that the girdle is uniform and the edge is parallel to the table. If the length of the stone is several times its width, it usually is necessary to alter the position of the lap stick or the faceting head to obtain the correct inclination of the facet. If this is not done, the end facets are lapped too steeply. This change is shown at *a* and *b* in Figure 7–75. Use a contact gauge to assure constant inclination of the facets (Fig. 11–15).

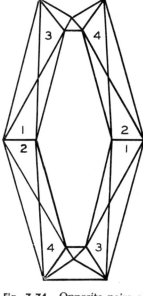

**Fig. 7-74.** Opposite pairs of facets cut.

The American brilliant cut (Fig. 7–33) is an elaboration of the double brilliant cut. It has an additional row of quadrilateral facets which occupy the position of the star facets of the double brilliant cut. This style of cutting may be developed in several ways, the most practical of which is as follows. The stone is prepared in the usual manner and cut as the double brilliant cut. However, instead of forming the usual triangular star facets adjoining the table, these facets are overcut so that they are pentagonal in shape. The star facet less steeply inclined is developed at the point where the two sides of the pentagonal facet join the table (Fig. 7–76). This triangular-shaped facet should be cut so that the base which forms one side of the table extends from the center of each pentagonal facet on the table edge to the center of its adjoining facet, and the apex opposite the table meets the top main facet in a point. After the front of the stone has been finished, the back is finished in the style of the double brilliant cut.

The twentieth-century style of cutting (Fig. 7–34) is not only one of the most elaborate examples of facet work, but the effect obtained with a properly finished stone is excellent. The front and back of the twentieth-century cut are in the rose-cut form, that is, the facets in a series of rows, less steeply inclined, extend from the girdle to a point (apex) at the top and at the bottom of the stone, the conventional flat table and culet facets being absent. In working a stone having this style of cutting, a greater amount of preparatory work is advised. The stone should be carefully roughed and finish-ground to the correct size and proportion, being particularly careful to lap the front and the back slopes as accurately as possible. The stone will then have a double cabochon appearance with pointed surfaces on both sides of the girdle. The facets may be placed in several ways, starting with the quadrilateral star facets which meet in a point on the top of the stone. The remaining rows follow, more steeply inclined, which is the method often used in fashioning the rose cut. An alternative method may be used, in which the girdle facets are made first, continuing to the top, each row being less steeply inclined.

The usual method is to treat the stone as a double brilliant cut. First, the main facets are blocked out in two rows, starting with the main facets extending from the girdle, and finishing the main facets in the second step which meet in a point at the top of the stone. The other facets, which have the position of the sixteenths in the regular brilliant cut, are formed midway between the girdle facets and the pointed star facets at the top. These facets, when completed, have a rhombus form, and the last row to be completed consists of the triangular-shaped facets bordering the girdle.

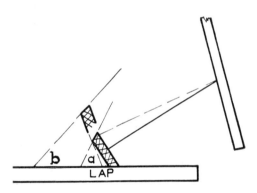

Fig. 7-75. Change of facet angle on stones of unequal dimension.

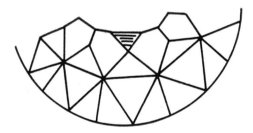

Fig. 7-76. Developing star facet.

After polishing the ground facets and scribing indicator lines on the girdle edge, the stone is reversed upon the lap stick, accurately re-cemented, and the back of the stone is finished. The simplest way to finish the back is to grind two series of steplike facets in the proper position, starting with the first series extending from the girdle to a point midway between the girdle and the culet. The second series of steps, less steeply inclined, extending from the midway point to the culet, meet in a point.

The girdle edge should be left a little thicker than usual so that the girdle facets to be cut last will not cut through and ruin the outline. After both main step facets have been cut, the hexagonal facet is developed on the edge formed by the two adjoining main facets in the first series. This facet, which will ultimately become hexagonal in outline, should be developed to a size where the second series of main facets become pentagonal in outline.

The fourth series, the quadrilateral-shaped girdle-edge facets, is finally cut, after which all are polished.

The Portuguese cut (Fig. 7–38) usually is placed upon stones of large size. A large number of facets in rows are cut on the front and the back of the stone, the number of which vary according to the size of the stone and the whim of the artisan. The facets usually are triangular or rhomboidal in shape, the average number disposed about the table being 32. The style shown in Figure 7–38 has three successive rows of triangular facets, two rows of rhomboidal, and a final row of triangular facets arranged between the table and the girdle. On the pavilion or back of the stone from the girdle to the culet, five rows of facets are cut in the following order. One row consists of triangular facets, one row of rhomboidal facets, two rows of triangular, and one row of pentagonal facets. In cutting a stone in this style, if the faceting is done by hand, it is best to cut the main crown facets first. These are developed in the usual manner. Opposite facets are cut first, then those on the quarter, eighths, and so on, until the 32 are equally developed about the girdle. The triangular girdle facet is readily formed by lapping the joining edge of the main facets, this series being more steeply inclined. By raising the pointed end of the lap stick to a higher position in the back rest and by cutting facets on the edges of facets already cut, the other series is finished.

After the second rhomboidal set has been finished, the remaining facets are finished in triangular shape. After the front of the stone has been finished, the back or pavilion is completed in like manner.

Stones of large size, cut in this style, are very difficult to finish by hand. Therefore, because of the accuracy and rigidity of the mechanical faceting head, it may be used with distinct advantage for this work, for the beauty as well as the accuracy of the workmanship depend upon the proper spacing as well as flatness of the facets when the stone has been polished. An alternative form, referred to as Scotch cut (Fig. 7–39), sometimes is seen on large circular stones usually made of yellow or brown transparent quartz, called Cairngorm or Scotch Topaz. The facets are arranged in series or rows, and the majority are rhomboidal or square in shape, the style actually being a step cut applied to a round stone. The number of facets in each row may vary from 24 to 32. Where the facets converge to form the culet, the number usually is halved and this portion is treated in various ways according to the ideas of the cutter. The usual practice is to arrange the facets in a starlike form (Fig. 7–40).

The rose cut (Fig. 7–41) is a style usually reserved for small round stones. These stones are prepared in the same manner as a round cabochon form. The stone is rough and finish-ground, and prior to cementing to the lap stick, the flat surface, which is the back of the stone, is lapped flat on a pewter lap. This surface should be up when the stone is cemented to the lap stick, and the flat surface should be set accurately and truly. The stone then is lapped to size, the back is finished, and the stone then is reversed upon the lap stick and the front is faceted. It is best to grind a true cabochon stone first before applying the facets; thus, an accurately formed domed surface will have been prepared which will enable the operator to place the facets truly. In developing the initial facets, the first series about the point at the apex of the stone is cut. Two main facets directly opposite each other are finished so that the joining edge bisects the stone. The position of the stone and the lap stick is then rotated 60 deg., and two additional facets are cut in like manner. By a further rotation of 60 deg., the third set of opposite main facets is cut and, when completed, the crown of the stone will have six triangular facets uniformly spaced about the top (Figs. 7–41 and 7–43).

Occasionally, eight facets are cut; but in the majority of rose-cut stones, six facets are the rule. The second row of main facets, cut at the same radial setting extending from the girdle edge, joins the facets previously cut. These should be cut so that both sets, top and bottom, are of equal length. The third series of facets, triangular in shape, is spaced about the girdle, and these facets are cut in the same way as previously prescribed under the double cut.

The double rose (Fig. 7–44) is a form in which the rose cut is applied to two domed surfaces both of which have a common girdle and, except for the facets, it is identical to the double-cabochon form.

Other styles of the rose cut may be seen from time to time, but the treatment is the same as outlined before. The Briolette (Fig. 7–47) shows an unusual style, where facets are in parallel rows. A change in the initial setting of the stone is necessary, however, in certain forms. Briolettes, having circular or elliptical outlines, are cemented to the lap stick so that the longitudinal axis of the stone coincides with the axis of the lap stick. They are made in a variety of patterns or styles of cutting. The commonest form, however, has triangular-cut facets arranged in rows about the stone. The stone must be finish-ground to exact size and shape. The initial series of long facets are cut about the point, after which the triangular-shaped facets are developed by bisecting edges formed by two facets in the preceding row (Fig. 7–47).

Briolettes with a sharp girdle edge, similar to the double-rose cut, are treated in the same manner as the latter style, the stone being cemented so that the girdle edge is at a right angle to the lap-stick axis. The stone then is treated in a manner similar to cutting a rose-cut stone. The facets are started at the center or apex of the stone and continue in uniform rows, the number of which vary according to the size of the stone. A series of triangular facets border the girdle edge (Fig. 7–44).

## POLISHING FACETED STONES

The technique of polishing faceted stones differs slightly from that of cutting. The chief difference is in the abrasive used which is a very finely divided powder. The action of this powder, when applied to a suitable lap, slowly wears away the surface of the stone and leaves a bright surface in place of the dull one produced by the lapping abrasive. In the cutting or lapping the operator is concerned with the proper proportions as well as the systematic arrangement of the facets. In the polishing, however, these factors must not only be considered and maintained, but the facets must be perfectly polished, free from scratches, dull spots, or roundness, and all bounding sides must meet the adjoining facets in edges or points. It is also the duty of the polisher to correct inequalities on the cut stone and, as the texture as well as the grain of the stone varies in different species (and on occasion in the same stone), requiring also the use of different polishing powders, it is obvious that a wide experience is necessary in order to satisfactorily polish all faceted stones.

Furthermore, the condition of the lap surface, rough or smooth, as well as the moisture content of the polishing material on its surface, from wet to dry, together with the lap speed also are variable. They not only change with different species of stones, but they also may vary in the polishing of a single stone.

The surface of the polishing lap should be scored with a sharp knife having a thin blade, such as those used in leather work, so that the wet polishing powder will adhere. The scoring may be done by making cuts in the lap surface from the center outward, in two or more directions tangent to the center, continuing the cutting until the entire surface is uniformly crisscrossed with score marks. During this operation the lap is held stationary, and it is moved from time to time as the scoring progresses. An alternative method, one which is less tedious and quicker, employed by most lapidaries, is to score the lap while it is rotating. This is done by holding a sharp knife at an angle to the lap face. The knife blade digs into the surface and begins to chatter and thus rapidly covers the surface of the lap with numerous small cuts (Fig. 5–15). This operation is continued, and by moving the knife blade outward, the entire surface of the lap is covered with small cuts. By holding the knife blade so that it points successively in two directions, right and left, the cuts will be respectively inclined in a diagonal grid pattern. The surface prepared in this manner is ideal for polishing large flat facets. If only one polishing lap is available, a portion of its surface should be worn smooth for polishing small facets or for polishing those stones which require a smooth lap.

In polishing faceted stones, a tin lap is used in the majority of cases. The lap should be perfectly true and balanced so that vibration is eliminated. As a general rule the laps used in lapidary shops are from ½ to 1 in. thick. However, equally good results may be obtained by fusing a thin lap of tin, from ⅛ to ¼ in. thick, onto a thicker brass lap. The unit then is trued and balanced. In special cases, wood, copper, bronze, or zinc laps may be used.

In the first attempt at polishing faceted stones on a tin lap, the same care and judgment should be exercised as that shown in the first attempt at cutting. The stone should be of moderate size and the facets should be as large as possible so that, when a number of facets in the same series are being polished, little difficulty will be experienced in polishing

Fig. 7-77. Polishing faceted stone.

all alike. A comfortable position before the lap bench, free of strain and tension, should be acquired before the work of polishing is attempted. The forearms should be parallel to and resting upon the bench top. To properly charge or break in a newly scored lap requires a few moments only. The polishing powder may be applied dry to the wet lap, or it may be mixed to a thick paste which is applied to the lap near the center with a thin wooden paddle (Fig. 7-77). At the same time, the material is rubbed into the surface with a flat piece of agate. In a short space of time, the rough ridges of the scored lap become burnished down by the agate and, if examined, the stone will exhibit a degree of polish. When learning to polish on a flat tin lap, it is customary to polish flat specimens of all types of stone. Thus, by careful observation, noting the effect of a lap speed and the action of the polishing material on the surface being polished, valuable experience is gained before an attempt is made to polish a small surface on a faceted stone. Specimens from ½ to 1 in. in area are ideal for this purpose. After the surface of a stone has been properly lapped, the stone as well as the hands must be scrubbed thoroughly to remove all traces of grit, for absolute cleanliness is necessary in order to polish stones. In the initial polishing, the lap speed should be about 400 r.p.m. Wet polishing powder should be applied to the surface of the lap near the center, with a small wooden paddle or a swab of cloth. After an adequate charge of powder has been applied, the stone is firmly held in contact with the rotating lap. The stone is moved radially across the lap surface, or it may be held near the outer edge of the lap which would tend to polish the stone more rapidly because of the greater amount of lapping surface available per revolution of the lap. If the stone is examined after a few moments of work, it will be observed that portions show a polished appearance as well as rough scratches and dull spots left from the cutting lap. Polishing then should be continued until all rough or dull spots left by the cutting lap have been removed. Numerous scratches may be seen in the surface of the stone. Provided that the polishing material as well as the lap surface are clean and free of grit, these scratches are invariably due to the wetness of the polishing material. To finish the surface of the stone so that it is free of scratches, the polishing material is permitted to dry out upon the surface of the lap until it is merely damp. In this condition the action of the wheel and the powder will pull and tug the stone which will result in a brightly polished surface. Should the lap become completely dry before the scratches on the surface of the stone have been entirely removed, the polishing powder remaining on the lap should be dampened by lightly touching it with a wet paddle. Some skill is required to maintain the polishing material with the proper amount of moisture so that the work may be finished. To prevent too rapid drying after the polishing material has reached the proper consistency, the speed of the lap may be slowed. To prevent motor stalling, the lap spindle should be provided with a brake or a slipping belt or clutch arrangement. Although the hand-driven lapidary bench has been derided and belittled by the uninformed as being antiquated, this apparatus possesses definite advantages. This is particularly true in the polishing of faceted stones for, when the critical moment has been reached, the polishing action and the speed of the wheel may be controlled perfectly.

In recent years numerous mechanical devices have become available that permit infinite changes of speed without loss of torque. The Graham transmission, which permits rapid change of speed to any r.p.m., is ideally suited for a lapidary polishing bench. This unit enables the lapidary to operate the polishing lap at maximum speed in initial polishing and then at greatly reduced speed for finishing, and because the maximum torque is retained at slow speed, the greatest degree of efficiency is attained.

Stones of the chalcedony type, such as the agate, bloodstone, carnelian, onyx, and sard, usually may be polished without slowing the lap. However, as the texture of the majority of stones varies, it is obvious that, as soon as the operator will learn to control the lap speed as well as the wet polishing powder, he will be conditioned to start on facet work. Working on the lap surface near the spindle, where the surface speed is less, has the same effect as slowing the lap speed.

If a reasonable amount of experience in the polishing of flat specimen pieces has been acquired, the various stones cut in the table-cut style may be polished. In the table-cut stone, the bevel edge joins the table facet in a sharp edge. As a precautionary measure, this sharp edge is "broken." That is, a small flat surface (beveled edge) is polished on the sharp edge at an angle between the side bevel edge and the table. To perform this operation, the lap stick is held at an angle, so that the sharp edge is in contact with the lap surface and in such a position that the lap surface travels along the edge of the stone. The stone is moved slightly back and forth, across the surface of the lap, to prevent grooving, and it is lightly but firmly held onto the lap. The purpose of this beveled edge is to prevent the bevel facet from chipping where it joins the table, which would also introduce particles of the stone into the polishing material and thus cause deep gouges to appear on the polished surface of the stone.

When all top edges have been polished, the table is polished next. The lap stick is held in a vertical position, the first three fingers of the hand grasping the stick near the cemented stone, the stick passing between the second and third fingers as shown in Figure 7–59. Held in this manner, the stone is pressed to the lap surface and the polishing proceeds. At this stage it becomes apparent why a stone of moderate size should be selected, for the table is sufficiently large to enable the operator to hold it onto the lap and develop a flat uniformly polished surface. If a small stone were selected, it would be impossible to finish properly unless some mechanical device were used to hold the lap stick in the proper position.

After considerable skill has been attained, facets as small as 6 mm. may be polished as previously outlined. The normal tendency is for the stone to tilt on the lap surface thus rounding the facet. After the table has been finished in a satisfactory manner, the side facets are polished.

In polishing the side facets, the lap should rotate in a clockwise direction for right-handed workers, so that the direction of the lap travel is away from the stone. This operation is similar to cutting the facets,

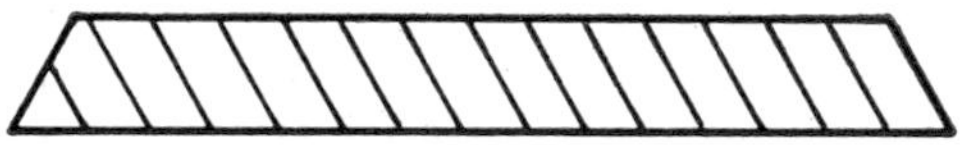

Fig. 7-78. Correct angle. Facet evenly polished.

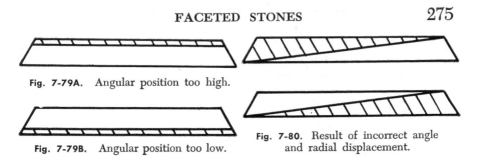

**Fig. 7-79A.** Angular position too high.

**Fig. 7-79B.** Angular position too low.

**Fig. 7-80.** Result of incorrect angle and radial displacement.

the polishing material being used instead of the cutting abrasive. With the polishing lap prepared with wet polishing powder, the pointed end of the lap stick is placed in the proper hole in the back rest so that the flat beveled facet, when pressed to the lap surface, will be evenly polished (Fig. 7-78).

The same holding position specified for cutting facets is used in polishing. The stone end of the stick is held by the first three fingers, the forefinger resting on the stick opposite the facet to be polished and the pointed end of the stick lying across the palm of the hand.

A trial is made to see if the angularity of the lap stick is correct by touching the facet to the lap for a few seconds or less. From the bright polished mark made by the lap, the proper angularity of the lap stick may be determined. If the polish mark shows a line near the table (A, Fig. 7-79), the slope or angle of the stick is too great and needs to be lowered on the back rest, by placing it in a lower series of holes. If the polished line is near the girdle edge of the stone (B, Fig. 7-79), the angle or inclination of the lap stick is too little and the pointed end should be raised to a higher position. The radial position also should be checked and, if the facet is polished more on one end than on the other (Fig. 7-80), suitable pressure in a twisting manner will correct the error. This, however, must not be overdone for it may develop a rounded facet or overdevelop it. The facet, when finished, should show the polish evenly distributed from the table to the girdle. Polish on the facet, re-sulting from the various positions listed in the foregoing, is shown in Figure 7-78.

The same results are obtained if the lap stick is held in a mechanical head or fixture. When the correct position has been found in which the lap works across the facet evenly, the polishing lap should be kept wet, if needed. Fresh polishing material should be added from time to time and the facet should be worked until all cutting abrasive marks have been polished out. The polishing material should be worked toward the spindle to prevent being thrown off by centrifugal force. If the facet has been cut unevenly, due to a slight turning of the lap stick during the cutting, looseness of the stick in the holder, or an insecure fixture itself, or, if the lap is not flat, it will become evident the moment the facet is placed upon the polishing wheel at the correct angle. The high portion will immediately show up, and a considerable amount of time and prolonged work must be resorted to before the facet has been completely worked flat and the rough-cut portion has been removed. As a rule, the facet is worked for several seconds and is then examined to ascertain the progress made and to apply correction, if necessary. The amount of time required depends upon the type of stone, the size and flatness of the facet, and the skill of the operator.

After the facet has been completely flattened, the polishing material is controlled so that it is just wet enough to polish without leaving scratches. This varies with different stones, but chalcedony of different types may be polished with the damp polishing material without difficulty. It is of the greatest importance that the operator learn to distinguish between the marks left by the polishing material and the scratches caused by grit. The polishing marks are practically uniform, while the marks left by grit are coarse and often gouge deeply into the surface of the stone. This does not apply to stones having peculiar grain structure which will be discussed later.

Having polished the first facet successfully, the facet directly opposite usually is polished next, and in like manner the remaining facets are finished. Stones having rectangular and square outlines are easier to work than the octagon form often used for ring stones. The long facets in the latter style may be polished without difficulty, but considerable practice is necessary before the small corner facets may be finished perfectly. There is a tendency to round the small corner facets if it is polished without a mechanical facet device.

The top left and bottom right corner facets usually may be polished without trouble, but the two opposite corners are more difficult. Circular or elliptical table-cut stones also are finished in like manner. The bevel edge is polished by working a section at a time, oscillating the stone until the section is polished, and then continuing the process until the entire facet about the stone has been finished.

In polishing step-cut stones, the top step facets adjoining the table are polished first. As they are steeply inclined, the small polished protecting edge given to the table-cut stone is not required, because the interfacial angle is such that chipping is improbable. In polishing the top facets, one facet is finished parallel to the girdle edge and the opposite matching facet is finished in like manner. Every effort should be exercised to prevent the facets from becoming overdeveloped through prolonged working, or tapered and out of alignment with the girdle edge. Thus, an unsymmetrical table would be formed, *i.e.*, the sides are not parallel to the girdle edge or the table would be off center.

The end facets are polished in a similar manner with the same care so that all facets in the same series are uniform. The facets in the next series, more steeply inclined, then are polished similarly.

In finishing the successive rows of facets, the condition of the lap should be controlled so that the polishing material on the lap surface will leave a brightly polished facet, free from scratches or blemishes, and that the polishing operation may be concluded when the facet reaches the proper development. If this is not done, and difficulty is experienced in obtaining the proper polish on the facet just as it reaches the correct size, it may be necessary to repolish the whole series of facets in the same row so that they will all be of the proper size or width. The ability to control the polishing operation, so that the facets are brightly polished and matching facets are of equal size, is an art that the beginner lapidary must learn at the earliest possible time if finished work is to be done. On large stones, it is well to polish the table first, but on small to medium-sized stones, the table facet may be polished last. This is the usual practice in commercial lapidary shops, and is a timesaving procedure. When polishing the table first, a special fixture is required to hold the stone rigidly to the lap surface in a vertical position. Most mechanical faceting equipment have attachments of this kind. If this is lacking, polish the table by hand. The usual procedure is to heat the cement and, as it becomes plastic, the stone is tilted so that the table is at an angle of 45 deg. with the axis of the lap stick (Fig. 7–81). By holding the lap stick at the same angle, with the pointed end in the back rest, the table comes in the same plane as the lap. Some adjustment of position generally is needed, which is determined by trial, after which the table is polished in the same manner as the regular step facets.

In this manner the table facet is polished first. This procedure is advised when working on peridot, zircon, or spinel, as it is often necessary to polish the surface from different directions, altering as required.

After a satisfactory polish has been attained, the stone and cement are heated and the stone reset in its original position with the table normal or at a right angle to the axis of the lap stick. After considerable

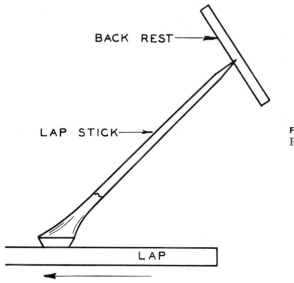

BACK REST

LAP STICK

LAP

Fig. 7-81.
Polishing small table.

practice, the stone may be reset within a small degree of its original position which lessens the necessity for making repeated corrections in angularity with respect to the lap surface during subsequent polishing operations.

Having finished the front or crown, the stone is reversed upon the lap stick, centered truly, and the back of the stone is cut as previously described. In polishing the back facets, those about the culet should be finished first, being careful to polish these parallel with the girdle edge. The succeeding step facets, more steeply inclined, are polished in the same manner as the top step facets, and care is taken to maintain all matching facets of uniform width. The purpose of polishing the facets in the order stated, which is opposite to the order for cutting, is to correct any inequalities or overdeveloped facets. A slight adjustment or correction in position is carried out at the girdle edge.

Polishing facets from the girdle upward results in dulling or minutely scratching the adjoining portion of facets which already have been polished. After some experience in polishing has been gained, it is possible to determine if the facet to be polished is flat on the lap by the sound emitted. If the facet is flat on the lap, the tone will be dull and low pitched as compared to the screechy, higher pitched sound produced when the facet is not true on the lap surface. During the polishing operation, the stone being polished should be moved back and forth through a small arc on the surface of the lap to remove the polishing scratches and to prevent grooves from developing in the lap.

All other styles of cutting are treated in a similar manner. The series of facets adjoining the table are polished first, after which the other series or rows of facets, more steeply inclined, are finished until the girdle edge is reached. In the French cut (Fig. 7–13), star cut (Fig. 7–26), and Cardinal cut (Fig. 7–16), the facets which are less steeply inclined, extending from the girdle to the table, are polished first. The table thus is formed truly, after which the remaining facets, more steeply inclined and forming the girdle outline, are finished. In polishing the long triangular-shaped facets, where the apex or point receives the initial polishing action when placed upon the lap, there is a tendency for the facet to become grooved. The groove extending from the point may cross the entire facet. To remove this defect and to produce a perfectly polished facet, light pressure and a lateral movement of the facet on the lap should be used without the application of fresh polishing material. Polishing equipment used in Switzerland holds the stone so that the polishing action is across the facet, thus eliminating this difficulty.

In polishing stones having circular or curved girdles, as single cut, or brilliant cut, the same principles of polishing are followed as previously described. Large table surfaces should be polished first, after which the crown facets are polished. All facets in the same series or row are equally developed and perfectly polished.

On long, narrow stones, particularly those having curved outlines, elliptical, marquise, or pear shaped, some difficulty will be experienced in the hand method of cutting as well as polishing the end facets. This is due to the angularity and the distance the end of the lap stick is from the facet being polished, which causes the stick to be turned slightly when the facet is placed in contact with the lap and results in rounding the facet. This trouble can be avoided by recementing and offsetting the stone (Fig. 7–82). Thus, the axis of the lap stick will more closely coincide with the axis of the section of the stone being worked, resulting in better control.

Fig. 7-82. Offsetting long, narrow stone to facilitate polishing.

Because of the rigidity of the mechanical holder, the end facets on long narrow stones can be polished with greater accuracy.

In polishing the facets on the crosscut (Fig. 7–17), the same procedure is followed. In all of the styles that have cross facets or series of facets that are radially disposed, two methods of treatment are possible. The facets may be polished by treating opposite pairs of facets, those which have been cut at the same angle and position on opposite sides of the stone, or, if desired, the right- and left-hand facets adjoining may be polished consecutively, exercising care to polish all facets in the same series equally. In small to medium-sized stones where the table surface is polished last, the top facets adjoining the table are overdeveloped a small amount, so that a small amount of material is left on the table for working. As the table facet becomes fully developed, the polishing material is controlled upon the lap surface so that the facet will be perfectly polished and the corners will meet adjoining facets in points.

## POLISHING, SPECIAL TREATMENT

While some faceted gem minerals may be polished with ease, and a number of them may be similarly treated without difficulty, many, by reason of peculiar grain or crystal structure, require the greatest degree of skill, experience, and patience in polishing. The art of polishing is further complicated by the fact that a number of different kinds of laps as well as polishing materials are necessary to successfully treat all stones. Experience has shown that, for best results in polishing, all stones used for gems may be classed in groups, each of which requires different treatment as listed in Table 11.

### TABLE 11.   RECOMMENDED PROCEDURE IN POLISHING FACETED STONES

*Lap used.*   Maple, boxwood, or optical pitch; also pewter
*Polishing medium.*   Tin oxide
*Substance.*   All stones, 6 and under on the scale of hardness; e.g., feldspar, glass, lapis lazuli, malachite, opal, flourite, obsidian, lazulite, etc.

*Lap used.*   Tin
*Polishing medium.*   Tin oxide
*Substance.*   Axinite, benitoite, californite, diopside, cordierite, danburite, hiddenite, idocrase, jadeite, kunzite, nephrite, phenacite, rhodonite, sphene, wernerite, Beryl (aquamarine, emerald, morganite, golden beryl, goshenite) Quartz (rock crystal, amethyst, citrine, smoky quartz) Chalcedony (agate, carnelian, chrysoprase, onyx, sard, bloodstone, jasper)

*Lap used.*   Tin
*Polishing material.*   Linde A5175, Damascus ruby powder, or levigated alumina
*Substance.*   Cassiterite, chrysolite, epidote, hematite, peridot, spinel (also synthetic spinel), "titania" (synthetic rutile), topaz, tourmaline, zircon, fabulite (a new synthetic)

*Lap used.* Tin or zinc
*Polishing material.* Tripoli
*Substance.* Alexandrite, chrysoberyl, cat's-eye, ruby, sapphire (cabochon stones); also synthetic corundum

*Lap used.* Bronze
*Polishing material.* Tripoli
*Substance.* Ruby, sapphire, also synthetic ditto

*Lap used.* Tin or zinc
*Polishing material.* Diamond powder No. 6 or finer
*Substance.* Ruby, sapphire, also synthetic ditto; all chrysoberyl and corundum cabochon cut

*Lap used.* Boxwood or maple.
*Polishing material.* Diamond powder No. 6 or finer
*Substance.* All chrysoberyl and corundum cabochon stones for final bright finish

*Lap used.* Iron
*Polishing material.* Diamond powder No. 5
*Substance.* Diamond

It will be observed that, as the hardness of the stone increases, harder laps as well as harder polishing powders are required, although the tin lap together with the proper polishing medium is used to polish a greater number of faceted stones than any other combination. Besides the mechanical difficulty which arises in the polishing of elongated faceted stones, only a few varieties, the most common of which is beryl, may be polished without difficulty.

Certain varieties of a single mineral species may be polished with ease, while others are worked with difficulty. This may be observed in quartz. The cryptocrystalline varieties are polished without difficulty while the crystalline varieties require greater care and skill. Rock crystal and the light-hued amethyst and citrine are only slightly more difficult to polish, while the deeply tinted varieties of amethyst, cairngorm, and Spanish topaz require considerable skill to polish brightly and free from scratches. In most cases, any difficulty of this nature may be overcome by a slowly rotating polishing wheel with the polishing powder slightly damp but not dry. Most of the scratches extend across the facet, those about the girdle being particularly difficult to eliminate. By polishing a small bevel at the girdle edge, much of this trouble may be overcome.

This difficulty of polishing often is met with in the dark or deeply tinted varieties of tourmaline, particularly the dark green crystals from Brazil. Another difficulty encountered in this stone is in polishing the table which is ground parallel to the longitudinal axis.

Polishing this surface across the longitudinal axis is most difficult for there is a pronounced tendency to scratching and scoring. If, however, the stone is recemented so that the polishing lap works along the longi-tudinal axis of the crystal, the facet will be polished without difficulty.

This peculiarity of grain is not constant but varies with different gems. The light-hued pink and green stones may be polished without difficulty from any direction. This characteristic also is to be observed in other gem minerals. Beryl has such a fine structure that it may be polished with ease from any direction. The crystalline quartzes sometimes show minute etch figures when polished. Topaz is difficult to polish if the flat table surface is on a cleavage plane. Zircon, spinel, and peridot possess soft spots which require the greatest amount of skill and experience to finish correctly.

Thus, it will be noted that great variance in gemstones makes a universal polishing technique impossible. The following is a discussion of stones in common use which require special treatment.

## TIN LAP WITH TIN OXIDE

Initial polishing of deeply colored varieties of transparent quartz, amethyst, cairngorm, smoky quartz, and "Spanish topaz" is done with the lap and polishing material on its surface at normal, final polishing with slow speed and the polishing material just damp. The polishing powder should be maintained at the proper dampness and not be permitted to become completely dry. This can be effected by the periodic application of the slightly wetted paddle, by which means the polishing powder is manipulated on the lap. Fine quality tripoli may also be used, but as this polishing material is much harder than the quartz, a brilliant polish on the facets is more difficult to develop. Maximum degree of polish is obtained by slow speed and careful control of the wetness of the polishing tripoli.

The dark-hued varieties of tourmaline may be polished with some difficulty. The table surface, if large, usually is polished first. By altering the position of the stone on the lap stick so that the polishing action on the stone is parallel to the longitudinal axis, this difficulty will be elimi-nated. Overheating should be avoided as the green tourmaline may split because of basal parting which is characteristic of this mineral. While tin oxide is invariably used, levigated alumina or Damascus ruby powder also may be used with advantage in difficult cases. Linde A-5175 powder is excellent in this case.

Despite its fine texture, the emerald (beryl) often is difficult to finish perfectly because of the numerous flaws and cracks that are present in most specimens. Small portions of the stone adjacent to flaws or cracks may grizzle or chip which requires prolonged and careful work to correct. This adds materially to the cost of cutting. Large cracks also may become filled with polishing material or abraded portions of the lap, resulting in an unsightly stone. The removal of this material often is difficult or impossible. Similar experiences may be observed in polishing feathered or flawed stones of other kinds, such as amethyst citrine, or tourmaline. Parting planes, occasionally encountered in aquamarine, ruby, and sapphire, present a difficulty not easily overcome.

These parting planes, which extend to the surface, may leave a small crack at which point the stone often grizzles or chips. The elimination of these faults requires the greatest care, delicacy of touch, a smooth and well-controlled lap, and patience.

In polishing faceted glass gems on the tin lap with tin oxide, the lap should be smooth and the polishing powder should be applied sparingly. A larger quantity of water should be used than normally, because the powder used is a thin, creamy mixture. The usual procedure is to apply the powder and then apply a small quantity of water to the lap surface by means of the paddle to thin the mixture. Sudden stopping of the lap will also produce a brighter facet.

## TIN LAP WITH LEVIGATED ALUMINA, RUBY POWDER, OR LINDE A-5175 POWDER

A number of stones in common use require an alumina polishing powder for successful treatment. For this purpose, either levigated alumina or Damascus ruby powder gives equally good results.

In the garnet group, the hard, clear varieties, as almandite, pyrope, and grossularite, may be polished without difficulty. Special care, however, should be taken to prevent overheating which may result in cracking the stone. Particular attention should be devoted to the work when polishing large facets such as the table. Garnets often contain faults such as cracks, feathers, cavities, or inclusions which may be impossible to eliminate. When these faults extend to the surface of the stone, the difficulty of satisfactorily finishing the facet is greatly increased. Essonite is rarely free of cavities, and these also are common in almandite. When these faults are present, the polished surface of the stone may become pitted or streaked. Occasionally a cavity near the surface may spall or chip out like a percussion mark, and the stone may require repolishing or recutting.

Because the demantoid is softer, it requires greater care in polishing. The best results are obtained with a slowly running lap and polishing powder that is nearly dry.

Chrysolite and peridot (varieties of olivine) are treated in a manner similar to the garnet. These stones, however, often possess soft spots or areas which may prove difficult to finish, the tendency of the stone being to rub or wear away without polishing. Often a high polish can be attained only with the aid of sulphuric acid as a wetting agent with the polishing powder. This peculiarity of grain or texture (soft zones) also may be observed in the zircon. In polishing these stones, the work proceeds normally with a smooth polishing lap and the polishing powder just damp. In polishing the facets on the soft areas, the powder is permitted to dry out, the lap is rotated slowly and, with gentle pressure, the facets are successfully completed. Soft spots in these stones can be polished only with the polishing powder run to dryness on the lap. If the polishing material is wet or damp, the facets will be lapped away without a trace of polished surface.

Topaz may be polished without difficulty (except as noted) although, being a harder stone, the time required to polish each facet or the entire stone usually is greater than that of stones of similar size mentioned before. If the table of the stone has been cut on a cleavage plane, difficulty will be experienced in polishing. This can be overcome by a slowly rotating polishing wheel, with careful pressure and the polishing material nearly dry. Better results are achieved through lapping the table surface a few degrees tangent to the cleavage plane. If the table surface is parallel to the longitudinal axis, polishing should be done in this direction.

Linde polishing powder A-5175 has been found to be excellent in polishing demantoid, chrysolite, and peridot.

Synthetic spinel, which lacks the difficulty in polishing caused by a cleavage plane, closely resembles topaz in texture and is polished in a similar manner. Certain types of synthetic spinel, e.g., synthetic tourmaline, are more difficult to polish than others. The lighter varieties, as a rule, are easy to polish.

Natural spinel is more difficult to polish than the synthetic type. This is not only because of the uneven structure, but sometimes it is because of the twinning which causes complex structure or grain. Large surfaces are particularly difficult to polish, and may require great care and skill to finish successfully. It is often necessary to alter the position of the stone so that the lap works along the surface of the facet from a different

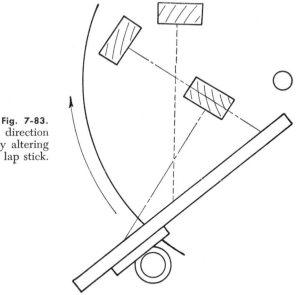

Fig. 7-83.
Lap-polishing direction
changed by altering
position of lap stick.

direction (Fig. 7–83). Sometimes twin crystals are cut, in which case polishing may be performed with the greatest difficulty because of the opposite direction in which the grain or structure of the stone is formed. This is particularly noticeable if the twinning plane is on the table facet, when the facet will show the plane in a sharp dividing line while it is being polished. One portion of the facet will be brightly polished while the other may be dull. A slowly turning lap, nearly dry polishing material, and careful and delicate application, as well as skill and experience are necessary to finish this stone. One of the difficulties encountered is the shifting of the stone, held by the cement, from the heat developed by the friction of the stone on the lap. This can be avoided by carefully controlling the lap speed, the length of time the facet is polished, as well as the consistency of the polishing material on the lap. Linde spinel powder has proved to be very effective in polishing stones mentioned herein.

Chrysoberyl and alexandrite are polished successfully on a tin lap with tripoli. These stones, which are harder than the others previously listed, requires a greater amount of time to finish.

The corundum gems, ruby and sapphire, usually are polished on a copper or bronze lap, using fine tripoli. Rottenstone also will give satisfactory results if it is of good quality. In certain cases (polishing cabochon stones), boxwood or tin laps and the finest diamond powder (No. 6) are utilized for polishing.

To perfectly polish rubies and sapphires, a number of the facets may require polishing from a different direction. This characteristic of grain or crystal structure is most often observed in polishing the table. Occasionally it may be necessary to alter the position two or more times before the action of the polishing lap will produce a satisfactory surface. The latest practice, particularly in the commercial polishing of synthetic ruby and sapphire, is to polish on a tin or zinc lap with diamond powder.

Inclusions as well as flaws, cracks, cavities, and bubbles add to the difficulty of polishing. On large, hard stones, considerable pressure may be necessary to polish or finish the facet and, if numerous flaws are present in the stone, the danger of breakage always is present.

Unusual stones, or stones not generally seen in the commercial field, are regularly cut and polished by the lapidary. Hematite, which is frequently seen, when carefully polished resembles the black diamond. Cassiterite, which is less frequently seen, is treated in like manner. Both of these stones are difficult to polish, but when properly finished they possess a high degree of luster. Best results are obtained by polishing on a tin lap with diamontine polishing powder. Lacking this, Linde powder is used. Maximum brilliance is the result of a slowly rotating lap with the powder dry or nearly so. In polishing stones of this type, it is necessary to thoroughly clean the lap of other powder, and to prepare the lap surface by polishing several stones at one time, or to have a lap reserved for this purpose.

Apatite occasionally is used as a gemstone. Because of its brittle structure, with a pronounced tendency to crack when overheated either in cementing on the lap stick or in polishing, it requires the greatest care in handling and polishing. The facet is first worked on the tin lap with wet polishing powder. As the facet approaches maximum development, the powder is permitted to dry out, and with a delicate touch on the dry or nearly dry lap, the facet is carefully finished. Prolonged application at this stage, resulting in overheating, may cause the stone to crack. Streaks and gouges are typical marks on the facet while it is being polished, and these are very difficult to remove while the facet is brought to maximum development as well as a brilliant polish.

Benitoite may have areas which will prove troublesome in polishing. The difficulty is that facets have a tendency to develop streaks or minute gouges. Proper control of the lap speed, wet polishing powder, and light pressure are necessary to overcome this fault. As a general rule, the light-tinted stones are less difficult to polish than those that are of a dark hue.

Other gem minerals that are sometimes cut and polished for use as gems are albite, amber, andalusite, andradite, augelite, axinite, cordierite, danburite, diopside, dioptase, epidote, euclase, fire opal, fluorite, kornerupine, kyanite, moldavite, obsidian, orthoclase, phenacite, rhodolite, sphalerite, sphene, vesuvianite, and wernerite.

Translucent and opaque stones, which also are faceted and require special care, are nephrite (New Zealand jade), and lapis lazuli. Best results usually are obtained on a dry slowly rotating lap. Exceptions to this rule have been observed where normal conditions (damp powder and regular lap speed) have prevailed.

Lapis lazuli varies considerably in texture and in hardness. Satisfactory results are obtained on a slowly running tin lap with tin oxide nearly dry. Difficulty in polishing may be experienced when dense concentrations of pyrite are present in the stone, because the pyrite gathers particles of the lap, or when stones are soft and granular. Excellent results are obtained by using Linde A powder in the usual manner.

From the foregoing it will be observed that, although the operation of polishing faceted stones is similar to that of cutting or lapping, because of the great difference in the variety as well as in the texture of the materials to be polished, the art of polishing is one which requires a greater amount of experience. Occasionally, new or unfamiliar gem minerals are sent to the lapidary for finishing into faceted stones. If the substance is fine grained enough for this purpose, the facets are cut in the usual manner, after which the initial attempt at polishing should be made on the tin lap using tin oxide. Should the results obtained prove to be unsatisfactory, other polishing powders or laps should be used until a satisfactory finish has been produced. Control of the lap speed as well as the condition of the polishing powder on its surface also should be tried wherever necessary in the manner previously outlined.

CHAPTER 8

# Drilling Holes in Stones

DRILLING holes in stone is one phase of lapidary art which varies from a simple mechanical function, whereby steel drills are used for drilling soft substances like shell, malachite, and onyx marble to the difficult task of piercing the hardest stones, such as ruby, sapphire, and diamond, which can be done only with the use of diamond drills.

The type of drill may vary; thus, for drilling small holes in soft stones, a flat steel drill (Fig. 8–1) will give best results. These drills may be purchased or they can be readily made from tool steel. Steel needles are frequently utilized for this purpose, the blade of which is flattened by heating red hot and then forging. The steel is hardened by heating and quenching in water and then tempered, after which the point is ground to the correct angle and clearance. Drills of this type are particularly useful for drilling pearls. The conventional twist drill also may be used for this purpose. Holes up to ½ in. in diameter may be drilled in various substances whose hardness does not exceed four on Mohs' scale. To drill holes of large size, a pilot hole, that is, a hole drilled with a smaller drill should be drilled first, after which drills of larger size are used. The drill's speed is slow even though the drill is made of high-speed steel, the peripheral speed being about 20 ft. per minute. The abrasive action of the stone on the steel is high; therefore, the point of the drill must be sharpened frequently.

Should an attempt be made to drill stone at too high a rate of speed, the drill point will be quickly abraded. With the loss of its cutting edge, therefore, the ensuing friction will generate sufficient heat to crack the stone or ruin the drill or both. To prevent chipping, the hole may be countersunk to a size slightly larger than the diameter of the drill.

Another type of steel tool which may be utilized for drilling is the steel burr, commonly used in dental operations or for steel die sinking. Their use, however, is limited and they are better used as auxiliaries to the regular drill. In recent years, hard alloys have been successfully used for drilling substances which have an abrading action upon steel. These alloys, cemented tungsten, tantalum, and titanium carbides, or combina-

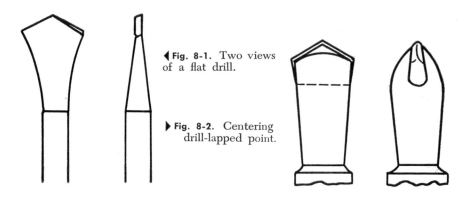

◀ **Fig. 8-1.** Two views of a flat drill.

▶ **Fig. 8-2.** Centering drill-lapped point.

tions, are formed in small briquettes. When suitably mounted and properly handled, they will give excellent service. Small diameter tungsten carbide (Carboloy) rods now are available; and more recently, drills and burrs made of this product are available in many sizes.

For drilling purposes, a small carbide blank is inserted in a milled slot in a properly machined steel shaft (Fig. 8–2), and is brazed in place. The tool then is ground and lapped on a diamond lap, the point of the drill being ground similar to the common flat steel drill (Fig. 8–1). Because of its great hardness (greater than that of corundum), a properly made and sharpened drill will readily penetrate stones in hardness to six on the scale. Marble and soft stones are easily drilled at fairly high speed and the drill is operated dry. When drilling glass or harder stones, however, water is necessary as a coolant and the drilling is done with the article submerged, using light pressure on the drill. When drilling a glass object such as glass plate, for instance, before the drill breaks through, the object should be reversed and the hole drilled from the other side to avoid chipping.

Holes of various sizes may be drilled in thin sections of stone by means of a ball-shaped tool to which abrasive, either diamond or silicon carbide, is applied, thus gradually producing a concave depression (Fig. 6–95). By applying the tool to opposite sides of the stone, a hole may be readily ground through the slab. The maximum thickness of the slab which may be drilled in this manner is slightly less than twice the diameter of the ball tool used.

The round ball-shaped tool also may be used as a small lap for enlarging existing holes. This method is quicker than lapping with a tapered lap, and it is less likely to break or chip the stone which might happen if a drill were used. Large holes may be formed by using grinding wheels which operate in a similar manner. This method is used on stones of little value, where one or two pieces only are required and regular tube drilling equipment is not available. For the economic drilling of holes over ¼ in. in diameter, tube drills are preferred.

If soft stones are to be drilled with holes larger than ½ in. in diameter, thin steel tubing charged with No. 100 silicon carbide will give satisfactory results. Boron carbide abrasive also may be used.

The end of the tube should be serrated or notched (Fig. 8–3), so that the abrasive will work under it, thus forming a cylindrical saw. In operating a tube drill of this type, best results are obtained by submerged drilling, with the abrasive in the form of a thin mud. Drilling progresses in easy stages, and the tube is raised periodically to ensure a sufficient charge of abrasive under the working end of the tube. A considerable amount of heat is generated as the tube enters into the substance being drilled, and care should be exercised to prevent cracking the stone. While the loose-abrasive type of tube drill is particularly useful for drilling holes in glass and softer minerals, it may also be used in drilling quartz al-

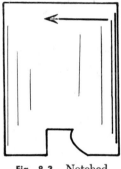

Fig. 8-3. Notched tube drill.

though a greater amount of time will be required to do the work. For example, a number of disks 2 in. in diameter were cut from quartz (jasper) slabs about ¼ in. thick. For this purpose a steel-tube drill, 2 in. in internal diameter, with a wall thickness of 1/32 in., rotating at 750 r.p.m. required an average of 20 minutes to pierce the slab. The abrasive used was silicon carbide No. 220 grit.

To drill stones harder than glass, a diamond drill is the most economical as well as the most satisfactory and efficient. Four distinct types are used in lapidary work. They are the solid-metal type, the inserted diamond-tip type, the diamond charged, and individually diamond-set tube. The latest development consists of diamond grain bonded with sintered metal or metallic alloys.

The solid-metal type is used for drilling small holes in thin stones. Its chief use, however, is in drilling hard stone for wire-drawing dies or for bearing jewels. Steel needles may be used and these should rotate at a high speed, usually from 5000 to 7000 r.p.m. A small quantity of fine diamond dust, mixed with a few drops of olive oil, is placed upon the stone at the point to be drilled, and the rapidly rotating steel drill gradu-

Fig. 8-4.
Diamond-drilling
equipment.

ally wears a hole through the stone. The drill is lifted at regular periods so that the diamond powder may lodge under the point, and the actual working of the drill point on the stone being only a few seconds. Since this process is a lengthy one, such drilling is usually done on automatic machines (Fig. 8–4). Small-diameter steel tubes also will produce excellent results if used with diamond grit No. 300 in oil.

Small diameter 1 to 1.5 mm. hypodermic needles are excellent for drilling small holes. When used with No. 300 diamond grain in oil with a precision drill press, a speed of 3500 r.p.m. will be ample.

A small quantity of the diamond oil mixture is placed upon the stone where the hole is to be drilled, and the rapidly rotating tube is brought in contact with it. A slight pressure follows for a few brief moments, after which the drilling tube is retracted, and the cycle is repeated. These pulsations are continued at a rate of approximately 60 per minute, the diamond oil mixture being added when required by means of a small splinter or a small, fine hair brush.

The rate of drilling will vary according to the toughness of the material. Amethyst, and rock crystal, can be drilled at the rate of 7 mm. in ten minutes. Spinel and corundum require about twice the time to drill, while a 1.5 mm. diameter hole drilled through a jadeite bar, ½ in. thick, required nearly two hours to complete. For drilling the latter gem, diamond-tipped tools are best.

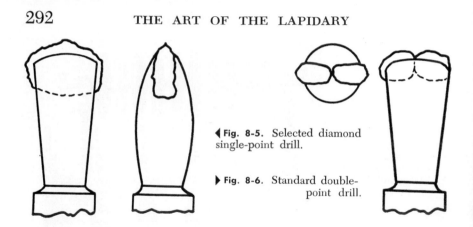

◀ **Fig. 8-5.** Selected diamond single-point drill.

▶ **Fig. 8-6.** Standard double-point drill.

In hard stone most of the holes are drilled with the standard type drill which has a small diamond set in the end of a metal rod (Figs. 8–5 and 8–6).

As a general rule, these drills are made by the lapidary who uses them. In the majority of cases the bow drill method is used, in principle little improved over the method used by the ancient Egyptians (Fig. 8–7). In making drills, the highest degree of skill is required, for not only must the drills be accurately made, but good judgment also must be exercised in the selection of suitable carbonado, and their proper fixing and setting in the point or drilling end of the tool. In drills 2 mm. diameter and smaller a single carbon is the rule, and in larger sizes two carbons may be used.

In making the drills, a suitable metal rod is prepared by filing a slot in the end, into which the carbon is set. It is further secured by careful peening so that the metal is hammered about the stone or the stone may be brazed in place. A stone of suitable size should be selected. One that is about the same width as the diameter of the drill, with a flattened triangular form, will be ideal for a single-point tool. If two stones are to be used, flattened, slightly tapered stones of equal size and type should be selected. After peening or brazing, the surplus metal is carefully ground away until portions of the diamond are exposed and full clearance is obtained on the sides as well as the point. The drill then is tested on an agate block, with a drop of oil, and further clearance adjustments are made if necessary. This can be determined by a microscopic examination of the metal surrounding the diamond which will show, by wear, if more material should be removed. The performance and the life of the drill vary considerably because of the many factors involved. These are the type of metal used for the drill, the method of setting, security of the

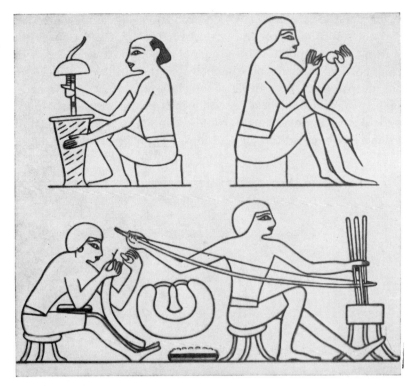

**Fig. 8-7.** Early application of the bow drill in ancient Egypt. Upper, drilling vase; lower, drilling beads.

stone, the type, durability, and toughness of the diamonds, the size of the drill and the method of application, as well as the nature of the stone and the depth of the hole to be drilled. Even under the best conditions, diamond drills are delicate tools, and unusual care should be exercised in their operation. Although most lapidaries and stone drillers use the bow drill, a small lathe with the drill operating in a horizontal position may also be used (Fig. 8–8). A modern diamond drill, developed and used by the author and illustrated in Figure 8–9, possesses many advantages. When used in a precision drill press, the result is accurate and positive control at all times, as well as greater production, longer life, and lessened possibilities of stone breakage.

In recent years, the sintered alloy diamond drills have become very popular. Diamond particles of No. 80 or 100 grit, held by sintered tungsten carbide, have been found to be the most satisfactory as well as durable in sizes 2 mm. and under. These small drills must be used with considerable care and skill to prevent breakage as they are delicate and do not stand much pressure. Most of these sintered type drills will work if correctly handled. The principal difficulty experienced is in the sintered portion shearing off the body of the drill, particularly when drilling deep holes. These drills should be operated at high speed 5000 to 7000 r.p.m. and used in a precision drill press with a light pressure.

As there is widespread amateur interest in lapidary work, the problem of drilling has been solved by the introduction of numerous automatic

Fig. 8-8.  Horizontal drilling on onyx bar in a lathe.

Fig. 8-9. Drilling holes in a petrified wood section for a clock, with a solid diamond drill. A small dam of putty retains the coolant.

drilling machines. Small diameter tubes which may be had in a variety of metals or alloys, including steel, silver, and bronze, are utilized with diamond grit No. 300 as already described. A drilling machine of this kind is illustrated in Figure 8–10. Drilling through stones in one pass using automatic drilling machines minimizes the possibility of breaking the stone or the tube used in drilling.

Before drilling has begun, the stone to be drilled is spotted; that is, a small concave is ground at the point where the hole is to be drilled. The small concave often is made by using a small, ball-shaped, diamond-charged wheel moistened with oil, although water may serve and is used in many cases. The tool is held in the chuck of a small lathe and is rotated at high speed. The stone to be drilled is held in the hand or is fastened to a lap stick. It is brought in contact with the rotating tool at the point where the hole is to be drilled, and the concave is developed to a size slightly larger than the drilled hole. The slight edge which remains protects the stone from chipping during the drilling operation. Proper preparation of the work for drilling is of great importance where the bow drill is used. With the drill held in the precision drill press, because of the greater rigidity and accuracy, the spotting may be dispensed with if the hole is to be drilled through a flat stone at a right angle to the surface. If necessary, a special centering drill may be used. A tool of this type, similar in construction to Figure

**Fig. 8-10.**
Taylor drilling machine.

8–2, consists of a stout metal shank into which a sharp-edged, pointed diamond is affixed.

All drilling with diamond drills should be done submerged, or an adequate supply of coolant, usually water, must be directed to the drill point at all times. Failure of the supply of coolant, which also washes away the abrasive particles of stone removed or abraded by the drill point, may cause the stone to crack. Also, the ground or abraded particles of the stone removed by the drill cause undue wear on the metal shank holding the diamond which will materially shorten the life of the drill.

As a general rule, flat stones, after spotting, are cemented to a steel plate, and the hole is drilled through the stone. As the drill approaches the bottom of, or the opposite side of, the stone, the pressure on the point should be lessened so that the drill will not break through, and chip the other side. In drilling holes through stones of greater thickness, particular care should be taken as the hole becomes deeper. Pressure on the drill point should endure for a few seconds only, after which the drill should be withdrawn a slight amount (about ½ to 1 mm.), to be certain the coolant will reach the drill point and the cycle is repeated.

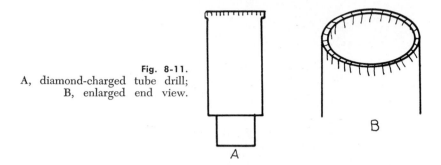

Fig. 8-11.
A, diamond-charged tube drill;
B, enlarged end view.

Small diameter metal tubes up to 6 mm. diameter may be used successfully with diamond grain in the manner already described. A tube
3 mm. diameter operating at 3000 r.p.m. using diamond grit No. 300,
in oil, will drill a hole in agate to a depth of ½ in. in twenty minutes.
Higher speeds to 5000 r.p.m. are more economical when using tubes
½ to 1 mm. in diameter.

Diamond charged tube drills (Figs. 8–11 and 8–12) in sizes from
⅜ in. in diameter and upward are not difficult to make. The usual practice is to mount the tube on a steel arbor having a shank diameter of
¼ in. to ⅜ in. which permits ready entry into most drill press chucks.
The tube is mounted on this adapter by a force fit and by means of
the shank, the body of the tube is turned truly in a lathe and the end
of the tube faced square. A small hole, ⅛ in. to 3/16 in. according to
the diameter of the shank, is drilled through the latter. This enables the
operator to insert a steel rod into the hole to drive out the core resulting
from drilling. Without this aid, it would be very difficult to remove the
core when the drilling has been completed (Fig. 8–13).

After facing the tube end, notches are cut into the tube face by
means of a sharp knife. These notches should be spaced about 1/16 in.
apart and cut about 1/16 in. deep. A thick paste made with heavy oil
and No. 100 diamond grit is then prepared and this diamond-oil mixture
is then thoroughly wiped into the cuts in the tube. A wiper made from
round leather belt, or a thick slice of neoprene is fine for this.

The diamond charge is thoroughly embedded in the prepared tube
end by peening. The prepared tube end is slipped onto a hard steel
mandrel slightly smaller in diameter that has been securely fastened
in a bench vise. By means of a small hammer the serrated tube end
is gradually closed by hammering and the diamond grains are thoroughly
embedded and tightly held in the closed slots. After closing the tube

**Fig. 8-12.**
Drilling large holes in glass-jar tops for lamps, with a diamond tube drill, ⅜-in. diameter. A dam of putty retains the coolant.

end, the face should be treated in like manner by peening and as a final precaution, the side wall of the tube once again is gone over by a thorough light hammering.

After this preparation, the surplus grit is wiped away and the tube is then ready for drilling. A diamond tube drill made in this manner is actually a cylindrical diamond saw (Figs. 8–11 and 8–13).

Operating speeds from 1500 to 1800 r.p.m. will give satisfactory results with tube drills up to ¾ in. in diameter. Tube drills from one to two inches in diameter should be operated at proportionally lower speed.

A dam of putty or placticene is built around the spot where the hole is to be drilled (Fig. 8–12) and a coolant, usually water is placed into the cavity thus formed. A well-charged drill will commence cutting a hole once the rotating drill is brought in contact with the stone or object to be drilled.

If a slab is to be drilled to form a ring (Fig. 6–93 and 6–94 A and B), a watch or clock case (Fig. 8–14), it should be cemented to a slab of agate or an aluminum cement plate and the latter securely held in a vise

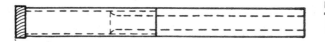

**Fig. 8-13.**
Tube drill adapter, ⅜-in. shank.

Fig. 8-14.
Desk clock,
Rhodonite case,
70 x 92 mm., 11 mm.
thick; Nephrite base
37 x 87 mm., 12 mm.
thick (author's creation).

or fixture. A depth stop on the drill press may be adjusted to limit the travel of the drill so the stone is not damaged when the drill pierces the slab. If the depth stop is set so a millimeter of stone remains to be drilled and the stop is then carefully adjusted to limit the travel of the drill in small amounts, brittle and fragile stones can be drilled without trouble.

It is in forcing the drilling and through a lack of sensitivity in the last millimeter that most damage occurs. The drill may suddenly penetrate the cemented face of the stone and as the hole diameter is less owing to the lack of clearance (Fig. 8–15), the tube drill may be forced into this restricted area with the result that the drill face will tear and the diamond charge will be lost, and the drill will be ruined. The slab being drilled is invariably broken at the same time. Sintered core drills also are subject to this damage and occasionally the sintered core may be stripped from the tube to which it had been brazed.

In operation, the drill press feed is maintained for a few seconds, after which the tube is withdrawn or retracted slightly. Two or three mm. is sufficient to permit the coolant to flow under the drilling face and then the cycle is repeated. If the core drill does not cut freely, it should be recharged or the charged portion refreshened by lapping on a fine grinding wheel, e.g., No. 220 grit. The small portion of the metal removed in this manner permits the exposed diamond grains to function properly.

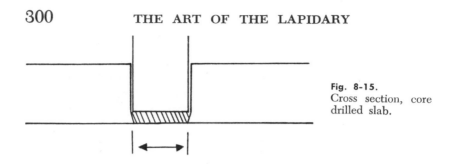

Fig. 8-15.
Cross section, core
drilled slab.

Persistent attempts to drill with a core drill in poor condition in the hope that it eventually will condition itself can only result in damage to the stone being drilled. This is particularly true in stones having low resistance to changes in temperature, *e.g.*, rock crystal.

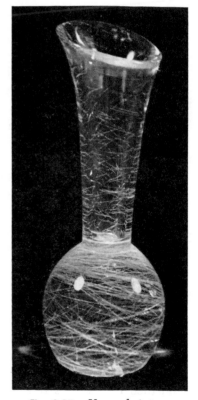

Fig. 8-16. Rock crystal vase, actinolite inclusions; amethyst violets, 14 kt. gold stems and mountings; 89 mm. high, 45 x 54 mm. wide (author's creation).

Fig. 8-17. Venus hairstone bud vase, 114 mm. high, 43 mm. dia. (author's creation).

Production drilling machines that introduce the coolant through the body of the tube drill are able to drill continuously.

Careful and intelligent handling of a diamond core drill is imperative if long life and satisfactory service is expected. It should be remembered at all times that the weakest part of the drill is the portion that holds the diamond grain in place.

In drilling deep holes, 2 in. to 3 in. and over, a copious supply of coolant is needed and the tube face should cut freely. A poorly charged drill or one that has become worn through continuous use should be avoided.

In the formation of small bottles or vases (Figs. 8–16, 8–17, and 9–18), blind holes are drilled to the depth required and the core is removed by carefully tapping the top edge of the core at an angle. If the drilled stone is flawless, the core will usually break at the bottom and the cylindrical shaped core is most easily removed. Because of the tendency for rock crystal and other similar types of the quartz family to fracture in an irregular rhombohedral manner, the core often will break in this manner (Fig. 8–18), and the remaining stub left at the bottom of the hole must be removed by end milling if it is desired to flatten the bottom of the hole, a necessity in transparent gemstones (Figs. 8–16 and 8–17). This is a time consuming operation and it is done by placing a mixture of wet silicon carbide and water in the cavity, and utilizing a round steel rod the diameter of the core removed as a lap held in the drill press chuck.

By a downward pressure, the end of the cylindrical steel rod coming in contact with the portion of the core remaining and through the medium of the abrasive present becomes a small diameter lap, and the stone is gradually worn away.

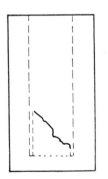

Fig. 8-18.   Irregular break in core.

A diamond charged end mill or lap will cut away the material more quickly. After all of the remaining core has been removed, the hole may be smoothed and polished or the cavity may be developed further (Fig. 9–18). In polishing the cylindrical cavity in the small vise (Fig. 8–16), after the core was completely removed and the bottom lapped flat, a true cylindrical steel lap, slightly smaller than the diameter of the hole, was used in like manner with FFF silicon carbide and water. By a constant up-and-down motion, the lap being used in a drill press (which is ideal for this purpose), the entire cylindrical surface was ground uniformly smooth and all of the gouges and grooves left by the core drill were removed.

First polishing was by substituting a wooden lap for the steel rod, and using FFF silicon carbide abrasive. A surprising degree of smoothness and polish is obtained in this manner. After all of the lap scratches have been removed, the vase as well as the drill press is thoroughly cleaned of all grit particles and a wood polishing lap is used with tin oxide to develop the final polish. Tripoli or levigated alumina used before the tin oxide will hasten the operation, although this introduces an additional step.

A variation in the cavity form of a small bud vase is shown in Figure 8–17. The cavity is formed by three stage core drilling (Fig. 8–19), after which the remaining material is removed by a special formed lap (Fig. 8–20). Polishing follows as already described.

In grinding out the cavity to form the snuff bottle or perfume flacon (Fig. 9–18), the round tool was used, as the cross section of the bottle is oval. If the bottle has a round cross section, a bent gouge (Fig. 8–21) will greatly reduce the working time. During the grinding operation a metal tubular guard is fastened in the opening to prevent accidental grinding of the mouth of the bottle. This precaution is necessary as

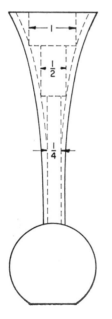

▲ Fig. 8-20.   Venus hairstone bud vase and conical lap.

◀ Fig. 8-19.
Vase, core drilling in three steps to form conical cavity.

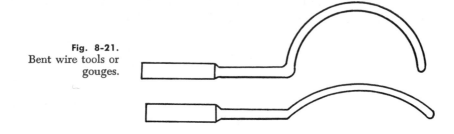

Fig. 8-21.
Bent wire tools or
gouges.

the shank of the tool would easily grind the hole oversize and possibly ruin the bottle.

In drilling holes at an angle to the surface, a deep countersink or concave should be made in the stone at the point where the hole is to be drilled, to insure correct starting of the drill point, and the stone should be set at the proper angle. A clamp or vise may hold the stone in the proper position if such a device may be utilized without danger of the stone's slipping or twisting.

Whenever a form (spheres or pendant drops) must be drilled which cannot be securely held in the proper position by a vise or clamp, it should be cemented to a suitable plate or fixture with lap cement or sealing wax, and adjusted to the proper position. Cement chucks of various types, plates, or cups are ideal for this purpose. Figure 8–22 shows a drill set up for spheres and drop forms. Threaded screw eyes or pegs are cemented into the hole so that the article may be suspended from a cord or a chain.

Occasionally, two or more holes are drilled in a stone at an angle so that they intersect. One hole is drilled at the proper angle and to the required depth and, after resetting or recementing the stone, the second

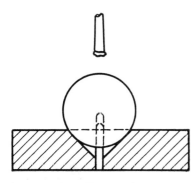

Fig. 8-22. Drilling jig for spheres.

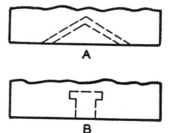

A

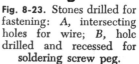

B

Fig. 8-23. Stones drilled for fastening: A, intersecting holes for wire; B, hole drilled and recessed for soldering screw peg.

hole is drilled. As the drill point nears the hole which has been drilled, the pressure should be lessened, and the tool should be operated in such a sensitive manner as to prevent the point from suddenly breaking through the thin wall which separates the two holes. This can be done by adjusting the stops on the drill press, limiting the travel of the drill. Failure to exercise this precaution may cause the drill to break through, the drill point to be broken, and the diamond being torn out; or, the stone being drilled may be broken by the drill.

As a general rule, intersecting holes of this type should be drilled with the included angle as near 90 deg. as possible. This is to provide for the easy passage of a suitable wire or loop for suspension or holding (Fig. 8–23).

Beads of all kinds are formed by drilling holes through an object so that it may be strung on a cord. In the majority of cases, the beads are spherical or have some regular geometrical form. Occasionally, however, irregular objects such as branch coral or nodular turquoise are used as beads.

All soft substances are drilled with a steel drill, the most common article being the pearl. If carefully handled, pearls may be drilled through in one pass. However, it always is best to drill from opposite points, so that the hole meets within the pearl. This prevents the surface from chipping or breaking out, which usually happens when the drill becomes dull or worn.

In drilling pearls or spheres, a special chuck or centering device is used so that the hole is drilled through the center of the sphere. This chuck consists of a conical receptacle securely fastened concentric with the drill spindle. In drilling pearls where very small diameter holes are required, a guide bushing is necessary to prevent the drill from wandering. A metal plate, with a hole of the required size, is secured above the conical centering mechanism so the hole will guide the drill through the center of the pearl. Figure 8–24 shows a drilling fixture of this type, in which the guide plate is pivoted so that it may be swung aside to facilitate easy handling of the pearl. In an alternative method, the guide bushing is fixed to a clamp which securely holds the pearl and prevents its turning. A thin lining of leather or plastic tape on the conical surfaces prevents turning as well as marring the surface of the pearl. After the pearl has been drilled halfway through, it is located by means of a guide pin which fits in the center of the conical holder. This accurately sets the pearl in line for the final drilling, thus the hole is concentric when finished. If sharp, well-ground drills are used, the pearl may be drilled in

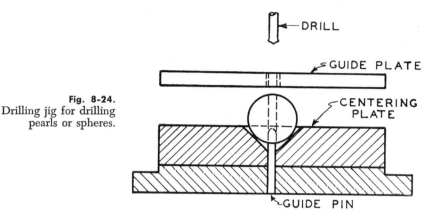

**Fig. 8-24.**
Drilling jig for drilling
pearls or spheres.

one pass. Spherical forms made of stone may be held in a similar manner when drilling for use as beads. Cubes or other forms, such as conical or olive, must be held in special fixtures or they must be cemented to plates. Hard stones for beads should be drilled from both sides to prevent breaking.

Drop forms, for suspension, may be drilled with the hole parallel to the longitudinal axis or at a right angle thereto, in which case the hole is made as small as possible. Figures 6–61 to 6–63 illustrate bead forms in use for necklaces or other articles of jewelry.

As a general rule, beads have a uniform cross section, but in some cases they have two dimensions and may be lenticular or conical in form.

REAMING is resorted to whenever existing holes must be enlarged and where it is not practical to redrill the hole to the size desired. Occasionally holes must be enlarged to fit tubes or pegs to fasten stone settings or medallions, or the position of one or more holes must be altered slightly to accommodate special settings. For this purpose, arbors or reamers of various sizes are used (Fig. 8–25). These tools, made of soft steel, invariably are tapered or conical, and in some cases they may be cylindrical. When charged or used with a suitable abrasive, usually fine diamond powder, they form efficient laps.

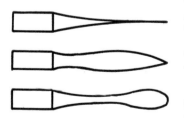

**Fig. 8-25.** Various types of reamers.

Operating speeds may vary from 1500 to 3500 r.p.m. according to the size of the tool, the amount of material to be removed, and the nature of the substance being lapped or reamed. As the function of a reamer is to remove a small amount of material only, speeds in excess of 3000 r.p.m. rarely are used.

If diamond powder No. 3 is used with the tool, an initial charge is given to it by rolling the tool between two slabs of agate, having first placed a drop of diamond dust in oil on the surface of the agate. Although olive oil is best for this purpose, good results are obtained by using medium body machine oil. From eight to ten drops are added to each carat of diamond dust, and the mixture is thoroughly stirred before using. An alternative method for charging is to rotate the tool in the lathe and to hold the agate plate against it, applying the diamond and oil mixture. After a tool has been thoroughly charged, it is only necessary to keep it moistened with a moderate application of oil during operation, and from time to time to freshen its cutting ability, a drop of diamond dust in oil is added. Common practice is to apply the lubricant with the finger. Reamers, made by incorporating diamond grain in a sintered alloy, recently introduced, are excellent for this purpose.

As a rule tools of this kind are charged with coarse diamond grit. They cut very rapidly and should be operated at speeds in excess of 3500 r.p.m. Extreme care should be used so the tool will not seize the work, which could result in stripping the diamond charge from the tool, thus ruining it and possibly the work also.

When using a reamer or other tool to enlarge an existing hole, a light touch should be used and the stone must not be forced. This is important where the stones are thin and narrow and the hole being lapped is a large proportion of the width of the stone. Undue force or pressure should be avoided for this will not cause the tool to work faster but may cause the stone to seize, and the wedging action of the tapered reamer or lap may easily split the stone into two pieces. Sharp-edged stones, which seize on the tapered lap and wrench out of the fingers, also may cause cuts and bruises.

Small spherical laps also may be used for reaming and these are less likely to cause seizing although the resultant hole reamed may not be straight.

Occasionally drilled holes must be polished. This is necessary where a special effect is desired, as when a hole is drilled in a transparent gemstone. Holes are polished with small-diameter laps or wires of steel or copper with fine diamond powder, usually No. 4 or 5. The work progresses until all of the internal grooves and irregularities of the hole have been removed. After the hole has been lapped smooth, the initial polishing is done with No. 6 diamond powder on small-diameter laps made of hard wood, horn, or plastic. Tripoli or tin oxide may be used as a substitute for the diamond powder, particularly on holes of larger size.

Countersinking, counterboring, and recessing operations on hard stone are performed with the use of diamond-charged tools of various types (Fig. 8–26). Tools having ball- or spherical-shaped ends, as well as conical forms, are used for countersinking, and disk or cylindrical forms are used for recessing and counterboring.

Occasionally, it is necessary to hollow out articles in stone, such as cases or boxes of various types, so that the bottom portion and the side walls are flat and at a right angle to each other. To accomplish this in a satisfactory manner, cylindrical laps of various sizes are used, beginning with the largest size which can be utilized, and finishing with the smaller diameter to form the corners of the aperture. All the laps used are diamond charged on the flat end as well as on the cylindrical surface so that proper cutting is assured. Positive stops control the depth of the tool so that the bottom surface is lapped in a uniform manner. If the stone which is so treated is transparent and the recessed surface is to be polished, suitable laps, together with a polishing material, are operated in a similar manner, and the surface is brought to a high degree of polish. An article of this type, a watchcase made of rock crystal, is shown in Figure 6–85.

Grooving, whether internal or external, is performed with the use of diamond-charged, disk-shaped wheels of various sizes. All of the functions described and performed with the use of diamond powder as an abrasive also may be performed with the use of silicon carbide, although the operation will require a greater amount of time and frequent truing or reshaping of the wheels used. In cases where a large stone is treated,

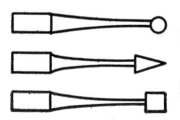

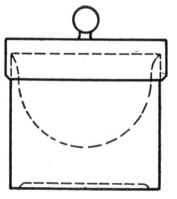

◀ Fig. 8-26. Ball cone, and wheel cutters.

▶ Fig. 8-27. Diamond-powder pot with cover.

the use of silicon carbide is naturally less costly and the rough preliminary work may be done with this abrasive.

When drilling, reaming, and similar operations are to be performed
on stones of certain types, oil should not be used with the diamond
powder. For example, on feathered or cracked stones, such as rose quartz,
amethyst, or rock crystal, where the oil, which becomes black from
working, may lodge in the cracks or crevices causing unsightly stains
or blemishes, which are impossible to remove, water is used instead.

Likewise, in various operations on jade, water on the lapping tool
facilitates the cutting, and stones like turquoise, which may become
stained, are better worked by lubricating the tools with water.

The small pot or container (powder pot, Fig. 8–27) in which the diamond dust and oil mixture is contained, should be made of solid metal
for stability, thus minimizing the danger of tipping and spilling the
contents.

Thin sheet-metal cups should be avoided.

# CHAPTER 9

# Engraving, Carving, and Sculpturing

ENGRAVING, carving, and sculpturing are performed on all types of stones, from the softest, talc, to the hardest, diamond. The unit may be so large that it may weigh several hundred pounds or so small as to weigh only a fraction of a carat. In the art, carving and sculpturing include all articles used for ornament or utility such as dishes, bowls, bottles, vases, jars, flowers, statues, and the like. Engraving, however, refers to gems, usually of small size, upon which are incised figures or images of various types. These are usually mounted in rings, brooches, and the like, and they generally are used for personal adornment.

In the group of engraved gems, there are several distinct types, such as intaglio, cameo, chevct, seals, crests or coats of arms, and encrusted gems.

The *intaglio* (Fig. 9–1) is the oldest form of the engraved gems

**Fig. 9-1.**
Cylinder seals.
Upper: impression
of Babylonian
cylinder, of jasper,
about 2600 B.C.,
depicting Gistubar
strangling a lion,
actual size.
Lower: Persian
cylinder seal, of
jasper, sixth century
B.C., actual size.
Left: cylinder seal;
right: impression.
Darius on a lion
hunt.

and in ancient times, it was extensively used for sealing purposes. The stone itself was engraved with some device, often the likeness of the owner, and the image which was carved into the stone left a depression which, when pressed upon a plastic material, produced a likeness in relief.

The earliest forms of intaglio were the Babylonian seals. These were engraved upon cylinders of stone (Fig. 9–1), through the center of which a hole was pierced to permit suspension from a cord, so as to be ready for instant use. The cylinders were rolled upon the damp clay leaving an impression and, after baking, a durable record remained. Many thou-

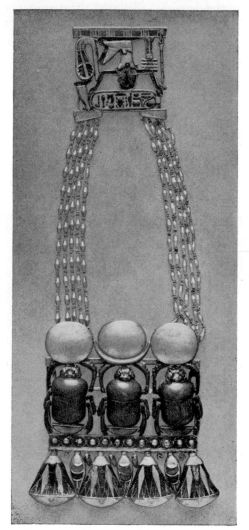

Fig. 9-2.
A pectoral with gold beads and scarab ornament, from the tomb of Tut-Ankh-Amen. The scarabs are cut from lapis lazuli.

**Fig. 9-3.**
Indian onyx cameo, eight layers
in black, brown, and white.
Ptolemy II and Arsinoe II, 3rd
century, B.C. Size 115 by
113 mm.

sands of these clay tablets remain to this day, many of which bear impressions of seals attesting to the validity of the contract or agreement inscribed in the baked-clay record.

From Babylonia, the custom of sealing all letters and documents spread to Egypt. The forms of the earliest seals were similar to those used by the Babylonians, but the Egyptians soon introduced a new form, called the *scarab* (Fig. 9–2). One surface was elaborated formed into a beetle and the flat back opposite was reserved for engraving with hieroglyphic characters. The scarab was usually pierced with a hole parallel to the flat surface so that it could be mounted in a ring and used as a seal when needed. To other parts of the ancient world, with development of civilization, the custom of sealing spread first to the islands in the Aegean and then to the mainland. To these people, the scarab (which had a religious significance to the Egyptians) had little meaning, so that the beetle was removed entirely, producing a form known as the *scaraboid*.

With the development of the art, the scaraboid form gradually changed, and was finally replaced by a cabochon form. The engraving usually was on the flat surface and commonly upon the convex surface as well, and all of the stones were set in metal bezels or rings.

During the Augustan era, the cameo (Figs. 1–2, 9–3 and 4), an engraved gem with the figure in relief, became popular. Although earlier examples are known, this form was used exclusively as an ornament, and the wealthy Roman delighted in a lavish display. Nearly all articles in his home were set with these gems.

Miniatures and busts in cameo, seen occasionally in full relief, represent the highest degree of artistry (Figs. 9–4, 5, and 6).

**Fig. 9-4.** Upper: Cameo portraits of Hon. George Morey and Horace Greeley. Lower: bracelet cameos by Wm. M. Hunt, American painter, of four Hunt brothers.

In the middle ages, crests and coats of arms engraved in stone were introduced, and the custom of sealing was revived which endured until the end of the past century.

The *chevet* is a modern introduction. It is a shallow cameo cut in such a manner that the entire figure lies below the surface of the surrounding stone; thus the engraved figure in relief is protected by the higher rim surface.

TECHNIQUE. For the purpose of engraving on hard stone, tools made of mild steel or iron, charged with a suitable abrasive, are used. As a general rule, a No. 4 or 5 fine diamond powder is used, although for certain purposes silicon carbide is more satisfactory. The use of the latter abrasive, however, is limited in scope. The tools, which are accurately turned, have cutting heads of great variety as to size and form, similar to those in Figure 4–5, sphere or ball shape, wheel or disk, cylin-

**Fig. 9-5.**
A rock-crystal bust of Francis Joseph
of Austria, from author's collection.
Height, 61 mm.

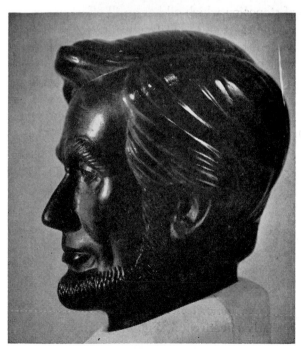

**Fig. 9-6.**
Abraham Lincoln (dark
blue Australian Sapphire
by Norman Maness).
Size: $2\frac{9}{16}$ in.
high, $1\frac{3}{4}$ in. wide,
2 in. deep, weight
1318 cts.

drical, oval, sharp edge, or conical. A convenient material from which these tools can be made is precision-ground mild steel (called needle rod), 3/16 or ¼ in. in diameter. The average length of the tool is 2 in. This material, which is accurate as to size, may be held in a collet chuck in a small lathe, and the point may be readily turned to the desired shape. The diameter of the rod will provide tools large enough for most purposes. Occasionally, tools with a larger diameter are required. These usually are wheel types or saws. Tools of this type can be turned from solid stock, or the wheel or disk-shaped unit may be a shrunk or forced fit on the ¼-in. arbor. After the tools have been turned truly, they are charged by rotating them in contact with an agate plate, to which a drop of diamond dust in oil has been added. It is customary to keep the diamond dust in oil in a small pot. A carat of powder mixed thoroughly with 10 to 12 drops of oil will be of proper consistency. Care should be used in charging the surface of special formed tools so as to preserve the contour.

After the tools have been thoroughly charged, they require only the addition of a lubricant to enable them to cut freely. From time to time, a fresh charge of diamond dust in oil is applied, or a small quantity of the powder may be thorcughly mixed with the lubricant which is applied to the tool. While oil is used in the majority of cases, there are a number of stones on which oil has an ill effect and water is used to advantage to enable the tool to cut freely. Turquoise is an example where oil would cause discolorization, and when working jade, better results are obtained with the use of water.

To become proficient in the art of engraving gemstones, manual dexterity is not only necessary, but the artistic ability of the individual must be developed to the highest degree for this art is actually sculpture in miniature. It is important, therefore, that the student gem engraver possess the ability to draw and to model figures rapidly and accurately.

As a first step, the student should learn the functions of the variously shaped diamond tools with which the engraving is done. Large, ball- or oval-shaped tools are used for the rapid removal of material or concave work in intaglios or wherever engraving is done in the face of a stone. The smallest ball- or oval-headed tools are used for the fine detail work after the main portion of the figure has been blocked out. The bud, wheel, and conical forms also are used for this purpose.

Small saws or large, wheel- or cylindrical-shaped tools are used for the rapid removal of material in cameo work, the small saw being particularly effective (A, Fig. 9–7). Small, knife-edged disk tools are used

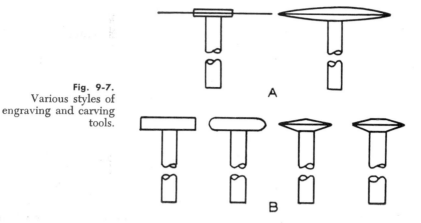

Fig. 9-7.
Various styles of
engraving and carving
tools.

A

B

for making fine lines or for outlining as shown in *B*, Figure 9–7. As a general rule, intaglio cutting is less tedious than cameo cutting, because of the smaller amount of material to be removed unless exceptional detail is required, as for example, a finely molded portrait with a polished surface.

Fig. 9-8. Engraving intaglio.

In preparing a suitable stone, such as some variety of chalcedony (carnelian, sard, etc.), for an intaglio, it has been customary in the past to remove the surface polish by lapping and then to draw the outline upon the stone with a metal stylus. The surface then is repolished upon the satisfactory completion of the engraving.

Equally good results are obtained by covering the surface of the stone with a coat of thin white lacquer or similar material, drawing the figure on the surface when the coat is dry, and then carefully tracing the outline with a diamond stylus. After the outline has been traced upon the surface so that it will be permanent, the stone is cemented to a short lap stick, so that it may be conveniently handled. The operator then assumes a comfortable position and is ready to proceed (Fig. 9–8).

The lathe should be capable of speeds up to 8000 r.p.m. without injury to the bearings, for operating speeds sometimes reach this number. However, speeds from 2000 to 4000 r.p.m. usually are sufficient. Tools should be held in a collet chuck, accurately, so that the cutting end will rotate truly and without chatter. The outline on the stone may be further protected or defined by a light cutting with a sharp knife-edged wheel, or the worker may block out the outline with correctly shaped tools that have been provided. The bulk of the surface to be hollowed out is removed with the largest tools, and the detail work is finished with smaller tools. Simple forms should be attempted first, learning to control the tool and the work so that it will follow where the operator wills.

From time to time the progress of the work may be checked by making a wax impression. Plasticine is a good material for this purpose. Then, by gradual grinding with correct tools accurately applied, the work is brought to completion.

While the average commercial intaglio may be produced without great difficulty, to accurately and artistically engrave a portrait likeness requires the greatest degree of skill and artistry.

Occasionally, intaglios are polished. Oftentimes as much time is spent on the polishing as was required in the cutting, for the finely molded work and sharp detail must be retained. This can be done only by means of small polishing wheels of the same size and shape as the cutting wheels. Small points or wheels made of ivory, boxwood, maple, rosewood, or horn, as well as metal wheels made in tin, bronze, and copper may be used. The finest diamond powder, No. 6, is used, and when the small wheels turn at high speed with this abrasive, a fine finish is obtained. A high, glossy surface is obtained by using a polishing powder such as tin oxide, alumina, or tripoli, according to the nature of the stone.

While the majority of intaglios are cut in stones of one color as specified, unusually attractive gems may be produced by using stones of contrasting color. On such stones as black and white onyx, sardonyx, or carnelian onyx, one layer of which is quite thin, the figure is cut through the thin upper strata into the contrasting background.

A gemstone of this type, frequently seen during the Roman era of the first and second centuries A.D., called the aegyptilla was very popular. This gemstone, now called nicolo, is an onyx of two layers. The uppermost layer is a bluish-white chalcedony through which the figure is cut into the black onyx layer beneath it, and the contrast is very pleasing.

In cameo cutting, the same tools and equipment are used, the sole difference in the work being that the subject is carved in relief in the stone. As a general rule, the stone chosen for cameo work will consist of two or more parallel layers of contrasting colors, such as black and white onyx, sardonyx, carnelian onyx, or onyx jasper. The head or figure to be worked is cut in one layer, and the contrasting color serves as the background.

Occasionally cameos are cut from a stone of uniform color, such as those made of jasper, carnelian, or sard, but these are rarely as attractive as the gems cut from material having a background which shows the engraving to the best advantage.

As the entire surface is to be carved, the polished surface on the top layer of a cut stone may be removed, and upon this surface the design or figure is drawn with a stylus. The outline is carefully traced with a small, sharp-wheel tool, and large areas in the field are blocked out and removed by sawing wherever possible. After the bulk of the background has been removed, the figure is molded with the largest tools available. The final detail work or modeling then is done with the smaller tools.

Chevets are engraved in a similar manner, usually in stones of a single color. The entire head or figure is carved into the surface of the stone, leaving a border surrounding the outline. Very interesting effects can be produced in such stones as carnelian, onyx, or sardonyx, which have two or three layers. Thus, a head in one color may be surrounded by a border of contrasting color and, if a third layer is visible, the background may be the latter.

Seals, crests, coats of arms, or inscriptions are made in a similar manner. The majority of these works are in intaglio. Although widely used generations ago, these engraved gems are now rarely seen.

Encrusted gems may be seen in large numbers at the present time. These stones, which usually are of a uniform color, have the design engraved in the surface of the stone. The engraved portion then is fitted with a sponge gold burnished into place and made level with the surface of the stone. The design of the older pieces usually consists of a floral piece, or a spray of flowers. Sometimes the bud or flower was further ornamented with small precious stones of various types. Present-day styles have monograms or initials as well as emblems.

To secure the metal in the engraved outline or shallow depression, deep grooves are cut with a narrow sawlike disk tool. The cuts are made in the center of the leaves, stems, or lines, in the design as the case may be. By burnishing, the metal is forced into these slots and there securely anchored.

## CARVING AND SCULPTURING

Carving and sculpturing are akin to engraving, the chief difference being the size and the nature of the article. While engraved gems usually are small in size and are designed to be worn in rings, pins, brooches, carved gems may vary in size from a small bud, bead, leaf, or flower weighing a carat or less, to articles of large size, vases, bowls, etc., which may weigh a hundred pounds or more (Fig. 9–17).

Objects in carved stone may be seen in an infinite variety. The most commonly used are bowls and vases of all sizes and shapes, boxes, leaves, flowers, snuff bottles, as well as birds, animals, and figures of every description. The number and variety are limited only by the ability and ingenuity of the artist (Figs. 9–9 to 9–24).

In general, the technique and principles involved in producing articles carved in stone are the same as those of cabochon cutting. The stone

**Fig. 9-9.**   Leaf pins. A. Anthurium, frosted rock crystal, 32 x 51 mm., white gold set with red spinels. B. Dogwood, rock crystal, 49 x 52 mm. yellow and green gold; center cluster, Chatham emeralds. C. Varigated Ivy, 37 x 37 mm., jaspar green and cream color, yellow gold stem (author's creations).

**Fig. 9-10.**
Frosted rock crystal pin, stylized seahorse,
20 x 50 mm. Demantoid eyes,
pink and yellow gold
(Francis J. Sperisen, Jr., creation).

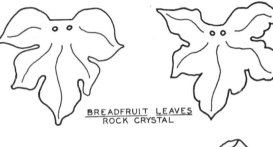

BREADFRUIT LEAVES
ROCK CRYSTAL

**Fig. 9-11.**
Template designs of
stylized leaf and flower
ornaments.

GINGER FLOWER
WHITE CHALCEDONY

GARDENIA
ROCK CRYSTAL

KUKUI
ROCK CRYSTAL

ANTHURIUM – ROCK CRYSTAL
PISTIL–CALIBRE RUBIES

IVY
GREEN AND RED
CHALCEDONY

All of these are produced, as previously outlined, by rough- and finish-grinding, drilling or piercing, azuring or elongating drilled holes, finish sanding, and polishing. For this purpose a large number of tools of all sizes and shapes are required. In azuring, extreme care must be taken to prevent small stems or thin portions from breaking off.

This breakage may be caused by the wedging action of the tool jamming in the cut or through the twisting of the stone during the operation, especially where wheel tools of large diameter are used. All of the work should be treated as delicately as possible, and at all times during the operations the individual's undivided attention to the work is of paramount importance. A moment's lack of concentration may cause the article being worked to be completely ruined.

Fig. 9-13. Jade vase with chains and handle. Varicolored white, green, and mauve. Height, about 10 in.

Fig. 9-14. White jade vase 700 years old. Height, 12 in. Weight, less than a pound.

Fig. 9-15.
Perfume vase of
varicolored jade.
Height, about 9 in.
Created by S. T. Koo.

Snuff bottles, bowls, vases, or containers may be seen in a great variety of forms from the most simple, finished with a smooth polished surface, to forms of the most complex nature. Such articles, as well as vases, have been made entirely surrounded with branches, leaves, and flowers attractively and delicately entwined about the body in full relief (Figs. 9–13 to 9–16). Jadeite and nephrite are particularly favorite materials for carving of this nature. They are followed closely by chalcedony of various types and colors. Rose quartz, rock crystal, and amethyst, as well also are favorites, and lapis lazuli is commonly used (Fig. 9–16).

The altar of the Sacred Jade Pagoda (Fig. 9–17), a masterful example of modern jade carving, was conceived by Chang-Wen-Ti, and the work was executed through his guidance and direction. All of the pieces were cut from a mighty boulder of jadeite weighing 18,000 lbs.

So elaborate and detailed is the work that it required the untiring effort of 150 artisans ten years to complete. Weight of the finished pagoda is only 75 lbs.

Piercing and enlarging the inside of a vase or a snuff bottle is a laborious task. The initial core may be removed by tube drilling (A, Fig. 9–18) after which the aperture is enlarged by using ball-shaped grinding tools with abrasive grain (B, Fig. 9–18). The maximum size to which the aperture may be ground is limited by the diameter of the opening through which the grinding tool is inserted. On transparent gem minerals used for these articles, more work is required because the interior must be polished. This operation is performed in a manner similar to the polishing of concaved pieces, the sole difference being the type of lapping and polishing wheels used. The greatest care is necessary to produce a smooth, evenly ground inner surface, so that the time involved in the polishing operation will be reduced to a minimum. Deep gouges should be removed by careful grinding so that the surface may be smoothed without difficulty. This is done with 1-F abrasive grain followed by FFF, using wooden laps. After the surface has been

Fig. 9-16.
Lapis lazuli vase.
Height, about 10 in.
By S. T. Koo.

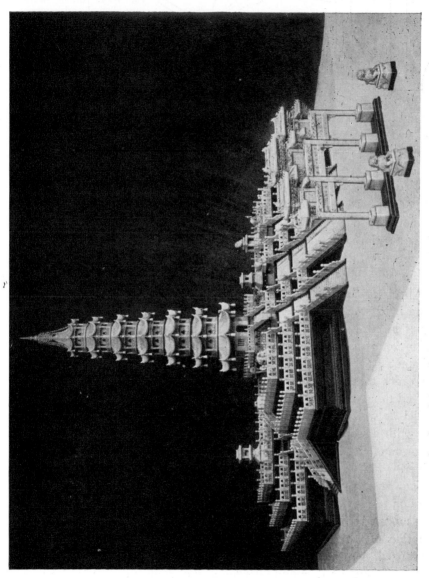

**Fig. 9-17.** The altar of the Sacred Jade Pagoda. Green jade pagoda with seven interlocking tiers, swinging bells, and connected chain on top spire. Height, 50 in.; base width, 13 in.

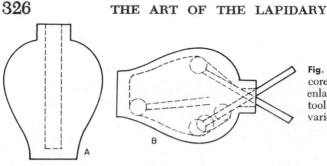

**Fig. 9-18.** Small bottle core drilled and cavity enlarged with ball-shaped tool. Tool shown in various positions.

thoroughly lapped to a uniform degree, it is further polished with FFF grain and a felt lap. Final polishing is done with tin oxide on felt, tin, or leather laps.

Because of the small size of the laps used, the lapping and polishing wheels wear out rapidly and they must be constantly replaced or serviced. To expedite matters, an ample supply of these items is necessary and should be on hand.

Bowls and vases may be made by removing the central portion in different ways, the simplest of which is by grinding (Fig. 6–80). Small grinding wheels may be used if the stone is soft or not too large and the wheels made of iron or steel used with wet abrasive are best to use on hard stones. Although this method is the most practical for the inexperienced, several hours of grinding are required to finish a small bowl or cup made of agate or chalcedony approximately two inches in diameter (Figs. 6–87 and 6–89).

In order to reduce the grinding time, the central portion may be removed to a considerable extent by sawing (Fig. 9–19A). A number of parallel as well as cross cuts are made in the central portion of the stone with a small diamond saw and the tabular pieces remaining are broken out (Fig. 9–19B), after which grinding proceeds in the original manner.

A cup saw may also be used for this purpose (Fig. 9–20). However, operation of a saw of this kind requires considerable skill and dexterity. The saw, made from thin sheet iron, is fashioned in a spherical form, the radius of which corresponds to the radius of the section that is to be removed. A saw of this kind is usually used as a mud saw with wet abrasive, although a diamond charged saw of similar design is also practical. The saw is firmly fastened to a spindle or arbor ⅜-in. shank diameter, reduced to ⁵⁄₁₆ in. at the saw end.

Prior to the sawing operation, a circular groove is ground around the top portion of the object to be hollowed out (Fig. 9–21), which serves

Fig. 9-19A. First sawing to form concave for compote.

Fig. 9-19B. After cross cuts and removal of partitions.

as a guide for the passage of the saw. The object which is cemented to a special cup shaped lap stick is supported at a suitable height and the grooved section presented to the saw which rotates in a small lathe (Fig. 4–13). By careful turning, the saw progressively cuts a cup-shaped hollow in the object and a round cabochon like section is removed.

This is a desirable method to use where valuable gem material is being worked, for in this manner a unit of appreciable size is available for additional use. The small cup (Fig. 6–89) may also be hollowed out by the method used in fashioning large vases (Fig. 9–23). A central core is first drilled to a maximum depth and this is removed by careful tapping. A second core of larger diameter is also drilled to the maximum depth; a small diamond-charged saw the diameter of the original core fastened to a long spindle is introduced into the hole. By lateral pressure the wall of the second core is sawed through and this core in the form of a cylinder is readily removed. Successive cylindrical cores are removed in like manner. After all of the units were removed, they were successively lapped, polished, and engraved. This practice is commonly

Fig. 9-20. Cup saw.

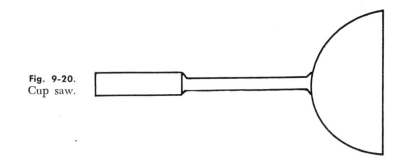

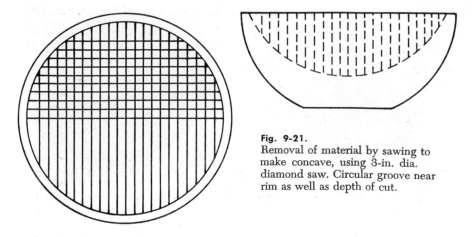

Fig. 9-21.
Removal of material by sawing to
make concave, using 3-in. dia.
diamond saw. Circular groove near
rim as well as depth of cut.

used by Chinese lapidaries in making vases (Figs. 9–13, 14, and 15).

An additional, but much more difficult, method is possible. It is useful
where valuable material is to be saved, as the vase can be hollowed
out to the maximum amount and a solid core removed. A cylindrical
core is first ground to the desired size and, for practical reasons, the
kerf should be at least ⅜₆ in. to permit entry of the quill bearing the
sawing units. This quill, having tubular projections fixed at the proper
radii, permits the projection end to enter freely into the kerf. Special
wire sawing units having a curvature common to the kerf are fastened
to steel rods that fit freely in the projection. By means of tension springs
and small levers fastened to the upper ends of the steel rods a radial
pressure is exerted on the latter so that the curved wire units at the
bottom of the kerf are in contact with the core and by rapidly rotating
the unit in a drilling machine, the core is cut in a lateral manner at
the base and finally removed. Although silicon carbide abrasive may be
used, the wire units may be charged with diamond to produce a more
practical sawing medium.

Grinding wheels, laps, and polishing wheels should be concentric and
should rotate truly without chatter, for the pounding or hammering
action of wheels and laps worn out of round would easily break a thin
bowl or other object.

Because the wheels used are small and the polishing action is slow,
there is a tendency to hasten the polishing action by increasing the
pressure. Such pressure would quickly generate heat which might crack
and ruin the article. Time and patience are of great importance in the
completion of intricate work.

**Fig. 9-23.** Double rock crystal vase, height, 259 mm. Italian, 16th century. Various mythological subjects, Judgment of Paris, Diana and Akteon, Leda, Venus and Adonis.

**Fig. 9-22.** Rock crystal pyramid by Dionysio Miseroni (1653–1677). Front view. Height, 1154 mm. Five units cut from single crystal.

**Fig. 9-24.**   Vase, compote, and seal. Compote of gray-green jasper, by the
artist lapidary, Kalugin, Russia, *circa* 1871.

Bowls, vases (Figs. 9–23 and 9–24), or other articles, such as a seal
handle (Figs. 6–76 and 9–24), sometimes are fluted. The flutes, either
concave or convex, may radiate from the center, or they may be in the
form of a spiral or helix (Fig. 9–24). Although the spacing of the flutes
may be done by hand with a fair degree of accuracy, best results can
be obtained only by mechanical means such as a dividing head of a
universal nature.

# CHAPTER 10

# Mosaic, Intarsia, Inlay, Parquetry

MOSAIC is that phase of the lapidary art where artistic compositions of every description are formed with colored stones which are carefully selected and skillfully fitted and cemented together to form a pleasing picture. Mosaics may vary in size from small ring stones to units forming table tops.

Two distinct types are in common use — the Florentine mosaics, also called intarsia, and the Roman mosaics. In Florentine mosaic (pietra dura, Fig. 10–1) exceptional skill is required in cutting and fitting the thin stones together, especially in the larger compositions where accurate fitting of carefully selected stones is necessary to match each colored portion of the original picture.

The Roman type of mosaic, also referred to as the Byzantine type, is used for cheap jewelry. It is formed of small stems of colored glass of uniform length, cemented in an upright position to a base to form a picture. In this construction the lapidary's art is usually not required. Scenic compositions of all kinds, sometimes very elaborate, also are produced in this style (Fig. 10–2).

The simplest form of Florentine mosaics are the small floral compositions (Fig. 10–3). More elaborate types illustrate figures or various types of scenes and architecture. A modern introduction, which is an elementary type of Florentine mosaic, is the opal doublet set in black onyx inside a border (Fig. 10–3). The use of the border was introduced to overcome the fault of chipping inherent in the usual opal doublet which has a very thin edge.

These stones usually are elliptical in shape and ground concave so that a uniform border about 1 mm. wide remains. The concave is ground in the usual manner, and after grinding, the recessing may be done by holding the stone against a small cylindrical diamond-charged tool rotating at high speed, or the work may be done with the aid of a drill press. The diameter of the tool should be of such a size that it will correspond to the minimum curvature of the cavity which is required to be cut in the stone.

Fig. 10-1. "Cavalier." Florentine-type mosaic made of varicolored marble and gemstones.

Fig. 10-2. Roman-type mosaic made of small stones 1 by 2 mm.

Because the opal to be inlaid is a thin veneer, the concave formed in the onyx should not be over 1 mm. deep. After this concave has been finished, the opal to be inserted is cut to fit the opening. It is then cemented in place by means of a black cement, usually black sealing wax, or asphaltum, after which the top surface of the stone is lapped flat or slightly convex. It is finally polished.

More elaborate and attractive forms may be seen in small floral pieces (Fig. 10-3) made in a similar manner. The flowers are made of opal in contrasting color, red, blue, and green; the leaves are green opal, and the stem is gold inlay. The onyx is prepared by engraving the design by means of small diamond-charged tools, after which the opals are cut to fit, and the gold stem is encrusted before the stones are cemented in place with the black cement. The entire unit is then lapped flat and polished.

By using the black cement, the vivid color of the opal is brought into prominence, and cavities or crevices remaining are filled thus forming a solid top free of contrasting border marks.

The Florentine mosaics usually are more elaborate although the materials of which they are made are softer. The majority are composed of soft stones, marble in a great variety of hues and tints, onyx marble and aragonite, glass in various colors, and occasionally, where rich color is desired, coral, turquoise, malachite, and lapis. Hard gem minerals also can be used for the same purpose.

A colored picture (Fig. 10–1) to be made in mosaic is chosen, and the various colors are blocked out. The stones of various types are carefully selected to match each color as perfectly as possible. The stones are cut into thin slabs, and in the small size mosaics these may vary from 1 to 2 mm. in thickness, according to the size of the finished article. In large pictures, the usual thickness of the stones is approximately 3 mm.

The respective slabs then are carefully ground to match that portion of the picture they are to represent. Long, slender-pointed pieces, such as stem or leaf sections, should be cemented to ground glass plates for support so that the slender sections or points will not break.

Fine grinding wheels should be used. Sandstone or lens edging wheels are best for this purpose if the softer materials are used, and a No. 240 silicon-carbide, medium-hard wheel will give good results for sizing and shaping the hard stones of the quartz variety, or jasper. Diamond-impregnated laps are excellent for this purpose.

As the stones to be fitted in the mosaic are in a great variety of

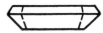

Fig. 10-3. Left: opal inlay onyx ring stone; right: opal doublet set in onyx.

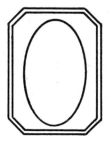

shapes, a large number of grinding wheels will be necessary, the contours of which are turned and trimmed to shape by means of a sharp diamond dresser.

Lead bushed wheels, 3 to 4 in. in diameter, will serve excellently. The wheel is firmly wrung onto a tapered threaded spindle and trued in place. Once these wheels have been firmly wrung onto the tapered spindle, so that a full thread is swaged in the lead bushing and the contour is trued with a diamond tool, they may be removed and replaced with the assurance that they will rotate truly when used at a later time.

A rest (Fig. 10-4) placed in front of and slightly below the center line of the wheel to support the stone during grinding is a necessity. Water is used throughout as a coolant. The outline of the stone to be cut is inscribed by means of a tracing of the original picture, or a template may be used instead. Because of the intricate nature of the work and the delicacy of the pieces to be cut, it is obvious that the greatest amount of care is required in working to avoid breakage.

As a general rule, the border section, which is made in black stone, is cut from one piece. The portion which is to contain the picture, usually the center, is carefully marked out and pierced. The remaining portions of the mosaic which form the picture itself are carefully fitted and cemented into place, and this process is continued until all portions of the picture have been completed.

Large mosaics, such as table tops, may have a floral display in the center, and at points equidistant therefrom additional floral pieces or

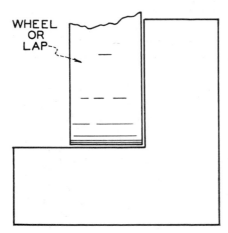

WHEEL
OR
LAP

Fig. 10-4. Table for contour grinding.

Fig. 10-5. Three-dimensional mosaic, 45 mm. (actual size). White chalcedony, brown jasper, black onyx, red garnet eye (author's creation).

sprays of flowers may be set in the solid surface. After all of the carefully fitted stones have been cemented into place and the cement has
thoroughly hardened, the surface is lapped flat and true, after which it
is polished.

Small mosaics may be handled without difficulty, and they are treated
in the same manner as any flat gemstone or specimen.

Fine abrasive, FFF, is used, preferably on a pewter lap which is
true and flat. After the entire surface has been flattened the desired
amount, it is carefully cleaned and polished. Mosaic made of hard gemstones will require polishing on tin or hardwood laps with tin oxide.
Softer stones may be finished on a special lap made by cementing thin
sheet felt to a flat lap, using No. 600 silicon carbide or 3-0 pumice as

**Fig. 10-6.**
White jade vase decorated
with gemstones.

abrasive materials for fine grinding, and then finish polishing on a flat leather wheel with tin oxide.

Large mosaics, as wall pictures or table tops, because of their size are difficult to handle. They must be finished in a stationary position in a rubbing bed such as those used in marble works, or by use of a flexible shaft outfit.

Mosaics made by the Chinese lapidary follow a different style. The stones are fitted into cavities cut into screens or other wooden objects, such as boxes, cabinets, etc. The topics usually are floral decorations, architecture, or garden scenes. The wood background is carved to receive the cut stone which is carefully fitted and cemented into place. Unlike the Florentine mosaic, which is flat, the inlaid stones in the Chinese mosaic are usually convex, and they are cut to resemble the original object as closely as possible in form and contour. Three dimensional mosaics (Fig. 10–5) are rare.

Occasionally, stone objects (vases or boxes) may be treated in a similar manner (Fig. 10–6).

## PARQUETRY

Parquetry is similar to mosaic. The stones, however, have regular geometrical outlines, and the compositions are geometrical rather than picturesque. This style of lapidary art was in vogue several decades ago when gold quartz jewelry was popular, and various types of quartz were cut to fit mountings having apertures of geometrical form. These mountings were to be seen in every form of jewelry, as rings, cuff links (Fig. 10–7), bar pins of all kinds, watch chains and watchcases, as well as knobs for canes. The stones for this type of work may vary in thickness from 1 to 2 mm., according to the size of the article. The thin slabs of material are cut to a close fit, the work being done on

Fig. 10-7.
Cuff links, California gold quartz inlay, black quartz center, and white quartz outer pieces. Diameter 15 mm.; center square, 6 mm.

a pewter lap with No. 220 or 240 silicon carbide. The individual pieces then are cemented in the respective openings with sealing wax or shellac, and the entire unit is lapped flat and polished.

Attractive combinations were made by using quartz of contrasting colors such as white, green, or black. Occasionally, the color of a piece of translucent quartz was heightened by the use of a colored cement.

Work of a similar nature may be seen where stones of contrasting color are used. The stones are carefully lapped to size and cemented together, and the entire unit is cemented to a common base having the same outline as the assembled unit. While articles of this type are sometimes used for personal adornment, the greatest use for parquetry is in articles used as boxes, or table tops.

The common checkerboard is an interesting example. Elaborate geometrical patterns may be used for taborets or trivets.

The usual practice in forming units of this type is to saw the material into slabs. By further sawing, the slabs then are cut to the required size or general shape. Accurate sizing follows in the usual manner on a flat lap with No. 220 or 240 silicon-carbide grain. The size of the stone should be carefully checked from time to time by the use of a millimeter gauge if the stone is to be square or rectangular, and a goniometer also can be used if an angular shape is desired, such as triangle, hexagon, or octagon. Where a large number of individual units are required, accurate sizing is of the utmost importance if a well-made unit is desired.

To facilitate this operation and to enable the operator to produce a large number of accurately cut and sized tiles, the mechanical dividing head shown in Figure 10–8 was designed by the author. Flat slabs of the required thickness are cemented to holders which fit into and are fixed

**Fig. 10-8.**
Dividing head on Sperisen Jr. lapidary machine. Size and shape of square and hexagon tiles shown are accurate to ± .001 in.

to the dividing head. This head is capable of radial adjustment sufficient to produce any desired number of flat surfaces, 4, 6, 8, etc. The entire unit may be raised or lowered at will by means of a vertical column. The sequence of the operation is simple. After the slab has been adjusted in place and the vertical position has been checked, the entire unit is swung against the horizontal rotating saw, which quickly removes one portion leaving a flat smooth surface. By maintaining the same vertical position and by merely indexing, the desired number of triangles, squares, hexagons, or other shaped tiles may be made with ease and accuracy.

If two opposite sides are finished in one position and the unit is then lowered a predetermined amount, a rectangular tile or other elongated form will result according to the number of times the device is indexed.

In sawing out slabs to form tiles of this type, it has been found that the abrasive bonded cutoff wheel 3760 resinoid or shellac bonded, well supported by the use of large flanges, will give excellent results. The edge thus produced will be sharp and clean with a freedom from chipping. Other type saws will break the stone off leaving small ends which can be removed only by subsequent lapping.

Through the use of gauge blocks (Fig. 10–9), the size of the tiles may be readily controlled. In the event that long, narrow, triangular,

Fig. 10-9.
Gauge block in use on Sperisen Jr. lapidary machine. Gauge block permits rapid change for size and dimension in sawing out blanks.

or wedge-shaped forms are required, the slabs should be cemented to a thin plate to reinforce the stone to prevent breakage.

If required, this dividing unit also may be used to lap the tiles to size permitting the tiles to be lowered in contact with a properly pre-pared lap. The size of the tile is controlled by the stops on the machine.

When the tiles have been finished, they are removed by heating and carefully cleaning in alcohol, after which they are ready for use. To properly support the tiles in use, they are cemented to a plate. The best material for this purpose is slate carefully lapped to size. After cementing and hardening, the top surface is carefully lapped flat and then it is polished as previously described. Small units are handled in the same manner as the polishing of flat specimens and large surfaces must be finished in the lapping bed or with a flexible shaft unit.

# CHAPTER 11

# Diamond Polishing

DIAMOND polishing, like engraving, is an exclusive branch of the lapidary art. This function consists of cleaving, sawing, rounding, and polishing. It is interesting to note that little change or improvement has been effected in generations in the technique or the equipment used in diamond polishing. Most of the improvement has been evidenced in the nature of the motive force used to drive the equipment.

The polishing equipment in Figure 11–1 shows a standard type used by most shops. Most of this equipment has been made in Belgium where most of the world's supply of diamonds are polished. Modern equipment (Fig. 11–2) for industrial use recently has been introduced. The laps,

**Fig. 11-1.** Diamond polishing standard equipment, showing mechanical dop clamped in tong being polished on lap.

Fig. 11-2. Diamond-polishing equipment.

made of cast iron, for polishing are similar to those used by the lapidary, but they are rotated at a much higher rate of speed, ranging from 2000 to 2500 r.p.m.

It is of the greatest importance that the lap and spindle be perfectly balanced so that vibration is eliminated. The lap spindle is of heavy construction, and the conical points are hardened and ground.

The bearings of the standard-type machine are made of lignum vitae, a very hard dense wood with an oily nature, and the lap surface is adjusted parallel to the table top. Special precision-type ball bearings are used on some of the new machines.

Whereas the lapidary uses a lap stick to which the stone is cemented, for cutting and polishing, and the numerous facets on the front or back of the stone are successively cut and polished with one cementing, the main facets on the diamond are polished one at a time, and after each is finished, the stone must be reset. This is necessary because of the grain or crystallographic structure of the stone, for it is possible to polish the diamond in certain directions only, that is, parallel to any one of the three crystallographic axes of the stone. The unit by which the diamond is held during polishing is called a dop; two types are used, the solder dop and the mechanical dop.

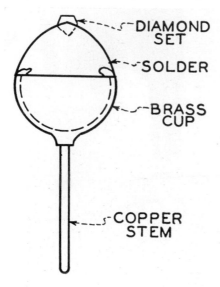

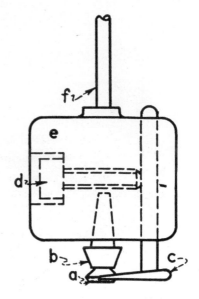

Fig. 11-3. Solder dop with set stone.

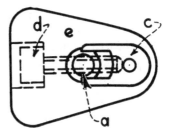

The solder dop (Fig. 11–3) which is generally used for small stones (usually five hundredths of a carat or less), consists of a metal cup (copper or brass) about an inch in diameter, in which solder in the proportion of two parts lead and one part tin is heated until it becomes plastic. The solder is then worked into a pointed dome and the stone is set and bedded therein so that only that portion which is required to be polished projects from the solder.

The mechanical dop (Fig. 11–4) is fitted with a small metal cup and a pronged foot which may be clamped in

Fig. 11-4. Mechanical dop. Side and bottom views: *a*, diamond in position; *b*, cup for holding stone; *c*, pronged clamp; *d*, clamp screw; *e*, mechanical dop body; *f*, copper stem for holding in clamp.

place, the diamond being securely held thereby. Both types of dops have stems of copper rod screwed into the body of the dop, and the rod is 3/16 in. in diameter. By this stem, the dop is clamped in a tong which is made of hard wood, to which is fixed a metal clamp that holds the dop in place during polishing. Two feet on the tong provide stability, and the unit is kept in place on the wheel by two steel rods clamped to the table in an upright position. These rods hold the tong in place and pre-

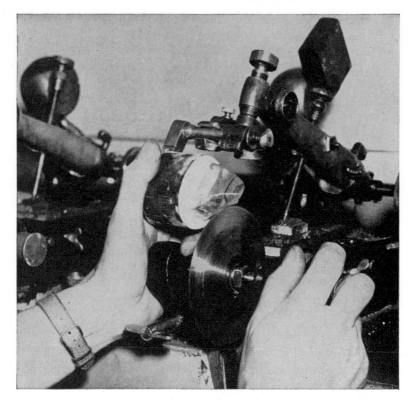

**Fig. 11-5.** Sawing Vargas diamond (726.60 ct.). This is the first sawing and the piece weighed 21.65 ct. Sawing time was five weeks.

vent radial movement of the dop caused by the thrust of the lap.

The copper rod affixed to the dop permits bending so that some adjustment may be readily made in order to place the stone on the lap in the proper position. Flat lead or iron weights are placed upon the top of the tong, when necessary, to bring greater pressure to bear upon the stone during the lapping of the main facets.

In preparing a rough diamond for polishing, the original stone may require cleaving and, if the maximum amount of finished weight is to be obtained, sawing also is resorted to. Sawing machines (Fig. 11–5) are used whenever it is necessary to part a diamond in a direction not possible by cleaving. These saws are made of phosphor bronze, about 4 in. in diameter and .005 in. thick. Diamond powder is used as an abrasive, and the saws rotate at a speed of 5000 r.p.m. As the majority of diamonds occur with an octahedral form, sawing must be resorted to in order to effect the maximum saving in weight. Sawing directions are illustrated

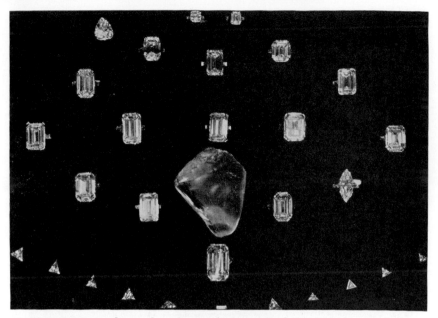

**Fig. 11-6.** Vargas diamond in the rough, center, and the 29 stones cut from it.

in Figures 11–7 and 11–8. Twinned crystals should be avoided for, while some difficulty is experienced when other gems of twinned nature are cut and polished, the crystallographic structure of the diamond is such that polishing may be accomplished only in certain directions, and the complex structure of twinned crystals often precludes the possibility of their economical polishing.

In former times, diamonds were shaped by rubbing one stone against another, the process being known as bruting, that is, roughing. The outline or shape of the stones polished varied only slightly from the outline of the original crystal (Fig. 11–9). At the present time, this work is performed on a lathe of special design (Fig. 11–11), and the resulting stone has a circular girdle. The stone to be cut is cemented to a cup-shaped conical chuck with hard diamond cement. The chuck

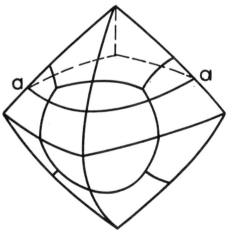

**Fig. 11-7.** Typical diamond crystal sawed for polishing two stones *a–a*.

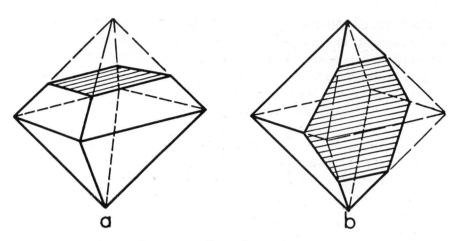

**Fig. 11-8.** Sawing directions in diamond parallel to face of cube inscribed in the octahedron.

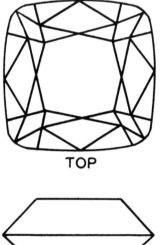

TOP

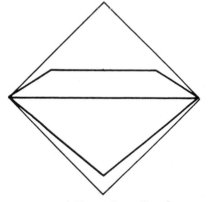

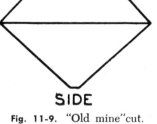

SIDE

**Fig. 11-9.** "Old mine" cut.

**Fig. 11-10.** Proportions of modern brilliant cut inscribed in outline of octahedron.

|  | 1 | 2 |
|---|---|---|
| Diameter | 100% | 100% |
| Height of crown | 14 | 16 |
| Depth of pavilion | 42 | 43 |
| Table width | 57 | 53 |
| Angle crown | 33 | 35 |
| Angle pavilion | 40 | 41 |

1. After Eppler and Klueppelberg.
2. After Tolkowsky.

is then screwed onto the spindle nose of the lathe which is solidly affixed to the faceplate of the machine. This faceplate is adjustable radially, the adjustment, if necessary, being made by means of light blows with a brass or lead hammer. The purpose of this adjusting feature is to quickly center the stone if it is not concentric with the axis of the lathe because of improper or inaccurate cementing, or to permit rounding of the stone in repairing chipped or broken stones.

In rounding a stone on the lathe, a hard stone, usually bort, is affixed to a turning tool holder (Fig. 11–11) which is used in a manner similar to any hand turning tool. The shank of the tool is rigidly supported by the crotch of the tool rest, and the movement of the tool is controlled by the hands and the arms. The shank of the tool, which is long, passes between the forearm and the body. By the necessary forward motion, the tool is brought in contact with the stone to be cut, which rotates about 400 to 500 r.p.m., and by carefully controlled pressure, the surface of the rotating stone is rounded. The girdle edge and the crown are usually finished first, the stone is then reversed on the cement chuck and, after centering, the conical back surface is finished (Fig. 11–12).

This operation, which constitutes the cutting of the diamond, actually bruting by mechanical means, prepares the stone for polishing. The stone is removed from the cement chuck, and cleaned of adhering

Fig. 11-11. "Bruting," rounding or initial stage in cutting and polishing a diamond.

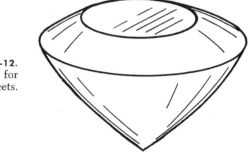

Fig. 11-12.
Diamond cut and prepared for
polishing facets.

cement. It is then secured in the dop for polishing the table, which is the first facet to be completed.

The stone is readily secured in position in the mechanical dop by means of the cup-shaped receptacle and the clamping foot (Fig. 11–4), or, if the solder dop is used, the stone is embedded in solder (Fig. 11–3).

The proper setting of the stone in the solder dop requires considerable skill which can only be acquired by practice. The cup-shaped dop is placed on a special gas burner and heated. Small disks of the solder are added until the cup is full, after which the temperature is controlled so that the solder becomes plastic and not molten.

Additional disks of solder are added to form a cone the shape of which is controlled by a broad, flat tweezer. After the additional material has become plastic from heating in the flame, the dop is removed by means of a cup-shaped tweezer and placed in a special wooden holder. The cone-shaped solder is molded by means of the flat tweezer, and any surplus solder which may be removed is caught in the cup-shaped portion of the dop holder. A small dent is made in the top of the cone with the pointed end of the tweezer, and the diamond is set therein. The diamond is embedded in place so that when the plastic solder is molded over its surface it is securely held and only the table surface to be polished projects above the solder. The conical surface of the solder is smoothed down by molding with the thumb (Fig. 11–13).

After the stone has been properly set, the dop is grasped by the cup-shaped tweezer and plunged into cold water. This is to develop a fine grain structure in the solder and to shrink it, thus holding the stone securely. Fortunately, because the diamond has a low coefficient of expansion it is not affected by this sudden change in temperature.

The dop is then held in the tong by means of the clamp which grasps the copper rod attached to the dop cup. The dop is inserted in such a manner that the cup is in the same plane as the feet of the tong

Fig. 11-13. Dop holder for setting diamond for polishing;
solder dops, burner, and tweezers.

and so that the table of the stone will be parallel to the lap surface when
the stone is brought in contact with it.

A trial application is made, and if the mark made by the lap on the
table surface indicates that this surface is not parallel, most of the adjustment necessary to bring it in the proper position is made by bending the
copper rod attached to the dop. Very slight adjustment of the stone
on the lap can be made by placing shims or cards under one or the
other foot of the tong.

As the stone can be economically polished only in the direction parallel
to a crystallographic axis, it follows that the table must be placed on the
lap so that the polishing action of the lap passes across the facet in a
direction parallel to the crystallographic axis selected. If an octahedron
has been selected for polishing and the table is cut at a right angle to
one of the optic axes, the polishing of the table may be accomplished
by placing it on the lap surface so that the lap travel crosses the facet
in any of four directions (Fig. 11–14).

As a general rule, after cutting or rounding an octahedron, four
splendent spots will remain on the girdle edge. These spots on the girdle
edge may be seen in brilliant contrast to the ground surface of the stone.

The four corners of the octahedron that have been removed in the

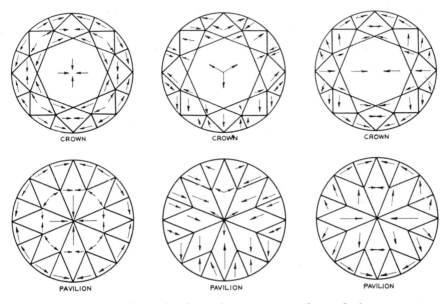

**Fig. 11-14.** Left to right: four-, three-, two-point diamonds showing polishing directions.

rounding of the stone are hard zones or points, and from this factor, the stone derives its name, that is, a four-point stone.

The splendent spots remaining on the girdle edge serve as distinguishing marks which enable the polisher to recognize the type of crystal and the orientation of the facets on the cut stone, and thus to employ the proper technique in polishing (Fig. 11–14).

Sometimes a stone is called a malformed octahedron, which is a crystal of octahedral habit showing irregular growth. As a result of this growth, one or more crystal faces have been suppressed so that the crystal has a triangular form or outline, or cleavages result from an octahedron. The table of the stone is lapped on the triangular face of the crystal, and the stone, after rounding, is referred to as a three-point stone. Polishing directions are illustrated in Figure 11–14.

Brilliants formed from diamonds of rhombic dodecahedral habit, with the table polished on a rhombic face, are referred to as two-point stones. In each case, the stone must be placed upon the lap so that the direction of the lap travel crosses the facet as nearly as possible parallel to a crystallographic axis, and this direction differs with respect to the types of crystals mentioned. The direction in which polishing may be effected with the least difficulty is shown in Figure 11–14.

After the proper position has been secured, weights are placed upon the top of the tong to increase the pressure of the stone upon the wheel, thereby increasing the rapidity of the polishing operation. The stone is examined from time to time to check the development of the facet. If the solder dop is used, it will require periodic cooling by quenching in water, for the heat generated by friction may cause the solder to become soft enough to release the stone, with possible damage to the stone as well as to the lap surface.

For the purpose of blocking out, the mechanical dop will prove to be superior in the saving of time as well as in convenience. After the table surface has been sufficiently developed, the polish marks left by the wheel must be removed to make a perfectly flat facet. These marks are caused by the lap surface becoming grooved and irregular through prolonged working upon the facet of the stone while it is maintained in one position. To eliminate these defects, the weights are removed, the tong is grasped in the hand, and the stone is placed upon a perfectly flat section of the lap referred to as the "polishing groove," which is reserved for this purpose. By a slow backward and forward motion of the stone upon the lap, the facet is trued perfectly flat.

The inner-half portion of the lap may be reserved for final polishing, and the outer surface is utilized for the preliminary work. Upon the satisfactory completion of the table facet, the culet directly opposite is finished in a similar manner. The dimension from the table to the culet, with respect to the diameter of the stone, is important. For a stone of ideal proportions, this dimension is 56–59 per cent of the width of the stone. The main front and back facets are polished at angles of 35 and 41 deg. respectively with the plane of the girdle. Figure 3–34 (see also Fig. 11–10) shows proper proportions in a perfectly cut diamond. In commercial cutting, these proportions are not always attained, and the majority of the diamonds may have a crown which is considerably lower than the ideal. Some diamonds have a crown that is but one quarter of the thickness of the entire stone.

After the table and culet facets have been finished, one of the top main facets is polished. A gauge (Fig. 11–15) is used to check the angularity of the slope. The facet directly behind the main facet then is finished, and again a gauge (Fig. 11–16) is used to check the angularity of the back main facet. In all cases the necessary correction of the angle is made by bending the stout copper rod attached to the dop, the initial adjustment having been made in the tong.

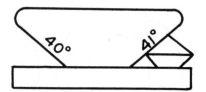

▲ **Fig. 11-16.** Gauge for checking angularity of main back facet.

◀ **Fig. 11-15.** Gauge for checking angularity of slope.

After the initial pair of facets has been completed (Fig. 11–17), the pair opposite are finished in like manner. Care is exercised to develop these equal to the first pair. At this stage, the edge formed by one of the crown facets with the table should be parallel to the edge formed by the opposite set, and the distance or width of the table should be

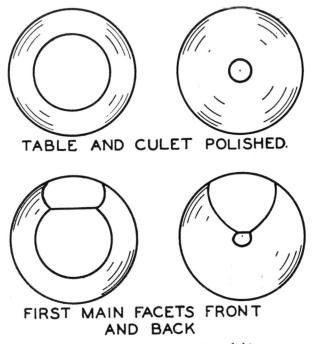

TABLE AND CULET POLISHED.

FIRST MAIN FACETS FRONT
AND BACK

Fig. 11-17. Successive stages in polishing.

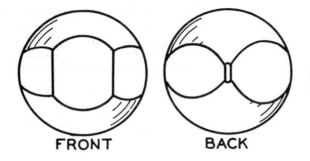

FRONT          BACK

Fig. 11-18. Main facets polished parallel.

approximately 60 per cent of the width of the stone (Fig. 11–18). Two sets of crown and pavilion main facets then are polished so that these will be placed at a position 90 degrees from those previously finished (Fig. 11–19).

In like manner, the remaining series of main facets are completed so that the finished or blocked-out form has a table and a culet facet, eight equally developed facets on the crown of the stone, and eight equally developed facets on the pavilion. The form or style of cutting now is called a single cut (Fig. 7–25). This style of cutting is reserved for small stones which weigh .04 ct. or less. Although it is possible to obtain full cuts (brilliant cut) on stones which weigh less than .01 ct., the majority of the small stones in commerce are fashioned in the single-cut style.

The double cut is formed by placing additional facets about the girdle edge (Fig. 7–27). A row of triangular-shaped facets, sixteen in number, are polished on the crown, and a matching row of equal number directly opposite are polished on the pavilion. When polishing the main facets, it is necessary to reset the stone in order to polish each facet, and for this purpose the mechanical dop is easier to use. It sometimes happens, how-

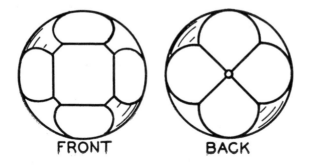

FRONT          BACK

Fig. 11-19. Opposite main facets squared.

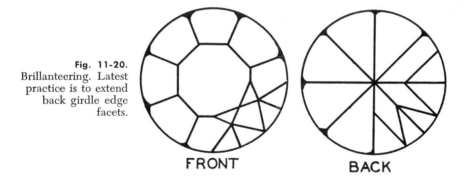

**Fig. 11-20.**
Brillanteering. Latest practice is to extend back girdle edge facets.

FRONT        BACK

ever, that the diamond powder, which is used in polishing, lodges in the brass cup or on the steel clamp which holds the stone; this may cause pitting of the polished facets should the stone become loose, or through prolonged working. This danger is never present when the solder dop is used.

In "brillianteering" or polishing the girdle and star facets about the table, one setting only is necessary for each pair of facets (Fig. 11–20). The proper adjustment is made by altering the position of the dop in the tong.

The brilliant cut (Fig. 7–28) is merely an elaboration of the double cut. It has in addition a single row of triangular-shaped facets disposed about the table between two adjoining crown facets. Other styles of cutting that have circular girdles as well as irregular forms and are adapted in the cutting of colored gems also are applied to good advantage in the diamond as well.

On large stones, the emerald cut (Fig. 7–10) is very popular at the present time. This style of cutting not only permits a saving in weight, but large stones may be used for rings whereas stones in the brilliant cut of the same weight would be too bulky for an artistic setting. Long, narrow crystals, which normally require cleaving or sawing to make two or more round stones, may be cut in the marquise cut (Fig. 7–36) which also is popular and results in a substantial saving in weight. (Rhombic dodecahedral crystals that have been flattened or malformed during growth often are found in a shape which is practically a marquise.)

Occasionally, the pendeloque and the briolette may be seen as well although, in the diamond, the latter form is rare. In every case the principles of polishing are the same. The stone is oriented on the lap so that the direction of travel of the lap across the facet is parallel to one of the crystallographic axes of the crystal, or as near as is possible in that direction.

In the past, the diamond has been engraved with inscriptions or in intaglio. This, however, is a tedious and laborious task, and the number of examples are few. Two notable examples are the Shah Diamond and the engraved diamond in the Field Museum called the DeVrees Diamond.

NOTE. In the diamond-cutting industry in Europe, particularly Holland, various names are given to the respective facets on a diamond by which the facets have a distinct relationship to crystallographic orientation. Thus, the main facets on the table side polished in the plane of the face of the octahedron are called bezeelen; those directly opposite on the culet side and similarly oriented are called the paviljoenen. The main facets formed at or adjacent to the interfacial angle formed by two faces of the crystal are called hoeken (corner facets).

The girdle-edge facets corresponding to the skew and skill facets are divided into two groups according to position, the eight bezeelhalfjes and the eight hoekhalfjes on the table side, and the eight paviljoenen-halfjes and eight hoekhalfjes on the culet side.

Encyclopaedie der Dimantnijverheid.
Dr. F. Leviticus, De Erven, F. Bohn, Haarlem.

# CHAPTER 12

# Applied Lapidary Art

DURING the past two decades, the diamond has rapidly gained importance for industrial use as a turning and boring tool. This use of the diamond, however, is restricted to the working of certain types of material such as turning and boring pressed paper, fiber, hard rubber, plastics, mica, and other substances which have an abrasive action on normal turning tools. Nonferrous metals such as the alloys of copper, tin, and lead (brass and bronze), as well as various types of aluminum alloys, are worked with efficiency and amazing economy with the use of diamond turning and boring tools. The diamonds are formed by lapping in the usual manner, after which they are set in properly designed and formed tool holders.

Besides the lapping and polishing of diamond tools, the lapidary, because of his skill, experience, and equipment, is often called upon to perform numerous functions for industrial purposes which are foreign to the true lapidary art. A number of technical applications are illustrated on the following pages.

Fig. 12-1. Knife edge and flat agate bearings for
scales, balances, etc.

**Fig. 12-2.** A crucible in synthetic sapphire. Diameter, 19 mm. Also tools used to grind concave. Crucible later polished inside and outside Used in scientific research work in World War II.

**Fig. 12-3.** Perfection eyecup and lotion container. The bottle stopper, a solid mass of glass, was ground into the shape of an eyecup.

**Fig. 12-4.** Agate mortar with pestle. Agate mortars are indispensable in many industries, for grinding chemical compounds and glazes.

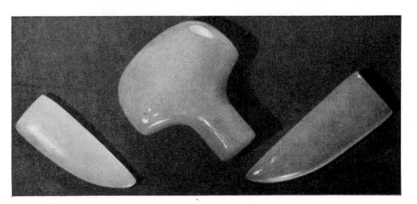

**Fig. 12-5.** Burnishers. Left and right for metal burnishing; center for leather work.

Fig. 12-6. Sawing off section of cemented tungsten carbide blank on a diamond saw, 4-in. diameter.

Fig. 12-7. Reaming hole to size in sintered tungsten carbide blast nozzle or metering bushing.

**Fig. 12-8.** Large model lever escapement Cap jewels and bearing jewels in ruby (syn.). Size of jewels, bearing 6 mm., cap 8 mm. dia. Movement, courtesy of Hubert Ritter, watchmaker, San Francisco, Calif.

**Fig. 12-9.** Nephrite paper knife. A. Sawed blank; B. Ground to shape; C. Finished knife, 190 mm. x 25 mm. x 4.5 mm. F. S. monogram two color gold, pink and green (author's creation).

**Fig. 12-10.** Rock-crystal bust, black jade (nephrite) plinth. Palladium wreath. 63 x 45 x 39 mm. (from author's workshop).

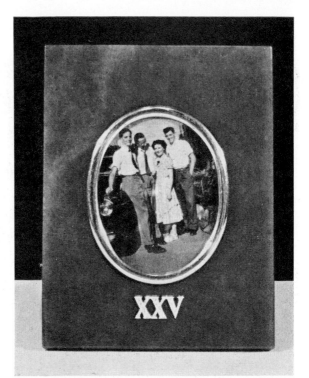

**Fig. 12-11.**
Nephrite jade picture
frame, 86 x 105 x 6 mm.
Yellow gold mounting,
numerals of white gold
and diamonds (author's
creation).

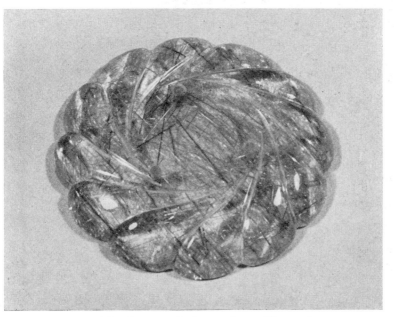

**Fig. 12-12.** Fluted Venus hairstone base, 65 mm. diameter
(author's creation).

**Fig. 12-13.** Black jade stem (98 mm. x 35 mm. x 16 mm.); octagon top (22 mm.), and pentagonal base (24 mm.), royal blue sodalite (from author's workshop).

**Fig. 12-14.** Black jade (nephrite) base, 3 x 4 in. (from author's workshop).

**Fig. 12-15.** Smoky crystal double cross lens cut, combination prism and cylindrical forms; 14 kt. y.g. free form shape (author's creation).

**Fig. 12-16.** Gold pin with Venus hairstone faceted prism (M. de Patta creation; gemstone cut by author).

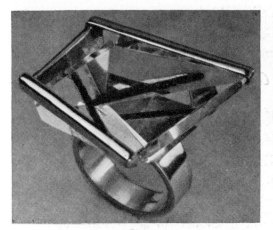

**Fig. 12-17.** Rock crystal finger ring, 14 kt. w.g., with single black tourmaline (M. de Patta creation; gemstone cut by author).

**Fig. 12-18.** Finger ring, 14 kt. w.g. Rock crystal plaque with needle-like inclusions of black tourmalines (M. de Patta creation; gemstone cut by author).

**Fig. 12-19.** Malachite box, 3½ x 4¼ x 2⅞ in. Restored by author.

# CHAPTER 13

# Reference Lists and Tables

## GEMSTONES

| | | | |
|---|---|---|---|
| Achroite | Carmazul | Fluorite | Lazurite |
| Adularia | Carnelian | Fowlerite | Lepidolite |
| Adularia | Carnelian onyx | Garnet | Limonite |
|   moonstone | Cassiterite | Garnierite | Magnetite |
| Agalmatolite | Cat's-eye | Golden beryl | Malachite |
| Agate | Chalcedony | Goshenite | Mala-cuprite |
| Alabaster | Chert | Graphic granite | Marcasite |
| Albite | Chiastolite | Grossularite | Melanite |
| Albite sunstone | Chlorastrolite | Gypsum | Moldavite |
| Alexandrite | Chloromelanite | Hambergite | Moonstone |
| Almandite | Chloropal | Hauynite | Morganite |
| Amatrice | Chromite | Hawk's-eye | Mother-of-pearl |
| Amazonite | Chrysoberyl | Heliotrope | Myrickite |
| Amber | Chrysocolla | Hematite | Nephelite |
| Amethyst | Chrysolite | Hiddenite | Nephrite |
| Anatase | Chrysoprase | Howlite | Novaculite |
| Andalusite | Citrine | Hyacinth | Obsidian |
| Andradite | Copal | Hyalite | Odontolite |
| Antigorite | Coral | Hypersthene | Oligoclase |
| Apatite | Cordierite | Iceland spar | Oligoclase |
| Aquamarine | Corundum | Idocrase |   sunstone |
| Aragonite | Crocidolite | Ilmenite | Olivine |
| Augelite | Danburite | Indicolite | Onyx |
| Aventurine | Datolite | Ivory | Onyx marble |
| Axinite | Demantoid | Jacinth | Oolite |
| Azurite | Diamond | Jadeite | Opal |
| Azurmalachite | Diopside | Jargoon | Orthoclase |
| Basanite | Dioptase | Jasper | Pearl |
| Benitoite | Dumortierite | Jet | Pearl blisters |
| Beryl | Emerald | Kinradeite | Pectolite |
| Beryllonite | Enstatite | Kornerupine | Peridot |
| Bloodstone | Epidote | Kunzite | Phenacite |
| Bowenite | Essonite | Kyanite | Plasma |
| Brazilianite | Euclase | Labradorite | Pleonaste |
| Cairngorn | Feldspar | Lapis lazuli | Prase |
| Californite | Flint | Lazulite | Prehnite |

Pyrite
Pyrope
Quartz
Quartzite
Rhodizite
Rhodochrosite
Rhodolite
Rhodonite
Rock crystal
Rubellite
Rubicelle
Ruby
Rutile
Sagenite

Samarskite
Sapphire
Sapphirine
Sard
Sardonyx
Satin spar
Scapolite
Schorl
Sepiolite
Serpentine
Siberite
Smaragdite
Smithsonite
Sodalite

Spessartite
Sphalerite
Sphene
Spinel
Spodumene
Staurolite
Steatite
Talc
Thetis hairstone
Thomsonite
Thulite
Tiger's-eye
Titanite
Topaz

Topazolite
Tortoise shell
Tourmaline
Utahlite
Uvarovite
Variscite
Verdite
Vesuvianite
Wernerite
Williamsite
Wollastonite
Zircon
Zoisite

## CHALCEDONY

Agate
Banded agate
Eye agate
Fortification agate

Iris agate
Moss agate
Ribbon agate (striped agate)
Variegated agate

## JASPER

Agate jasper
Brecciated jasper
Moss jasper

Orbicular jasper
Ribbon jasper
Variegated jasper

## OPAL

Black opal
Boulder opal
Common opal
Fire opal
Harlequin opal
Hungarian opal
Jasp opal (opal jasper)
Mexican opal

Moss opal
Nevada opal
Opal matrix
Opal prase (prase opal)
Opalized wood
Water opal
White cliff opal

## QUARTZ

Amethystine quartz
Asteriated quartz
Chrysocolla stained quartz
Chrysocolla inclusion in quartz
  (gem chrysocolla)
Gold quartz
Magnesite inclusion in quartz
Mariposite inclusion in quartz
Milky quartz

Petrified wood (also silicified,
  agatized, or jasperized wood)
Quartz cat's-eye
Rose quartz
Rutilated quartz
Sagenite
Smoky quartz
Tourmalinated quartz
Venus hairstone

## TRANSPARENT MINERALS USED FOR GEMSTONES

| | | | |
|---|---|---|---|
| Achroite | Cassiterite | Hyalite | Rhodolite |
| Adularia | Danburite | Idocrase | Rock crystal |
| Albite | Datolite | Indicolite | Rubellite |
| Alexandrite | Demantoid | Jacinth | Rubicelle |
| Almandite | Diamond | Jargoon | Ruby |
| Amber | Diopside | Kornerupine | Sapphire |
| Amethyst | Dioptase | Kunzite | Spessartite |
| Anatase | Emerald | Kyanite | Sphalerite |
| Andalusite | Epidote | Moldavite | Sphene |
| Apatite | Essonite | Morganite | Spinel |
| Aquamarine | Euclase | Obsidian | Spodumene |
| Augelite | Fluorite | Opal | Topaz |
| Axinite | Garnet | Orthoclase | Topazolite |
| Benitoite | Goshenite | Peridot | Tourmaline |
| Beryl | Hambergite | Phenacite | Wernerite |
| Brazilianite | Hiddenite | Pyrope | Zircon |
| Cairngorm | Hyacinth | Rhodizite | |

## STONES REQUIRING SPECIAL CARE IN HANDLING, CEMENTING, OR WORKING

*Soft stones, brittle stones, and stones possessing distinct weak cleavage planes*

| | | | |
|---|---|---|---|
| Adularia | Brazilianite | Hiddenite | Smithsonite |
| Albite | Chrysocolla | Jet | Sodalite |
| Amazonite | Copal | Kunzite | Sphalerite |
| Amber | Coral | Labradorite | Sphene |
| Apatite | Dioptase | Lapis lazuli | Spodumene |
| Augelite | Euclase | Malachite | Turquoise |
| Azurite | Fluorite | Opal | |
| Benitoite | Gypsum | Satin spar | |

## HARD AS WELL AS DURABLE STONES

| | | | |
|---|---|---|---|
| Achroite | Beryl | Chrysolite | Flint |
| Agate | Bloodstone | Chrysoprase | Garnet |
| Alexandrite | Bowenite | Citrine | Golden beryl |
| Almandite | Cairngorm | Corundum | Goshenite |
| Amethyst | Californite | Danburite | Grossularite |
| Andalusite | Carnelian | Diamond | Hawk's-eye |
| Aquamarine | Chalcedony | Dumortierite | Heliotrope |
| Aventurine | Chloromelanite | Emerald | Hematite |
| Basanite | Chrysoberyl | Essonite | Hyacinth |

Idocrase
Indicolite
Jacinth
Jadeite
Jargoon
Jasper
Kornerupine
Melanite
Morganite
Nephrite
Novaculite

Olivine
Onyx
Peridot
Phenacite
Plasma
Pleonaste
Prase
Pyrope
Quartz
Quartzite
Rhodizite

Rhodolite
Rhodonite
Rock crystal
Rubellite
Rubicelle
Ruby
Sapphire
Sapphirine
Sard
Sardonyx
Siberite

Spessartite
Spinel
Tiger's-eye
Topaz
Topazolite
Tourmaline
Vesuvianite
Zircon

## STONES HAVING FINE GRAIN OR TEXTURE

Achroite
Adularia
Albite
Albite sunstone
Alexandrite
Amber
Amethyst
Almandite
Anatase
Andalusite
Andradite
Apatite
Aquamarine
Augelite
Axinite
Benitoite
Beryl
Beryllonite
Brazilianite
Cairngorm
Carnelian
Carnelian onyx
Chalcedony
Chrysoberyl
Chrysolite

Chrysoprase
Citrine
Coral
Cordierite
Corundum
Danburite
Datolite
Demantoid
Diamond
Diopside
Dioptase
Emerald
Epidote
Euclase
Fluorite
Garnierite
Grossularite
Hambergite
Hessonite
Hiddenite
Hyacinth
Hyalite
Idocrase
Indicolite
Jacinth

Jargoon
Jet
Kornerupine
Kunzite
Melanite
Moldavite
Morganite
Mother-of-pearl
Obsidian
Oligoclase
Oligoclase
   sunstone
Olivine
Onyx marble
Opal
Orthoclase
Peridot
Phenacite
Pleonaste
Prase
Pyrope
Rhodizite
Rhodolite
Rock crystal
Rubellite

Rubicelle
Ruby
Rutile
Sapphire
Sapphirine
Sard
Sardonyx
Scapolite
Siberite
Spessartite
Sphalerite
Sphene
Spinel
Spodumene
Thetis hairstone
Titanite
Topaz
Topazolite
Tourmaline
Uvarovite
Vesuvianite
Zircon

## STONES HAVING GRANULAR TEXTURE, COARSE OR UNEVEN GRAIN

| | | | |
|---|---|---|---|
| Agalmatolite | Chromite | Lapis lazuli | Sepiolite |
| Alabaster | Chrysocolla | Lazulite | Serpentine |
| Amazonite | Dumortierite | Lepidolite | Smithsonite |
| Antigorite | Enstatite | Malachite | Sodalite |
| Aventurine | Gold quartz | Mala-cuprite | Staurolite |
| Azurite | Graphic granite | Marcasite | Thomsonite |
| Azurmalachite | Gypsum | Myrickite | Thulite |
| Basanite | Hawk's-eye | Nephelite | Tiger's-eye |
| Bloodstone | Heliotrope | Nephrite | Turquoise |
| Bowenite | Hematite | Novaculite | Utahite |
| Californite | Howlite | Odontolite | Variscite |
| Carmazul | Hypersthene | Onyx marble | Williamsite |
| Chert | Ilmenite | Oolite | Wollastonite |
| Chiastolite | Jadeite | Pectolite | Zoisite |
| Chlorastrolite | Jasper | Prehnite | |
| Chloromelanite | Kyanite | Pyrite | |
| Chloropal | Labradorite | Rhodonite | |

## STONES DIFFICULT TO POLISH

### CABOCHON

| | | | |
|---|---|---|---|
| Cat's-eye | Hematite | Nevada opal* | Sapphire |
| (oriental) | Labradorite | Pyrite | Smithsonite* |
| Cassiterite | Lepidolite | Ruby | Sphalerite* |
| Dumortierite | | | |

### FACETED

| | | | |
|---|---|---|---|
| Albite | Chrysoberyl | Hematite | Sapphire |
| Alexandrite | Chrysolite | Hiddenite* | Sphalerite* |
| Apatite* | Demantoid | Kunzite* | Sphene* |
| Augelite* | Diamond | Kyanite* | Spinel |
| Benitoite* | Dioptase* | Peridot | Topaz |
| Brazilianite* | Euclase* | Pyrite | Zircon |
| Cassiterite | Fluorite* | Ruby | |

* Stones requiring extreme care in handling.

## SCALE OF HARDNESS

### (*Ascending order from softest to hardest*)

| | | |
|---|---|---|
| 1. Talc | 2. Gypsum | Chrysocolla |
| Steatite | Copal | 3. Calcite |
| Alabaster | Amber | Iceland spar |

Satin spar
Aragonite
Onyx marble
Jet
Malachite
Azurite
Azur-malachite
Serpentine
Agalmatolite
Sphalerite
Coral
Ivory
Chiastolite
Rhodochrosite
4. Fluorite
5. Apatite
Odontolite
Smithsonite
Pectolite
Dioptase
Datolite
Variscite
Wardite
Thomsonite
Limonite
Hematite
Chiastolite
Moldavite
Sodalite
Beryllonite
Actinolite
Lapis lazuli
Rhodonite
Lazulite
Sphene
Opal
Nephelite
Bowenite
Diopside

Turquoise
Amatrice
6. Feldspar
Orthoclase
Amazonite
Albite
Moonstone
Sunstone
Labradorite
Scapolite
Moldavite
Obsidian
Zoisite
Rutile
Pyrite
Marcasite
Cyanite
Cassiterite
Prehnite
Chlorastrolite
Idocrase
Californite
Epidote
Benitoite
Kornerupine
Demantoid
Axinite
Olivine
Chrysolite
Peridot
Andradite
Nephrite
Jadeite
Dumortierite
7. Quartz
Chalcedony
Jasper
Rock crystal
Amethyst

Citrine
Smoky quartz
Spodumene
Kunzite
Hiddenite
Cordierite
Rutile
Tourmaline
Achroite
Indicolite
Rubellite
Zircon
Pyrope
Essonite
Melanite
Rhodolite
Grossularite
Spessartite
Danburite
Euclase
Andalusite
Phenacite
Almandite
Uvarovite
Beryl
Goshenite
Emerald
Aquamarine
Morganite
8. Topaz
Rhodizite
Spinel
Chrysoberyl
Alexandrite
Oriental cat's-eye
9. Corundum
Ruby
Sapphire
10. Diamond

NOTE. All gem species referred to are included in the Scale of Hardness Table for ready reference. In general, the species are listed in order of increasing hardness. On occasion, however, the exact order may vary owing to impurities, other compounds, elements or minerals.

# TABLES OF SPECIFIC GRAVITY AND REFRACTIVE INDEXES

The values listed in the tables are derived from authoritative listings, a number of which have been checked by the author. The authorities selected are credited as being the foremost in the gem science field and include the works of the following: Dr. Max Bauer, Dr. A. Eppler, G. F. Herbert-Smith, Robert Webster, and Messrs. B. W. Anderson and C. J. Payne, through the medium of The Gemmologist, N.A.G. Press, Ltd. To all of these the author expresses grateful acknowledgment.

## SPECIFIC GRAVITY

| | | | | | |
|---|---|---|---|---|---|
| Amber | 1.03–1.10 | Brazilianite | 2.99 | Oriental | |
| Copal | 1.03–1.10 | Phenacite | 2.95–2.97 | cat's-eye | 3.68–3.78 |
| Jet | 1.10–1.40 | Danburite | 2.99–3.04 | Pyrope | 3.69–3.78 |
| Opal | 1.97–2.20 | Lazulite | 3.00–3.12 | Malachite | 3.70–4.00 |
| Chrysocolla | 2.00–2.30 | Odontolite | 3.00–3.25 | Uvarovite | 3.77 |
| Sodalite | 2.13–2.29 | Tourmaline | 3.02–3.25 | Azurite | 3.80 |
| Aragonite | 2.19–3.00 | Andalusite | 3.10–3.20 | Zircon | 3.95–4.71 |
| Alabaster | 2.20–2.30 | Euclase | 3.10 | Zircon | |
| Thomsonite | 2.30–2.40 | Zoisite | 3.12 | group A | 3.95–4.14 |
| Hambergite | 2.35 | Spodumene | 3.18 | Zircon | |
| Obsidian | 2.33–2.60 | Kunzite | 3.13–3.31 | group B | 4.67–4.71 |
| Moldavite | 2.36–2.58 | Hiddenite | 3.13–3.31 | Zircon | |
| Moonstone | 2.50–2.55 | Apatite | 3.16–3.22 | group C | 4.30–4.71 |
| Serpentine | 2.50–2.70 | Fluorite | 3.18 | Andradite | 3.84 |
| Orthoclase | 2.56 | Diopside | 3.20–3.34 | Almandite | 3.85–4.20 |
| Variscite | 2.56 | Fibrolite | 3.25 | Sphalerite | 3.90–4.20 |
| Cordierite | 2.58–2.65 | Dumortierite | 3.25–3.35 | Corundum | 3.95–4.10 |
| Amazonite | 2.58–2.66 | Zoisite | 3.25–3.37 | Corundum | |
| Albite | 2.60 | Epidote | 3.25–3.49 | Ruby Burma | 3.95–4.00 |
| Chalcedony | 2.60 | Enstatite | 3.26–3.28 | Corundum | |
| Talc | 2.60–2.70 | Axinite | 3.29–3.31 | Sapphire | |
| Steatite | 2.60–2.70 | Jadeite | 3.30–3.33 | Siam | 3.97–4.01 |
| Coral | 2.60–2.70 | Kornerupine | 3.32 | Ruby Siam | 4.05–4.10 |
| Bowenite | 2.60–2.80 | Dioptase | 3.30–3.40 | Corundum | |
| Turquoise | 2.60–2.80 | Olivine | 3.30–3.50 | Sapphire | |
| Scapolite | 2.61–2.70 | Chrysolite | 3.30–3.39 | clear | 3.99 |
| Sunstone | 2.63–2.67 | Peridot | 3.30–3.50 | Corundum | |
| Rock crystal | 2.65 | Idocrase | 3.35–3.45 | Sapphire | |
| Pearl | 2.65–2.78 | Californite | 3.35–3.50 | Ceylon | 3.99 |
| Beryl | 2.66–2.90 | Rhodizite | 3.40 | Corundum | |
| Aquamarine | 2.68–2.70 | Staurolite | 3.40–3.80 | Sapphire | |
| Emerald | 2.66–2.77 | Sphene | 3.45–3.56 | Burma | 3.98–3.99 |
| Labradorite | 2.70–2.72 | Rhodochrosite | 3.45–3.60 | Corundum | |
| Calcite | 2.71 | Topaz | 3.50–3.60 | Sapphire | |
| Lapis lazuli | 2.76–2.94 | Diamond | 3.52 | Queensland | 4.00–4.05 |
| Wardite | 2.77 | Rhodonite | 3.53 | Spessartite | 4.00–4.30 |
| Morganite | 2.78–2.90 | Spinel | 3.60–3.63 | Sphalerite | 4.08–4.10 |
| Beryllonite | 2.80–2.85 | Grossularite | 3.60–3.70 | Rutile | 4.20–4.30 |
| Prehnite | 2.86–3.00 | Kyanite | 3.61–3.68 | Smithsonite | 4.30–4.65 |
| Pollucite | 2.86 | Benitoite | 3.64–3.67 | Hematite | 4.95–5.30 |
| Datolite | 2.90–2.99 | Chrysoberyl | 3.68–3.78 | Pyrite | 4.90–5.20 |
| Nephrite | 2.90–3.00 | Alexandrite | 3.68–3.78 | Cassiterite | 6.80–7.1 |

## REFRACTIVE INDEXES

| | | | | | | |
|---|---|---|---|---|---|
| Fluorite | 1.434 | Andalusite | 1.634–1.644 | Benitoite | 1.757–1.838 |
| Opal | 1.453 | Indicolite | 1.634–1.653 | Essonite | 1.76 |
| Obsidian | 1.495 | Apatite | 1.637–1.640 | Sapphire | |
| Moldavite | 1.50 | Spodumene | 1.651–1.677 | clear | 1.70 –1.768 |
| Pollucite | 1.52 | Phenacite | 1.654–1.670 | Sapphire | |
| Gypsum | 1.52 –1.53 | Euclase | 1.658–1.677 | blue | 1.764–1.772 |
| Adularia | 1.52 –1.53 | Fibrolite | 1.658–1.677 | Sapphire | |
| Moonstone | 1.52 –1.53 | Olivine | 1.658–1.686 | green | 1.770–1.779 |
| Albite | 1.525–1.536 | Peridot | 1.661–1.697 | Ruby | 1.768–1.776 |
| Cordierite | 1.53 –1.54 | Kunzite | 1.665–1.680 | Almandite | 1.78 |
| Hambergite | 1.53 –1.628 | Hiddenite | 1.665–1.680 | Zircon A | 1.79 –1.84 |
| Amber | 1.54 | Kornerupine | 1.667–1.680 | Zircon B | 1.93 –1.993 |
| Scapolite | 1.54 –1.57 | Dioptase | 1.667–1.723 | Zircon C | 1.795–1.995 |
| Rock Crystal | 1.544–1.553 | Axinite | 1.679–1.690 | Pyrope | 1.80 |
| Beryllonite | 1.553–1.565 | Diopside | 1.686–1.712 | Spessartite | 1.80 |
| Emerald | 1.565–1.593 | Rhodizite | 1.69 | Uvarovite | 1.85 |
| Aquamarine | 1.570–1.575 | Zoisite | 1.700–1.706 | Andradite | 1.888 |
| Beryl | 1.575–1.582 | Idocrase | 1.708–1.716 | Demantoid | 1.90 |
| Morganite | 1.580–1.588 | Kyanite | 1.712–1.728 | Sphene | 1.90 –2.02 |
| Brazilianite | 1.598–1.617 | Spinel | 1.72 | Cassiterite | 1.997–2.093 |
| Tourmaline | 1.61 –1.65 | Epidote | 1.733–1.768 | Sphalerite | 2.369 |
| Topaz | 1.611–1.637 | Grossularite | 1.744 | Diamond | 2.419 |
| Rubellite | 1.615–1.633 | Chrysoberyl | 1.747–1.756 | Rutile | 2.616–2.903 |
| Achroite | 1.619–1.636 | Pyrope | 1.75 | | |
| Danburite | 1.630–1.636 | Rhodolite | 1.75 | | |

## PHYSICAL CHARACTERISTICS OF PLASTICS

| | Sp. Gr. | R.I. | H. |
|---|---|---|---|
| Cellulose nitrate (celluloid) | 1.37–1.43 | 1.495–1.520 | 1.2 |
| Cellulose acetate (safety celluloid) | 1.29–1.35 | 1.490–1.510 | 1.5 |
| Acrylate resins | 1.18–1.19 | 1.495–1.510 | 2.5 |
| Casein | 1.32–1.34 | 1.54 –1.56 | 2.5 |
| Phenol Bakelite | 1.20–1.70 | 1.56 –1.67 | 2–2.5 |
| Urea Bakelite | 1.48–1.55 | 1.55 –1.62 | 2.5 |
| Vulcanite & Ebonite (hard rubber) | 1.15–1.20 | 1.60 –1.63 | 2. |

## PHYSICAL CHARACTERISTICS OF EMERALD

| | Sp. Gr. | R.I. |
|---|---|---|
| Germany (I. G. Farbenindustrie) | 2.66 | 1.564–1.566 |
| U.S.A. (Chatham synthetic) | 2.667 | 1.573–1.578* |
| Colombia | 2.698–2.715 | 1.565–1.570 |
| Brazil | 2.67 –2.70 | 1.566–1.571 |
| South Africa | 2.720–2.77 | 1.586–1.593 |
| Siberia | 2.70 –2.71 | 1.573–1.579 |

* Synthetic emeralds of recent production have a lower R.I. = 1.562–1.569.

## PHYSICAL CHARACTERISTICS

| | Sp. Gr. |
|---|---|
| Ivory dentine | 1.70–1.93 |
| Ivory vegetable | 1.38–1.42 |
| Bone | 1.90–2.10 |

## THE METRIC SYSTEM OF MEASUREMENT

1 Micron = ............................................... 0.001 mm.

### Measures of Length

1 Millimeter (mm.) = ...................... 0.03937079 in., or about 1/25 in.
10 Millimeters = 1 Centimeter (cm.) = .......................... 0.3937079 in.
10 Centimeters = 1 Decimeter (dm.) = .......................... 3.937079 in.
10 Decimeters = 1 meter (m.) = ...... 39.37079 in., 3.2808992 ft., or 1.09361 yd.
10 Meters = 1 Decameter (Dm.) = ............................... 32.808992 ft.
10 Decameters = 1 Hectometer (Hm.) = ...................... 19.927817 rods
10 Hectometers = 1 Kilometer (Km.) = .......... 1093.61 yd., or 0.6213824 mile
10 Kilometers = 1 Myriameter (Mm.) = ...................... 6.213824 miles
1 inch = 2.54 cm., 1 foot = 0.3048 m., 1 yard = 0.9144 m., 1 rod = 0.5029 Dm.,
1 mile = 1.6093 Km.
1 Ligne = 0.0888 in.; 1/12 Ligne = 1 Douzieme = 0.0074 in.

### Measures of Weight

1 Gramme (g.) = 15.4324874 gr. Troy, or 0.03215 oz. Troy, or 0.03527398 oz. avoir.
10 Grammes = 1 Decagramme (Dg.) = .................... 0.3527398 oz. avoir.
10 Decagrammes = 1 Hectogramme (Hg.) = ................. 3.527398 oz. avoir.
10 Hectogrammes = 1 Kilogramme (Kg.) = .................... 2.20462125 lbs.
1000 Kilogrammes = 1 Tonne (T.) = 2204.62125 lbs., or 1.1023 tons of 2000 lbs.,
or 0.9842 ton of 2240 lbs., or 19.68 cwts.
1 grain = 0.0648 g., 1 oz. avoir. = 28.35 g., 1 lb. = 0.4536 Kg., 1 ton 2000 lbs. =
0.9072 T., 1 ton 2240 lbs. = 1.016 T., or 1016 Kg.
1 Carat = 1/5 gm. = 200 mg. = 4 pearl grains.

### Measures of Capacity

1 Liter (l.) = 1 cubic decimeter = 61.0270515 cu. in., or 0.03531 cu. ft., or 1.0567
liguid qts., or 0.908 dry qt., or 0.26417 Amer. gal.
10 Liters = 1 Decaliter (Dl.) = 2.6417 gal., or 1.135 pk.
10 Decaliters = 1 Hectoliter (Hl.) = 2.8375 bu.
10 Hectoliters = 1 Kiloliter (Kl.) = 61027.0515 cu. in., or 28.375 bu.
1 cu. ft. = 28.317 l., 1 gal. Amer. = 3.785 l., 1 gal. Brit. = 4.543 l.

## METRIC CONVERSION TABLE

| | | | |
|---|---|---|---|
| Millimeters | × | .03937 | = Inches |
| Millimeters | = | 25.400 | × Inches |
| Meters | × | 3.2809 | = Feet |
| Meters | = | .3048 | × Feet |
| Kilometers | × | .621377 | = Miles |
| Kilometers | = | 1.6093 | × Miles |
| Square centimeters | × | .15500 | = Square inches |
| Square centimeters | = | 6.4515 | × Square inches |
| Square meters | × | 10.76410 | = Square feet |
| Square meters | = | .09290 | × Square feet |
| Square kilometers | × | 247.1098 | = Acres |
| Square kilometers | = | .00405 | × Acres |
| Hectares | × | 2.471 | = Acres |
| Hectares | — | .4047 | × Acres |
| Cubic centimeters | × | .061025 | = Cubic inches |
| Cubic centimeters | = | 16.3866 | × Cubic inches |
| Cubic meters | × | 35.3156 | = Cubic feet |
| Cubic meters | = | .02832 | × Cubic feet |
| Cubic meters | × | 1.308 | = Cubic yards |
| Cubic meters | = | .765 | × Cubic yards |
| Liters | × | 61.023 | = Cubic inches |
| Liters | = | .01639 | × Cubic inches |
| Liters | × | .26418 | = U. S. gallons |
| Liters | = | 3.7854 | × U. S. gallons |
| Grams | × | 15.4324 | = Grains |
| Grams | = | .0648 | × Grains |
| Grams | × | .03527 | = ounces, av'dupois |
| Grams | = | 28.3495 | × ounces, av'dupois |
| Kilograms | × | 2.2046 | = Pounds |
| Kilograms | = | .4536 | × Pounds |
| Kilog's per sq. centimeter | × | 14.2231 | = Lbs. per sq. inch |
| Kilog's per sq. centimeter | = | .0703 | × Lbs. per sq. inch |
| Kilogram per cubic meter | × | .06243 | = Lbs. per cubic ft. |
| Kilogram per cubic meter | = | 16.01890 | × Lbs. per cubic ft. |
| Metric tons (1,000 kilog's) | × | 1.1023 | = Tons (2,000 lbs.) |
| Metric tons (1,000 kilog's) | = | .9072 | × Tons (2,000 lbs.) |
| Kilowatts | × | 1.3405 | = Horse-powers |
| Kilowatts | = | .746 | × Horse-powers |
| Calories | × | 3.9683 | = B. T. units |
| Calories | = | .2520 | × B. T. units |

## TABLE OF USEFUL CEMENTS

| Trade Name | Setting | Solvent |
|---|---|---|
| Du-Co Household cement | Clear, light amber | Amyl acetate |
| Stronghold cement | Clear to light amber | acetate |
| Glyptal cement | Clear to light amber | acetate |
| Epoxy 220 cement | Light amber | Methyl ethyl ketone |
| Eastman 910 cement | | (slight action) |
| | White | Dimethyformamide |
| | | (slow action) |
| Pliobond cement | Light brown | Methyl ethyl ketone |

Du-co, stronghold and glyptal are generally used for cementing small settings to stones in inexpensive jewelry, e.g., pendants, stones, for necklaces or bracelets.

All may be used in the natural state or mixed with powdered pigments to act as fillers to fill cracks or holes in stones prior to polishing.

Epoxy 220, and other epoxy type cements have many applications and they are superior to the above where longer setting time is available.

Eastman 910 is a rapid setting cement having great strength but it sets white opaque and working time is limited.

Pliobond is excellent for cementing opaque objects, stone to metal, but it is slow in setting.

## A FEW DON'TS

Don't neglect cleanliness in all operations.

Don't fail to prevent grit contaminating polishing materials and apparatus.

Don't hurry an operation by greater pressure; a fraction of a second is all the time required to ruin hours of labor.

Don't grind on the side of an abrasive wheel not designed for that purpose.

Don't use grinding wheels too large for the grinding spindle.

Don't use apparatus too small for the job in hand.

Don't work in an absent-minded manner; think while you work; finished stones with blemishes that could have been removed are unsightly; stones cut too small cannot be made larger.

Don't attempt to shift belts while the machine is running.

Don't rough out stones on vertical wheels without using goggles or a shield to protect the eyes.

Don't handle stones carelessly; stones cemented to lap sticks should be placed so that they will not fall or strike a hard object.

Don't overload your equipment or motor.

**Don't take chances.**

# Vocabulary and Glossary

*Aegyptilla.* This gemstone described by Pliny corresponds to our nicolo which is an onyx of two layers. The thicker or back layer is black, and the upper layer, which is thin, is bluish-white chalcedony. The design in intaglio was cut through the thin layer, and the figure in the dark or black portion formed a pleasing contrast.

*Alcohol lamp.* A small heating element with a wick in which alcohol is used as fuel.

*American brilliant cut.* A modification of the ordinary brilliant cut. It has a total of eighty-two facets.

*Antwerp rose cut.* A stone with a flat back and a domed top about which is arranged a series of triangular facets.

*Axial.* Pertaining to an axis.

*Azuring.* Altering a round hole to one which has some geometrical form such as square, triangular, or rectangular.

*Back rest* (also Jamb peg or Gem peg). A mechanical contrivance with a number of holes arranged at various heights which act as a rest and support for the pointed end of a lap stick in facet cutting and polishing.

*Baguette.* A small step-cut diamond with a rectangular shape.

*Bort, Boart.* Impure diamond, and commercially any diamond crystal which is unsuited for gem use.

*Bow drill.* A device used for drilling holes where a drill is worked by a bow and string.

*Boxwood.* A yellowish, close-grained, hard wood.

*Brilliant cut.* A faceted stone totaling fifty-eight facets arranged in a definite pattern or design.

*Brillianteering.* That phase of diamond polishing wherein small triangular facets are placed about the stone next to the girdle.

*Briolette.* A drop or pendant stone with its entire surface faceted.

*Briquette.* A small object of compressed powdered material similar to a tile.

*Bruting.* Actually roughing. The act of roughing two diamonds by rubbing one against the other.

*Buff top.* A style of cut stone with a low, smooth-cut dome.

*Cabochon.* A cut stone of any geometrical outline with a flat back and a domed front, polished smooth without facets.

*Caliber cut.* Cutting very small stones to definite size and shape.

*Cameo.* A form of cut stone, gem material, or substance, wherein a figure or object is carved in relief.

*Carboloy.* A trade name given to a sintered tungsten carbide.

*Carbonado.* In the trade, "Carbon." A peculiar form of diamond usually without crystal form or cleavage planes, gray to brown in color, and opaque.

*Carborundum.* The trade name of the abrasive product sold by the Carborundum Company. Chemically, silicon carbide.

*Carving.* Gem carving usually refers to the grinding and polishing of intricate and artistic objects, such as bowls, vases, or figures.

*Cavity.* Crystallography; any small space within a crystal.

*Cement chuck.* A small brass tool used in mechanical bruting or roughing and rounding diamonds in a lathe, the diamond being cemented thereto.

*Cemented tungsten carbide.* Granulated tungsten carbide held by a bond of sintered cobalt, through compression and fusion (sintering).

*Cement plate.* A steel block used to manipulate the heated cement in cementing stones to lap sticks.

*Centering drill.* A special tool used to drill a countersink to guide a drill.

*Chevet.* An engraved gem having the figure in relief but cut so that all portions are below the top surface of the stone.

*Cleavage.* The property possessed by various minerals capable of being split along certain planes peculiar to the substance. These planes always are parallel to a possible crystal face.

*Cleavage plane.* The direction in a mineral in which cleaving takes place. Stones that are easily cleaved often show cleavage planes where a portion of the stone has been partly split. Often seen in kunzite.

*Cleavages.* The portions of a mineral which result from cleavage action.

*Collet chuck.* A split, cylindrical-shaped holding device inserted in the spindle of a lathe or other machine tool for holding tools or other articles accurately.

*Conchoidal.* A concaved, rippled, shell-like fracture.

*Coolant.* Any liquid used as a cooling medium, as for instance, water.

*Counterbore.* To drill and enlarge an existing hole a predetermined amount.

*Countersink.* To grind or lap a small concave or beveled edge on a drilled hole to prevent chipping, or to provide a seat for a conical-shaped setting.

*Cratex wheel.* A trade name of a special rubber wheel in which abrasive grain is embedded.

*Crest and Coat of Arms.* A style of engraving which depicts heraldry.

*Crosscut.* A faceted gem in which some of the facets are so oriented that when viewed from the top a crosslike effect is obtained.

*Crown.* The entire front of a faceted stone.

*Cryptocrystalline.* Formed of microscopically fine crystals.

*Crystal.* A regular polyhedral form characterized by a definite internal and external structure and a definite chemical composition.

*Crystal face.* A plane surface bounding a crystal.

*Crystalline.* A solid having regular molecular structure.

*Crystallographic axis.* One or more axes which pass through a crystal in definite directions. Axes of reference.

*Crystallography.* The science of crystals. Treating of the system and structure of crystals.

*Crystolon.* The trade name of the abrasive product sold by the Norton Company. Chemically, silicon carbide.

*Culet.* The small plane surface on the pavilion of a faceted stone parallel to the table or top facet.

*Cylindrical drill.* A drill made of metal in tube form to be used with abrasive for drilling large holes.

*Damascus ruby powder.* Trade name for a finely divided alumina powder used for polishing gemstones.

*Diamond drill.* A tool made of metal and set with one or more bort diamonds used for drilling.

*Diamontine.* A special powder used for polishing.

*Die sinking.* Intaglio cutting in tool steel for striking coins or medallions.

*Dop.* A mechanical contrivance made of metal used for holding stones (diamond) in polishing.

*Double brilliant cut.* A modified brilliant cut in which the main facets are divided to form two triangles.

*Double cut.* A faceted stone having two rows of triangular facets arranged in a definite manner.

*Double-rose cut.* A faceted stone in which the facets on both sides of the girdle edge are usually triangular in form and are arranged in series extending from the girdle to a point on the crown as well as on the pavilion.

*Emerald cut.* A faceted stone having an octagonal outline in which the facets are arranged in a series of steps.

*Encrusting.* The art of filling an intaglio design with incised lines, with a metal such as gold.

*Engraving.* The art of cutting designs or figures in various materials which, in the lapidary art, usually are gemstones.

*Facet.* Any flat surface usually cut on a gemstone.

*Faceting.* The art of cutting and polishing plane surfaces in a regular manner upon gemstones.

*Feathered or feathers.* Liquid-filled cavities, arranged in whisp or fan-like feather formations in the body of a gemstone.

*Flawed.* The imperfect condition of a gemstone.

*Florentine diamond.* A famous diamond with the facets arranged in a double rose-cut form. Wt. 137.27 ct.

*Florentine mosaic.* A mosaic in which the picture is composed of many stones carefully selected for color and tone, and carefully fitted and cemented together, to form a picture.

*Four-point stone, three-point stone, two-point stone.* In diamond cutting, these are terms used by the cutters and polishers which refer to the orientation of the facets with reference to the crystal form.

*French cut.* A faceted stone with the facets arranged in a particular design.

*Gauge.* Any instrument or tool used to check the outline or form of a cut or rough stone. Also refers to the thickness of sheet metal.

*Gem.* A substance, usually a mineral, suitable to be cut and polished and capable of being used for personal adornment.

*Geode.* A hollow nodule or concretion, the cavity of which is lined with crystals.

*Girdle.* That portion of a gemstone which defines its form or shape.

*Girdle facets.* Small facets on either side of a gemstone adjacent to the girdle.

*Glandular.* A form having a shape like a gland, oval.

*Goniometer.* A tool or instrument for measuring the angles of crystals, etc.

*Great Mogul.* The name of a celebrated diamond which belonged to the Great Mogul until 1739, since which time it cannot be traced.

*Grid pattern.* Having a pattern of crosslines similar to a grid.

*Grit.* A particle of abrasive material.

*Guide bushing.* A special bushing set in a fixture to guide the path of a drill.

*Heraldry.* A coat of arms; armorial bearings.

*High-speed steel.* A special tool steel.

*Holland rose cut.* A faceted stone with the facets arranged in a dome form and with a flat back.

*Hue.* A specific color. A tint is lighter than a hue and a shade is darker; that is, a lighter tint, or a shade darker.

*Indexing.* To accurately space or divide by mechanical means.

*Inlay.* To fit small substances into various formed cavities, such as mosaic.

*Intaglio.* A type of carved or engraved substance, usually a gemstone, in which the figure or design is engraved into the surface, forming a slight depression.

*Intarsia.* Same as mosaic inlay.

*Interfacial angle.* The angle formed by two adjoining faces of a crystal.

*Jamb peg* (gem peg). A mechanical device or rest used for cutting faceted gems.

*Jubilee cut.* A special design for faceted stones better known as the "twentieth-century cut."

*Knockoff stick.* A heavy stick used for knocking off the stones from the lap stick when they have been finished.

*Koh-i-noor.* A celebrated diamond from India owned by the British. Wt. 108.9 ct.

*Lap.* A flat disk made of metal to which loose abrasive grain is applied for the purpose of fine grinding flat surfaces on stone or other substances.

*Lapping.* Using a lap with abrasive to grind.

*Lap stick.* A special stick or holder used for manipulating gemstones during cutting and polishing.

*Lens cut.* A special type of faceted stone.

*Lenticular.* Having a lenslike form, e.g., a double cabochon.

*Levigated alumina.* A trade name for finely divided alumina powder used for polishing.

*Luster.* Condition of the surface of a substance which varies according to the polish attained and to the refractive index of the substance.

*Magna cut.* An elaborate modification of the brilliant cut, recently introduced.

*Main facets.* The principal facets cut on a gemstone.

*Malformed.* An unusual or abnormal form.

*Mechanical dop.* A special tool made of metal used for holding diamonds during cutting and polishing.

*Mechanical facet head.* A mechanical device used for developing and polishing facets on faceted stones in a regular geometric manner.

*Millimeter.* A unit of measurement in the metric system, 25.4 of which are equal to one inch.

*Mixed cut.* A faceted stone, the crown of which is brilliant cut and the back of which is step cut.

*Mosaic.* The name of a composition in which small stones are fitted and cemented together to form a picture or design.

*Negative crystal.* A small angular cavity in a crystal.

*Nicolo.* A chalcedony gemstone composed of two layers; the top or thinner layer usually is gray or bluish gray, and the back layer is black.

*Nodule.* A small rounded mass or rock or mineral, usually quartz.

*Normal to.* Perpendicular to or at a right angle.

*Octahedron.* In crystallography, an eight-sided figure in which the sides are equilateral triangles and the three axes are of equal length, mutually perpendicular.

*Onyx.* Black, or black-and-white, striped chalcedony.

*Orloff.* A celebrated diamond in the Russian Imperial scepter.

*Parquetry.* The art of cutting and arranging small tiles or other substances in a mechanical design or geometrical pattern, usually for tables and floors.

*Parting plane.* A direction of weakness in certain crystals caused by twinning.

*Pavilion.* The entire back portion of a faceted gemstone.

*Pentagonal.* A figure having five sides.

*Peripheral speed.* The surface speed in feet per minute or the distance in feet per minute that a disk or wheel would travel.

*Plasticene.* The trade name for a special modeling clay.

*Portuguese cut.* A special and elaborate type of cutting on gemstones.

*Quadrilateral.* A figure formed by four straight lines.

*Radial.* Extending outward from a common center.

*Reaming.* Enlarging an existing hole by means of a special tool.

*Recessing.* To form a cavity or to remove a portion from a substance at a predetermined depth.

*Recurved.* To curve in a different direction.

*Reflected light.* Light reflecting from a surface.

*Reflection.* The act of light reflecting from a surface.

*Refraction.* A change of direction when a ray of light passes from one medium to another of different density.

*r.p.m.* Revolutions per minute.

*Rhombic dodecahedron.* A twelve-sided figure in which the sides or faces have a rhombic form.

*Rhomboid.* A four-sided figure in which the angles are oblique and the adjacent sides are unequal.

*Rhomboidal.* Shaped like a rhomboid.

*Rhombus.* A four-sided figure having oblique angles and sides of equal length.

*Roman mosaic (Byzantine).* A type of mosaic made by placing and cementing vari-colored glass cylinders of small diameter in a vertical position to form a picture.

*Rose cut.* A faceted stone having a flat back and a domed front faceted.

*Rounding.* The act of grinding in a smooth manner the domed surface of a cabochon stone.

*Rubbing bed.* A horizontal polishing machine with a movable frame and head, attached to a rigid base, used in polishing large slabs or blocks.

*Safety edge.* A small chamfered or beveled edge placed upon a stone to prevent chipping.

*Sancy.* A celebrated diamond owned at different times by Queen Elizabeth, Cardinal Mazarin, and Louis XIV.

*Sanding (smoothing).* The act of smoothing the surface of a stone with an abrasive-covered cloth or paper.

*Sard.* Reddish brown to brown chalcedony.

*Sardonyx.* Chalcedony having alternate bands of sard and white zones.

*Sawing (slitting).* The act of parting a stone with the use of a thin metal disk to which an abrasive is applied.

*Scale of hardness (Mohs).* An arbitrary list of minerals ranging in hardness from the softest No. 1 (talc) to the hardest No. 10 (diamond).

*Scarab.* An engraved stone combining the cameo and the intaglio, having the convex portion engraved into a beetle and the flat portion engraved with an inscription or other device.

*Scaraboid.* A modified form of the scarab in which the engraving of the scarab is eliminated to form a domed surface.

*Scoring.* The act of causing indentations to appear in the surface of a lap with the aid of a sharp knife.

*Scotch cut.* An elaborate form of faceted stone usually of circular outline having a large number of small facets.

*Seal stones.* Flat-top table-cut stones used for the purpose of engraving a seal.

*Silicon carbide.* The chemical name of the artificial abrasive sold under various trade names such as Carborundum, or Crystolon, used by lapidaries.

*Silk.* An optical effect commonly seen in the corundum gems.

*Single cut.* A simple form of a round, faceted stone having a single row of facets on the front and back respectively.

*Solder dop.* A metal cuplike holder in which solder is melted and in which diamonds are held while being polished.

*Splendent.* Reflecting with brilliancy.

*Square cut.* Various types and designs of facet arrangement placed upon stones having square outlines.

*Star cut.* A faceted stone in which the facets produce a starlike display.

*Star facets.* The small, triangular-shaped facets surrounding the table of a faceted stone.

*Steel burr.* A small tool-steel cutter, the cutting head of which consists of numerous sharp-edged cutters.

*Step brilliant.* Alternate name for the mixed cut.

*Step cut.* A faceted stone having the facets arranged in parallel steps.

*Strass.* A special glass named for the inventor, having strong dispersive qualities.

*Stylus.* A sharp, hard-pointed scribing instrument.

*Submerged drilling.* Drilling holes with the article being drilled submerged in a coolant.

*s.f.p.m.* Surface feet per minute.

*Table.* The large uppermost facet on a faceted gemstone.

*Table cut.* Table-cut single bevel; table-cut double bevel. Flat, faceted stones having a broad table surface surrounded by a single bevel or facet in the single cut and by a similar facet row on the back of the stone in the double cut.

*Tangent to.* Meeting a line at a point without intersecting.

*Technique.* The details of any art.

*Template.* A metal plate having an aperture into which an article may be fitted to produce multiple units of the same size and shape.

*Three-quarter brilliant cut.* A modified form of the brilliant cut, having fewer facets.

*Tong.* The mechanical clamp that is used to hold a dop upon the lap.

*Tripoli.* An altered rock used for polishing.

*Tube drill.* A drill formed from a metal tube charged with an abrasive.

*Tweezer.* A small pair of hand tongs used for holding stones.

*Twentieth-century cut.* An elaborate modification of the brilliant cut.

*Twin crystal.* Crystals in which one or more parts, regularly arranged, are in reverse position with reference to the other part or parts.

*Twinning plane.* The plane in a crystal to which two portions are symmetrically placed.

*Van Berquem.* Conceded to be the originator of the modern art of diamond polishing.

*Venus hairstone.* Rock crystal containing needle or hairlike crystals of rutile.

# Selected Bibliography

*Introduction to the Study of Rocks and Minerals,* Austin F. Rogers (New York. McGraw-Hill Publ. Co., 1921); 3rd Ed., 1937.

*A Text Book of Minerology,* Edward S. Dana (New York: John Wiley & Sons, 1902); 4th Ed., 1951.

*Gemstones,* G. F. Herbert-Smith (New York: Pitman, 1958); 13 rev. ed.

*Gems & Gem Materials,* E. H. Kraus and C. B. Slawson (New York: McGraw-Hill Pub. Co., Inc., 1947).

*Gemmologists' Compendium,* Robert Webster, F.G.A. (London, England: N. A. G. Press Ltd., 1947).

*Gem Testing,* B. W. Anderson, B.Sc., F.G.A. (London, England: Heywood & Co., Ltd., 1958); 6th Ed.

*Popular Gemmology,* Richard M. Pearl, F.G.A. (New York: John Wiley & Sons, 1948).

*Getting Acquainted With Minerals,* G. L. English (New York: McGraw-Hill Pub. Co.).

*Edelsteinkunde,* Dr. Max Bauer (Tauchnitz, Germany: Chr. Herm, 1909).

*Gewerbliche Materialkunde, die Schmuck und Edelsteine,* Dr. A. Eppler (Stuttgart, Germany: Verlag von Felix Krais, 1912).

*Die Künstlichen Edelsteine,* Dr. Hermann Michel (Leipzig, Germany: Verlag von Wilhelm Diebener. G.m.b.H., 1926).

*The Gem Cutters Craft,* Leopold Claremont (London: Geo. Bell & Sons, 1906).

*The Curious Lore of Precious Stones,* Dr. George F. Kunz (Philadelphia: J. B. Lippincott, 1913).

*Traite des Pierres Gravees,* P. J. Mariette (Paris, 1750).

*The Science of Gems,* Archibald Billing (London: Daldy Isbister & Co., 1875).

*Natural History of Gems,* C. W. King (London: M. A. Bell & Daldy, 1870).

*Handbook of Engraved Gems,* C. W. King (London: M. A. Bell & Daldy, 1866).

*Gemmen und Kameen des Altertums und der Neuzeit,* Georg Lippold (Stuttgart, Germany: Verlag von Julius Hoffmann).

*Die Kameen im Kunsthistorischen Museum,* Fritz Eichler and Ernst Kris (Vienna, Austria: Verlag von Anton Schroll & Co., 1927).

*The Engraved Gems of Classical Times,* J. Henry Middleton (England: Cambridge Univ. Press, 1891).

*Engraved Gems,* Duffield Osborne (New York: Henry Holt & Co., 1912).

*Catalogue of the Engraved Gems in the Metropolitan Museum* (Rome: L'Erma di Bretschneider, 1956).

*Catalogue of the Engraved Gems and Cameos, Greek, Etruscan, and Roman in The British Museum,* H. B. Walters (London, England).

*Catalogue of the Engraved Gems in The British Museum, Post-Classical Period,* O. M. Dalton.

*Catalogue of Egyptian Scarabs, Etc., in The British Museum,* H. R. Hall.

*Meister und Meisterwerke der Steinschneidekunst in der Italienischen Renaissance,* Ernst Kris (Vienna, Austria: Verlag von Anton Schroll & Co., 1929).

*Dionysio Miseroni,* Heinrich Klapsia (Vienna, Austria: Verlag von Anton Schroll & Co.).

*Encyclopaedie der Dimantnijverheid,* Dr. F. Leviticus (Haarlem, Holland: De Erven, F. Bohn).

*Gemstones of North America,* John Sinkankas (Princeton, N. J.: D. Van Nostrand Co., Inc., 1959).

"Der praktische Brilliantschliff der Diamanten," *Deutsche Goldschmiedezeitung,* No. 25, 1939, Eppler and Klueppelberg.

*Diamond Design,* Leopold Tolkowsky.
*Diamond Tools,* Paul Grodzinski (New York: Anton Smit & Co., 1944).
*Diamond and Gem Stone Industrial Production,* Paul Grodzinski (London, England: N. A. G. Press Ltd.).
*Ancient Egyptian Materials and Industries,* A. Lucas (London, England: Edward Arnold Co.).
*A Roman Book on Precious Stones,* Sydney H. Ball (Los Angeles: Gemological Institute of America, 1950).
*The Ancient Maya,* Sylvanus G. Morley (Stanford Univ. Press, Calif.).
*200 Meisterwerke* (Vienna, Austria: Kunsthistorischen Museum, 1931).
*Glossary of Mineral Terms,* bulletin No. 35, U. S. Bureau of Mines.
*Handbook and Descriptive Catalogue of the Gems in the U. S. National Museum,* Bull. 118, Geo. P. Merrill (Wash., D. C.: Gov't Print. Off., 1922).
*Units of Weights and Measure,* U. S. Dept. of Commerce Publication No. M.121.
*Photomicrography,* Charles Patten Shillaber (New York: John Wiley & Sons, 1944).
*The Gemmologist* (London, England: N. A. G. Press).
*Rocks and Minerals,* bimonthly magazine, Peekskill, N. Y.
*The Mineralogist,* monthly magazine, Portland, Oregon.
*The Lapidary Journal,* bi-monthly magazine, 241 Twelfth St., Del Mar, Calif.
*Gems and Minerals,* monthly magazine, P.O. Box 687, Mentone, Calif.
*A Field Guide to Rocks and Minerals,* Dr. Frederick H. Pough, 3rd Ed.

# Index